CACHE TECHNICAL LEVEL

3

- ◆ Linda Wyatt
- ◆ Pete Wedlake
- ◆ Maria Ferreiro Peteiro
- ◆ Elizabeth Rasheed

Extended Diploma in
Health &
Social Care

DYNAMIC LEARNING

HODDER EDUCATION
AN HACHETTE UK COMPANY

The authors and publishers would like to thank the following for the use of photographs in the book.

Figure 1.2: © Peter Titmuss / Alamy Stock Photo; Figure 1.3: © Yuri Arcurs – Fotolia; Figure 2.2: © Lole –Shutterstock; Figures 3.1 and 8.1: © Monkey Business Images – Shutterstock; Figure 3.3: © Rido – Shutterstock; Figure 3.4: © Ocskay Mark – Shutterstock; Figure 4.1: © lassedesignen – Fotolia.com; Figure 4.2: © Montgomery Martin / Alamy Stock Photo; Figure 4.7 ©MiniMo; Figure 5.6: ESB Professional – Shutterstock; Figure 6.1: © SpeedKingz. – Shutterstock; Figure 6.3: A. Bandura et al.; Figure 6.7: © BSIP SA / Alamy Stock Photo; Figure 7.3: © Banksy via Wikipedia https://creativecommons.org/licenses/by-sa/3.0/deed.en; Figures 8.3 and 14.3: © Tyler Olson – 123RF; Figure 8.5: © kzenon – 123RF; Figure 9.3: © Clearview / Alamy Stock Photo; Figures 10.4 and 11.1: © Katarzyna Białasiewicz – 123RF; Figure 10.5: © Syda Productions – Shutterstock; Figure 12.26: © PhotoAlto / Alamy Stock Photo; Figure 12.27: © Juan R. Velasco – Shutterstock; Figure 14.1: © Graham Oliver – 123RF; Figure 14.2: © Cathy Yeulet –123RF; Figure 14.3: © Tyler Olson – Fotolia

Illustrations by Aptara Inc.

Although every effort has been made to ensure that website addresses are correct at time of going to press, Hodder Education cannot be held responsible for the content of any website mentioned in this book. It is sometimes possible to find a relocated web page by typing in the address of the home page for a website in the URL window of your browser.

Hachette UK's policy is to use papers that are natural, renewable and recyclable products and made from wood grown in sustainable forests. The logging and manufacturing processes are expected to conform to the environmental regulations of the country of origin.

Orders: please contact Bookpoint Ltd, 130 Park Drive, Milton Park, Abingdon, Oxon OX14 4SE. Telephone: (44) 01235 827720. Fax: (44) 01235 400454. Email education@bookpoint.co.uk Lines are open from 9 a.m. to 5 p.m., Monday to Saturday, with a 24-hour message answering service. You can also order through our website: www.hoddereducation.co.uk

ISBN: 9781510403123

© Maria Ferreiro Peteiro, Elizabeth Rasheed, Linda Wyatt, Pete Wedlake, 2017

First published in 2017 by

Hodder Education,
An Hachette UK Company
Carmelite House
50 Victoria Embankment
London EC4Y 0DZ
www.hoddereducation.co.uk

Impression number   10 9 8 7

Year   2021 2020

Cover and chapter opening photo © Bela Hoche – 123RF.com
Typeset in Aptara Inc.
Printed in Slovenia
A catalogue record for this title is available from the British Library.

Contents

How to use this book

This textbook will provide you with the knowledge and understanding required for the following qualifications:

The Technical Level 3 Extended Diploma in Health and Social Care (601/8435/8) and the Level 3 Extended Diploma in Health and Social Care (601/6110/3).

Please note that unit HSC DM3.1 Anatomy and Physiology for Health and Social Care is assessed by examination at Technical Level and excludes any skills-based outcomes.

Note: The legislation covered in this book is correct at the time of writing. However, you should keep up-to-date with any changes to legislation. The Children and Social Work Act 2017 was introduced just before the publication of this book, and is not covered here. This has meant changes to Local Safeguarding Boards and Serious Case Reviews. For further information on any changes that affect the content of this book, visit https://tinyurl.com/lt4dozz

Key features of the book

Learning Outcomes

LO1: Understand the key elements of development across human lifespan

1.1 Identify the life stages of human development

1.2 Describe social, emotional, cognitive and physical developments within each life stage

LO2: Understand theories of human growth and development

2.1 Describe theories of human growth and development

Prepare for what you are going to cover in the unit.

About this unit

The aim of this unit is to provide knowledge and understanding of human growth and development through the human lifespan. It will explore changes across the lifespan and theories of human growth and development. Finally, it will explain some of the significant life events and the potential impact these can have on individuals. This unit has relevance to health and social care in that practitioners work with people of all ages.

Understand some of the key issues with this short introduction to the unit.

LO1: Understand equality, diversity and rights in health and social care

1.1 Define the terms equality, diversity, inclusion and discrimination

Understand all the requirements of the qualification with clearly stated learning outcomes and assessment criteria fully matched to the specification.

 Key term

Duty of care – a care practitioner's legal duty to act in the individuals' best interests and keep them safe from danger, harm and abuse

Understand important terms.

Activity (AC 1.1, 1.2, 1.3)

Imagine you have been asked to produce a training session for care assistants in a new service that provides care and support to older people. Your training materials must include:

- a *definition* of the terms equality, diversity, inclusion and discrimination. A definition means that you need to state the meaning of these terms in a health and social care context.
- an *explanation* of how individuals' rights are promoted in health and social care services. An explanation means that you need to provide a clear account of your understanding, with examples of how individuals' rights are promoted and why.
- a *discussion* of ethical dilemmas that may arise when balancing individual rights and duty of care. A discussion means that you need to present and explain more than one ethical dilemma.

Prepare a slideshow or flipcharts for your training session to support the points above.

Test yourself with various tasks and knowledge-based questions to help enhance your understanding of assessment criteria.

Command word activity

Explain (AC 3.1)

Create a pamphlet aimed at new parents. It should explain the challenges and benefits of parenthood, and explain how a new sibling can affect the family dynamics.

Test your knowledge with activities specifically linked to command words, such as Describe, Explain, Evaluate and Analyse.

Case Scenario: Taking risks (AC 1.3, 5.1, 5.2, 6.1)

Jeremy is a mental health support worker to a young adult, Michael, who lives in a flat on his own. He provides support with day-to-day activities such as cooking, household cleaning and shopping. Part of Michael's plan of support, states that two support workers must always be present when supporting Michael with shopping as he can become very anxious when outside his home.

Consider real life issues and scenarios.

Take it further

For more information on promoting dignity in care visit the Social Care Institute for Excellence's (SCIE) website and their dignity in care video films: www.scie.org.uk

Enhance your understanding of a topic with helpful cross references, suggestions for further reading and research encouraging you to explore an area in more detail.

Classroom Discussion

Identify two examples of ethical dilemmas that may arise in health and social care (you can use any of the examples included in Table 1.1). For each one, discuss the reasons why it is an ethical dilemma, the conflicts that may arise when balancing individual rights and duty of care as well as different perspectives.

Work in groups to reflect on topics, discuss and share ideas.

✔ Check your understanding

1. What is the meaning of safeguarding adults?
2. Can you name the two principles that underpin the safeguarding of children?
3. Can you give two examples of how safeguarding protects individuals?
4. Can you give two examples of how health and social care practitioners can safeguard themselves when providing support to individuals?

Test your knowledge and understanding of each learning outcome.

Read about it

Argyle, M. (1972) *The Psychology of Interpersonal Communication*. Harmondsworth: Pelican.

Websites

Bridge School (2010) Speech Generating Devices accessed from: https://www.bridgeschool.org/transition/multimodal/sgd.php

HRA Our Committees Accessed from **http://www.hra.nhs.uk/about-the-hra/our-committees/section-251/**

Includes references to books, websites and other sources for further reading and research

		Assessment grading criteria	Assessment of learning / What you need to show
D1	1.1	Explain what is meant by 'safeguarding'	The explanation of safeguarding must: • show accurate understanding of the meaning of safeguarding • relate safeguarding to the context of health and social care.

Understand how you will be assessed and graded with these tables from the specification.

Acknowledgments

From Maria Ferreiro Peteiro:

Thank you for the constructive feedback from all those involved in this project, and thank you to Chris and my family for their endless support.

From Elizabeth Rasheed:

I would like to thank my family for being so supportive while I spent so much time writing.

Upon successful completion of this qualification, learners will be awarded the NCFE CACHE Technical Level 3 Extended Diploma in Health and Social Care 601/8435/8. This CACHE branded qualification is certified by the Awarding Organisation, NCFE.

HSC CM1
Equality, Diversity and Rights in Health and Social Care

Learning outcomes

LO1: Understand equality, diversity and rights in health and social care

1.1 Define the terms:
- equality
- diversity
- inclusion
- discrimination.

1.2 Explain how rights are promoted in health and social care services

1.3 Discuss ethical dilemmas that may arise when balancing individual rights and duty of care

LO2: Understand how to work in an inclusive way

2.1 Explain how to promote equality and support diversity

2.2 Describe how to challenge those not working inclusively in a way that promotes change

2.3 Explain how to support others in promoting equality and rights

LO3: Understand legislation and codes of practice in relation to inclusive practice in health and social care settings

3.1 Summarise legislation and codes of practice relating to equality, diversity, inclusion and discrimination

LO4: Understand the role of the health and social care practitioner in relation to inclusive practice

4.1 Evaluate the role of the health and social care practitioner in meeting individuals' needs through inclusive practice

About this unit

Promoting equality, diversity and human rights is essential for preventing discrimination when accessing health and social care services. Creating an inclusive environment for individuals is integral to providing high-quality and effective care and support.

In this unit you will learn about equality, diversity, inclusion and discrimination in relation to health and social care. Having an awareness of these terms is not enough; you must also know and understand how these can be put into practice on a day-to-day basis, across a variety of settings where care and support

are provided. You will also, therefore, learn more about how equality, diversity, inclusion and rights can be promoted and discrimination prevented in health and social care services.

An understanding of relevant legislation and codes of practice that underpin the promotion of equality, diversity and inclusion, will help you to further develop knowledge and understanding of inclusive practice and the role of the health and social care practitioner in meeting individuals' unique and diverse needs.

LO1: Understand equality, diversity and rights in health and social care

1.1 Define the terms equality, diversity, inclusion and discrimination

What does equality mean?

Equality means treating every person fairly and valuing every person as an individual. It also means supporting people's rights and ensuring every person has equal rights and opportunities to improve their lives and achieve their full potential through, for example, pursuing a career of their choice, learning a new skill or activity or being able to socialise with their friends.

Equality applies not only to the people accessing services and their parents, families and friends, but also to all those who work within health and social care services and external organisations such as Social Services and other **voluntary sector organisations** including the mental health charity MIND and the Royal National Institute for the Blind (RNIB) that provides practical support, information and advice.

Equality does involve...	Equality does not involve...
treating every person as an individual	treating every person the same
treating every person fairly	treating some people unequally
supporting every person's rights	not respecting every person's rights
providing every person with access to the same life opportunities as everyone else	denying some people access to the same life opportunities as everyone else

Key term

Voluntary sector organisations also known as third sector organisations and are not for profit such as charities

What does diversity involve?

Diversity involves recognising that every person is unique and different. Valuing the importance of these individual differences allows the sharing of different views and ideas as well as the development of a culture in which everyone can participate in. Figure 1.1 below provides examples of some of the differences that may exist between people that make them unique.

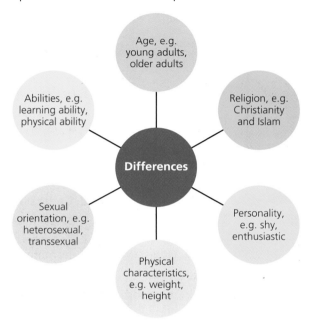

Figure 1.1 What makes you unique?

Key terms

Christianity a religion based on the life and teachings of Jesus Christ

Islam a religion followed by Muslims that teaches that there is one God (Allah) and that Muhammad is its prophet

Heterosexual a person that is sexually attracted to people of the opposite sex

Transsexual a person that may assume the gender role of the opposite sex and undergo treatment to acquire the physical characteristics of the opposite sex

Health and social care services in the UK reflect the diversity of the population including the needs of everyone who uses them and works in them. In order to be able to develop positive working relationships with **individuals** and **others** and provide safe, effective, compassionate and high-quality care it is important to find out and understand the diversity that exists in people's day-to-day lives.

Key terms

Learning disabilities refers to individuals who have a reduced ability to learn new skills, carry out daily living activities, understand complex information and interact with other people

Mental health needs refer to individuals that have a mental health illness that affects the way they think, feel and behave

Depression a low mood that continues for a long period of time and affects day-to-day living

Anxiety and panic attacks the physical and emotional negative sensations experienced as a result of worry and fear

Dementia refers to a group of symptoms that may include memory loss and/or difficulties with thinking or language

Alzheimer's refers to a disease that is the most common cause of dementia

Key terms

Individuals persons accessing health and social care services

Others parents/carers, family, friends, colleagues, external partners and health and social care practitioners

Activity

Read through the three case scenarios below that focus on different health and social care settings, and then answer the questions that follow.

Scenario 1: NHS hospital:

Andrei has been working as a health care assistant across a number of hospital wards for two years; Andrei works full time and variable day, night and weekend shifts. Mandy has six years of experience as a health care assistant and has worked across a number of different wards and hospitals. She works alongside Andrei but only on a part-time basis because she provides care and support to her elderly father who lives with her and her family.

Scenario 2: A supported living service

Robinson House is a supported living service for four individuals who have **learning disabilities and mental health needs** and require support with daily living. Dean is 44, has a mild learning disability and **depression** and lives on the ground floor; he likes going out to socialise with his friends. Liam, is 40, has a mild learning disability, **anxiety and panic attacks** and lives on the first floor; he likes spending time with his nephew. Ana, 40 and Marina, 42 have mild learning disabilities and depression; they share the top floor and enjoy gardening and going to the gym.

Scenario 3: A day centre

Trent Day Centre is a service for individuals who have **dementia**. A team of volunteers provide support to individuals to participate in a range of activities including singing, arts and walking. David has recently become a volunteer after having been diagnosed with **Alzheimer's**. Stuart has been a volunteer for three years and provides support to his father who attends twice a week. Lina has been a volunteer for four years and runs a Spanish group for all those interested in learning more about Spain, its language, food and music.

1. In what ways are health care assistants Andrei and Mandy different from each other in Scenario 1?
2. What differences are there between Dean, Liam, Ana and Marina in Scenario 2?
3. How do volunteers, David, Stuart and Lina differ from each other in Scenario 3?

What is meant by the term inclusion?

The term inclusion means a lot more than being included; it involves having a meaningful role in society as well as being supported to feel respected and develop a positive sense of well-being. Additional information about other key aspects of inclusion that is integral to high-quality care is provided below:

Individualised support

Nurturing confidence in one's own abilities

Controlling one's own life, care and support

Living life with a sense of belonging

Understanding and feeling respected and valued

Supporting positive relationships between individuals and others

Increasing participation in life opportunities

Openly engaging in community life and society

Nurturing support and commitment from others to fulfil own potential

What is the meaning of discrimination?

The term discrimination refers to the unfair or unequal treatment of an individual or a group. All those who access, live and work in health and social care services have a right not to be discriminated against. The Equality Act 2010 sets out the different types of discrimination that exist; you will learn more about these in Learning Outcome 3.

Discrimination usually occurs when an individual or group treats another individual or group worse than they would others because of their unique differences. Being discriminated against can lead to low life expectations, poor self-esteem, reduced mental and physical well-being, as well as a reduction in life opportunities. For example, if a young man who has autism is denied support to move to independent living because of his condition, then, not only is he being treated unfairly but he is also being prevented from living his life how he wants to and being denied the

Command word activity

Describe (AC 1.1)

Take it in turns to test your partner's understanding of the terms inclusion and discrimination in relation to health and social care. Agree on a definition for each.

opportunity and experience to learn and develop new independent living skills. If you were this young man, how would you feel?

Similarly, if a group of older people were denied access to a running group because of the running group's preconceived and unfair opinion that older people will be more at risk of acquiring serious injuries then this is disempowering this group of older people from pursuing their interests and engaging in their local community. Again, if you were in this situation, how would you feel?

1.2 Explain how rights are promoted in health and social care services

Individuals who access health and social care services must have their rights upheld. In the UK these rights form part of the Human Rights Act 1998 and are underpinned by the principles of dignity, equality and respect.

As well as the right to be treated with respect, equality and dignity, individuals in health and social care services also have the right to:

- privacy
- independence and choices
- be protected from danger, harm and abuse
- be involved in their care and support
- be provided with care, support and services that meet their needs, strengths, abilities, preferences and choices
- communicate and have information communicated to them using their preferred methods of communication
- access and be supported with understanding information relevant to them.

Take it further

For more information on relevant legislation in health and social care you will find it useful to read LO3 in this unit and Unit HSC CM8 (LO1).

The promotion of individuals' rights in health and social care enables care practitioners to provide good-quality, safe and effective care and support.

Promotion of individuals' rights to respect, dignity, privacy, independence and choice

The *right to respect* involves taking into account individuals' views, feelings and wishes such as addressing the individual by their preferred name, taking into consideration their feelings and preferences when discussing their current care and support needs. The *right to dignity* involves providing care and support to individuals that raises their **self-esteem** and enables them to feel valued such as speaking to an individual politely and in a way that is not undermining or demeaning and ensuring their *right to privacy* is respected when being supported with maintaining their personal hygiene, for example by having doors closed and curtains drawn.

The *right to independence* involves individuals being encouraged to do as much as possible for themselves within their own abilities in all aspects of their lives and being supported with living their lives fully and how they wish. It is important, because enabling individuals to complete independent activities brings with it control, a sense of achievement and **self-fulfilment** that can positively enhance both their mental and physical well-being. Promoting

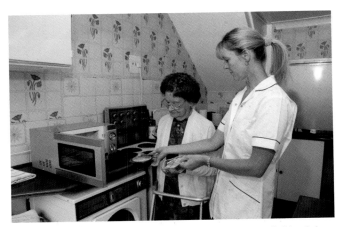

Figure 1.2 How can independence impact on individuals' lives?

independent activities will vary for individuals and may involve making a cup of tea, getting dressed, writing to a family member, visiting a friend, going out on public transport or learning a new hobby. Promoting independence can also positively impact on the relationships between care practitioners and individuals by instilling trust, encouraging positive interactions and developing happy memories of the time spent together.

The *right to choice* involves individuals being given all the information they need and in a form that they can understand to be able to make their own decisions in all aspects of their lives. This may involve day-to-day decisions such as what to wear, what to eat, what time to get up, what time to go to bed, how to spend the day as well as more complex decisions such as how their care and support is provided, that is, what services to access, how they would like the support provided and by whom.

Take it further

For more information on promoting dignity in care visit the Social Care Institute for Excellence's (SCIE) website and their dignity in care video films: www.scie.org.uk

Key terms

Self-esteem the value or confidence individuals place on themselves

Self-fulfilment following and achieving hopes and wishes

Promotion of individuals' rights to be protected from danger, harm and abuse

The *right to be protected from danger, harm and abuse* involves the promotion of individuals' safety from both actual and potential danger, harm and abuse by not only protecting individuals when these do occur, but also by preventing these from taking place. Danger, harm and abuse can occur in different environments; for example, in residential care settings, in individuals' own homes, in community settings such as the shops, park and on public transport. The risk of harm can involve different people including family members who live or care for the individual, care practitioners who support the individual, other professionals and members of the general public. Care practitioners can protect individuals from danger, harm and abuse by:

- identifying potential dangers, harm and abuse before they occur, e.g. a wet bathroom floor that may cause an individual to slip over; an individual who may be vulnerable to being taken advantage of because they have a disability

- reporting and recording dangers, harm and abuse when they occur, e.g. reporting a faulty television in a **nursing home** to the manager; recording in the incident book of a **day centre** that an individual had a fall; reporting and reporting potential **physical abuse** of an individual to the nominated **Designated Safeguarding Officer**

- keeping up to date with how to promote individuals' rights to be protected from danger, harm and abuse, e.g. by health and social care settings raising awareness through training, information updates, policies and procedures.

Promotion of individuals' rights to care and support that reflect their identity and diversity

The *right to care and support that reflects identity and diversity* involves accepting and valuing individuals' differences by getting to know who they are and supporting them to live their lives in line with their unique views, preferences and beliefs. This may involve supporting individuals to practise their faith and respecting individuals' beliefs in relation to the way all daily activities are carried out including, for example, in relation to:

- personal hygiene: e.g. preferences over being supported by a male or female carer

- eating, e.g. beliefs over whether to eat meat or vegetarian food

- dressing, e.g. beliefs over how to dress and what to wear.

Promotion of individuals' rights to effective communication

The *right to effective communication* involves care practitioners being aware of individuals' communication preferences and needs and using a variety of methods to communicate with

Take it further

For more information on effective communication you will find it useful to read Unit HSC CM4 (LO2).

individuals such as using key words and phrases, sign language, pictures, symbols, photographs or an interpreter. It is important because, when communication is effective working relationships between care practitioners and individuals can develop and, in turn, enhance the quality of the care and support provided through the development of mutual trust, respect and understanding.

1.3 Discuss ethical dilemmas that may arise when balancing individual rights and duty of care

Ethical dilemmas may arise in health and social care because care practitioners are supporting individuals to live their lives as they wish, which may conflict with their professional **duty of care** towards them. Table 1.1 provides details of different ethical dilemmas that care practitioners may face when balancing individuals' rights with their duty of care.

Key term

Duty of care a care practitioner's legal duty to act in the individuals' best interests and keep them safe from danger, harm and abuse

Classroom discussion (AC 1.3)

Identify two examples of ethical dilemmas that may arise in health and social care (you can use any of the examples included in Table 1.1). For each one, discuss the reasons why it is an ethical dilemma, the conflicts that may arise when balancing individual rights and duty of care as well as different perspectives.

Take it further

For more information on dilemmas when balancing the rights of the individual against the health and social care practitioner's duty of care, you will find it useful to read Unit HSC DM1 (LO2).

Table 1.1 Examples of ethical dilemmas

Ethical dilemmas	Examples
An individual's right to independence	Ana has dementia and gets confused and disorientated when out, sometimes for long periods of time. Ana wants to continue with her weekly visits to her daughter, who lives 3 miles away; Ana's carer is concerned about her safety and her getting lost.
An individual's right to choice	Jordan has depression and lives on his own. He prefers to stay in bed all day and chooses not to get up until 6 p.m. in the evening. Jordan's mental health support worker is concerned about his well-being and his lack of activity during the day.
An individual's right to confidentiality	Jolanda is 75 and has a good relationship with her son who visits her every day. Jolanda tells her home carer that her son asked her for money again and so she thought she had better give it to him. Jolanda tells her home carer to not tell anyone about this as she does not want her son to find out.
An individual's right to respect	Lina is 23 and has a learning disability. She has found out that she is pregnant and wants to have a termination. She asks her support worker to accompany her to the hospital. Her support worker holds religious beliefs that do not agree with terminations.
An individual's right to dignity	Aidan is 84 and lives with his wife who is his sole carer. The social worker visits and notices that Aidan is only partly clothed and not wearing any trousers. Aidan's wife explains that this is because it is easier for her when supporting him to use the toilet.

Activity (AC 1.1, 1.2, 1.3)

Imagine you have been asked to produce a training session for care assistants in a new service that provides care and support to older people. Your training materials must include:

- a *definition* of the terms equality, diversity, inclusion and discrimination. A definition means that you need to state the meaning of these terms in a health and social care context.
- an *explanation* of how individuals' rights are promoted in health and social care services. An explanation means that you need to provide a clear account of your understanding, with examples of how individuals' rights are promoted and why.
- a *discussion* of ethical dilemmas that may arise when balancing individual rights and duty of care. A discussion means that you need to present and explain more than one ethical dilemma.

Prepare a slideshow or flipcharts for your training session to support the points above.

 Check your understanding

1. What do the terms equality and diversity in health and social care mean?
2. What do the terms inclusion and discrimination in health and social care mean?
3. Give three examples of the rights individuals in health and social care have. How can these rights be promoted?
4. What is the meaning of the term 'duty of care'?
5. Give two examples of how and why ethical dilemmas in health and social care may arise.

LO2: Understand how to work in an inclusive way

Having gained a greater understanding about individuals' rights in health and social care and how equality and diversity underpin these, you will now learn more about how working in an inclusive way links to promoting individuals' rights to be treated fairly and in line with their specific needs.

2.1 Explain how to promote equality and support diversity

There are many different ways to promote equality and support diversity in health and social care to ensure that individuals feel valued.

Promoting equality

Some ways of promoting equality include:

- respecting the rights of individuals, e.g. to privacy, dignity, independence
- working in **inclusive ways** with individuals, e.g. as the experts of their own care and support, as citizens
- providing equal opportunities for individuals, e.g. using an individual's preferred communication methods to enable their participation, adapting the environment to meet individuals' learning and physical needs, such as by ensuring it is not cluttered and is accessible for individuals who have poor mobility
- being **impartial**, i.e. not allowing your own beliefs and values to influence the care and support that you provide to individuals
- not engaging in **discriminatory practices**, challenging and reporting all discrimination.

Supporting diversity

Supporting diversity can include:

- treating individuals as unique, i.e. with their own unique needs, preferences, wishes
- understanding and valuing individuals' differences, e.g. enabling individuals' choices and preferences over what to wear, what to eat
- taking into account individuals' differences, e.g. considering special dietary requirements and preferences, providing opportunities for individuals to share their beliefs
- supporting the **empowerment** of individuals, so that they can make decisions about their care and access services that meet their needs
- providing good-quality care and support that is centred on the individual, their unique likes, needs, abilities, preferences and fulfils care practitioners' duty of care.

Figure 1.3 Supporting diversity

Take it further

For more information on empowerment in health and social care, you will find it useful to read Unit HSC DM1 (LO1); and for supporting the communication needs and preferences of individuals, you will find it useful to read Unit HSC CM4.

Command word activity

Explain (AC 2.1)

Develop a short presentation that includes good practice examples of the different ways that health and social care settings promote equality and support diversity. To help you prepare your presentation you can search the internet for examples of organisations' equality and diversity policies and procedures, or you can visit health and social care settings and speak with the people who work in these. Remember to reference clearly the sources you used.

Key terms

Inclusive ways ways of working that provide individuals with equal opportunities so that they can be included

Impartial fair and objective

Discriminatory practices showing unfair treatment of individuals because of their differences

Empowerment enabling and supporting individuals to be in control of their lives

2.2 Describe how to challenge those not working inclusively in a way that promotes change

It is very important for health and social care practitioners to work in inclusive ways and equally important for them to know how to challenge those not doing so constructively and positively. For example, non-inclusive practices can include not responding to an individual because they do not make a fuss, not giving individuals the opportunity to make their own choices and decisions and not providing individuals with information in a format that they can understand and meets their needs. Non-inclusive practices may be deliberate or accidental; either way they must always be challenged and not tolerated or ignored. Not doing so may mean that working practices continue to become more discriminatory and that care practitioners fail in their duty of care. Here are some guidelines for how you can effectively challenge practitioners to work inclusively.

All non-inclusive working practices must be

- *challenged immediately* to make it clear that they are unacceptable and will not be tolerated
- *reported* to ensure the person with the appropriate authority, i.e. a manager can take the necessary action
- *recorded* to ensure that there is documented evidence of what occurred, who it affected and the actions taken
- *challenged in a positive and constructive way*, i.e. through a discussion with the person to ensure they understand why their work practices are non-inclusive

Case scenario: Lee (AC 2.1, 2.2, 2.3)

Lee is a health care assistant who works in individuals' own homes in the community. He assists individuals with daily activities including washing and dressing, eating and drinking and spends time talking with them when they are feeling anxious or in a low mood.

Jean is Lee's supervisor and this morning, together with Lee, she will visit an individual who Lee provides care to. This will form part of her monitoring visits to ensure that all health care assistants are working in inclusive ways. Jean is looking forward to her monitoring visit today, as having met Lee on one previous occasion she remembers him being very caring, positive and friendly.

On arriving at the individual's home, Lee explains to Jean that this individual is not very nice to him and that he doesn't really enjoy visiting him as he can be quite difficult at times. As the individual opens the door, he ignores Lee and welcomes Jean into his home. Lee walks through the individual's front room into his kitchen and begins to make lunch for him.

The individual tells Lee that he does not feel hungry as it is too early for lunch; Lee explains that he is running late and so he only has 10 minutes to eat his lunch. Lee places a sandwich in front of the individual; the individual begins to get agitated and says that he wants to have a hot lunch today. Lee turns around to Jean and says, 'You see what I have to put up with!'

1. How many examples of non-inclusive ways of working can you find?
2. What do you think about Lee's words to Jean both before and during the visit to this individual?
3. How could Jean support Lee?

- *challenged in a supportive way* that encourages individuals to change their **behaviour**, i.e. by suggesting training courses, **self-reflection**, relevant reading, shadowing of more experienced colleagues, being assigned a **mentor**.

Key terms

Behaviour the way a person thinks, feels and acts

Self-reflection thinking about a situation that occurred, what happened and what could have been done differently

Mentor an experienced person in an organisation who provides training and guidance

2.3 Explain how to support others in promoting equality and rights

Promoting equality and rights involves providing support to others that are involved in individuals' lives, such as their parents, carers, family, friends, colleagues, external partners and health and social care practitioners. This can take many forms and can include:

- suggesting others read the setting's relevant policies and procedures that support the promotion of equality and rights
- raising others' awareness of what different laws say about promoting equality and rights
- providing clear information and advice in relation to practices that promote equality and rights
- encouraging others to access training and development opportunities around the promotion of equality and rights in practice
- learning through modelling and peer observation are good practice methods for the promotion of equality and rights
- providing effective supervision, monitoring and guidance
- reflecting on feedback from others on examples of occasions when equality and rights have been promoted and when they haven't
- open and honest discussions with others in relation to the support they require with promoting equality and rights.

Classroom discussion (AC2.3)

Discuss the different ways to support others in health and social care to promote equality and rights. For each method of support demonstrate your understanding of the reasons why this method can be used and give examples of how to put it into practice.

Activity (AC 2.1, 2.2 and 2.3)

Work in pairs to produce a presentation for a group of informal carers that includes parents, family, and friends of individuals. Your presentation must include:

1. An *explanation* of how to promote equality and support diversity: an explanation means that you need to provide a clear account of your understanding with examples and details of how to promote equality and support diversity and why.
2. A *description* of how to challenge those not working inclusively in a way that promotes change: a description means that you need to provide detailed information about the different methods of challenging practitioners to work inclusively.
3. An *explanation* of how to support others in promoting equality and rights: an explanation means that you need to provide a clear account of your understanding with examples and details of how to support others in promoting equality and rights and why.

Check your understanding

1. Give two examples of ways that care practitioners can promote equality in a health and social care setting.
2. Detail the reasons why supporting diversity in health and social care is important.
3. Detail the consequences of not challenging those who work in non-inclusive ways.
4. Name three methods for challenging non-inclusive working practices.
5. Give two examples of ways to support others in promoting equality.

LO3: Understand legislation and codes of practice in relation to inclusive practice in health and social care settings

All working practices in relation to equality, diversity and inclusion in health and social care that you have learned about are underpinned by legislation. This legislation sets out the experiences that individuals should expect when accessing different services.

3.1 Summarise legislation and codes of practice relating to equality, diversity, inclusion and discrimination

UK and international legislation or laws are established by governments; and in the UK they are made official by Parliament. The following laws you will read about relate to equality, diversity, inclusion and discrimination and the promotion of individuals' rights:

European Convention on Human Rights 1950

The Convention was set up to protect people's basic human rights to lead lives that are fair, dignified and free from discrimination; the UK agreed to be part of the Convention and therefore agreed to protect the Convention's rights. If an individual's rights are not upheld and the individual is unable to address this through the UK's Human Rights Act 1998 (you will learn about this Act in this section) then the Convention provides the individual with the right to have their case listened to by the European Court of Human Rights.

United Nations Convention on the Rights of the Child 1989

The UN Convention on the Rights of the Child (UNCRC) sets out the rights that all children around the world have, as well as how adults and governments must work together to ensure

Take it further

For more information on the UNCRC you will find it useful to access Unicef's website and information pages: http://www.unicef.org.uk/UNICEFs-Work/UN-Convention/

Take it further

For more information on the Human Rights Act 1998 you will find it useful to read the Disability Rights UK's factsheet:

http://www.disabilityrightsuk.org/human-rights-act-1998-hra

that children's rights are promoted and upheld. The Convention placed children and their rights at the forefront and described the rights that all children have in relation to different aspects of their lives such as in relation to the right to education, health and well-being, protection from abuse and discrimination as well as having their views and feelings listened to, respected and taken account of.

The Human Rights Act 1998

Individuals also have basic human rights; the Human Rights Act sets out the rights and freedoms that everyone in the UK has. It states that public organisations (including the Government, the police and local councils) must treat everyone fairly and with dignity and respect.

The following human rights are the most relevant when you receive health or care services. These include the right:

- to respect for private and family life, e.g. the right to privacy in a residential care home
- not to be tortured or treated in an inhuman or degrading way e.g. the right of an individual who is in hospital to be supported with eating and drinking when they are unable to
- to liberty, e.g. the right of an individual who has dementia to not sleep in a locked room
- to life, e.g. the right of an individual's wishes over life-saving treatment not to be ignored
- not to be discriminated against, e.g. the right of an individual who has a physical disability to access a service's premises.

Activity (AC 3.1)

Work in pairs and read through an Equality Policy for a health, social care or children's service and discuss how the policy complies with different pieces of legislation and promotes individuals' rights.

The Equality Act 2010

The Equality Act 2010 makes it unlawful for individuals to be treated unfairly because of their differences. It sets out nine differences that are protected in law and refers to them as the 'nine protected characteristics'.

Figure 1.4 includes the nine protected characteristics stated in the Equality Act 2010.

1. Age: protects individuals from being discriminated against, **harassed** or **victimised** because of their age, i.e. young individuals, older individuals (see p. 13 for definitions)
2. Disability: protects individuals from being discriminated against because of their disability, i.e. physical disability, learning disability, a disability that impairs an individual's mental health

Figure 1.4 The nine protected characteristics of the Equality Act 2010 – do you know what they are?

3. Gender reassignment: protects individuals who have reassigned their gender from being discriminated against, harassed or victimised, e.g. an individual being refused access to a community based social evening group because of their physical appearance

4. Marriage and civil partnership: protects individuals from discrimination and victimisation because of marriage or civil partnership, e.g. being ignored when consulting with a group of residents because of being in a civil partnership which is only available to same sex couples

5. Pregnancy and maternity: protects individuals from discrimination and victimisation because of their pregnancy, or for taking or seeking to take maternity leave, e.g. withdrawal of a care service because an individual is pregnant

6. Race: protects individuals from discrimination, harassment and victimisation because of their race, e.g. exclusion from a mental health drop-in service because of an individual's ethnicity, place of birth or cultural background

7. Religion or belief: protects individuals from discrimination, harassment and victimisation because of religion or belief, e.g. where an individual with Christian beliefs living in a residential care setting is not supported to go to church on Sundays in line with their preferences

8. Sex: protects both male and female individuals from discrimination, harassment and victimisation because of sex (gender), i.e. unwanted conduct of a sexual nature

9. Sexual orientation: protects individuals from discrimination, harassment and victimisation because of sexual orientation.

 Key terms

Harassed unwanted conduct related to a 'protected characteristic'

Victimised when an individual is treated less favourably for making or seen to be supporting an allegation or complaint

Race an umbrella term that includes colour, ethnic origin, national origin and nationality

The Equality Act also sets out *four* main types of discrimination:

1. Direct discrimination occurs where someone is treated less favourably directly because of a protected characteristic they have or are perceived to have, someone they are associated with has (such as family, friend, colleague); e.g. to deny an individual good-quality care and support because of a protected characteristic.

2. Indirect discrimination occurs where a practice or system is applied equally to a group of individuals but does not take into account individuals who have a protected characteristic; e.g. a setting organising a social event but specifying that only younger individuals can attend; there are three older individuals who live in the setting who do not understand the reason for this as they also want to attend.

3. Harassment occurs when there is 'unwanted conduct', that is intimidating or violates a person's dignity and is related to a relevant protected characteristic, e.g. bullying, making inappropriate remarks that humiliate and cause offence.

4. Victimisation occurs where an individual is treated less favourably for making or seen to be supporting an allegation or complaint, e.g. an individual is treated less favourably by the care and support team for making a complaint against the service.

Activity (AC 3.1)

Select three out of the nine characteristics that are protected by the Equality Act and for each one provide an example of how individuals may be treated unfairly when accessing health, social care or children's services.

Command word activity

Summarise (AC3.1)

Develop a poster about the Equality Act. Sum up the key facts about the Act. Include how the Act supports equality, diversity and seeks to prevent discrimination.

The Mental Capacity Act 2005

This Act protects the rights of individuals who lack mental capacity by:

- enabling individuals to make decisions for as long they are able to, i.e. assuming capacity
- enabling individuals to make decisions in line with their views, needs and preferences that others may not agree with
- enabling individuals to make advance decisions about their future care and support, i.e. make decisions before they lose capacity
- appointing who they would like to make decisions on their behalf if they lose capacity, including the use of Independent Mental Capacity Advocates (IMCA) to represent those individuals who do not have anyone to support them
- ensuring all decisions made are in individuals' best interests.

 Key term

Mental capacity refers to an individual's ability to make their own decisions

Command word activity

Summarise (AC3.1)

Research the five key principles on which the Mental Capacity Act 2005 is based. Sum these up on a spidergram and include how they relate to the promotion of individuals' rights.

Command word activity

Evidence (AC3.1)

Produce a pocket-sized leaflet of the key facts of the Mental Capacity Act 2005.

Use the Harvard referencing system to produce an easy-to-follow list of all the sources of information that you've read and referred to.

Remember to use a minimum of two references that can be easily tracked and their validity confirmed.

Take it further

For more information on the Mental Capacity Act you will find it useful to read the Factsheet, 'Mental capacity and mental illness, The Mental Capacity Act 2005 (MCA)' produced by Rethink Mental Illness: **https://webcache. googleusercontent.com/search?q=cache:JPrnk3 GJDEwJ:https://www.rethink.org/resources/m/ mental-capacity-and-mental-illness-factsheet+ &cd=2&hl=en&ct=clnk&gl=uk**

The Health and Social Care Act 2012

The Health and Social Care Act 2012 brought with it many changes for the NHS, with the aim of improving the quality of health care provided and promoting individuals' rights to a fair and inclusive service. With this Act primary care trusts were abolished and replaced with clinical commissioning groups (CCGs). CCGs are responsible for commissioning the majority of health services in England, including emergency care, hospital care, community and mental health services; there are now more than 200 CCGs in England.

Under the Act the NHS and local authorities were given new responsibilities and duties to improve health and reduce health inequalities for the public, such as through the introduction of health and well-being boards that bring together different sectors including the NHS, public health, adult social care, children and young people's services and encourage them to work together in partnership to provide high-quality care and support that meet individuals' diverse needs.

Remember when recording electronic sources of information used to include the date you accessed the resource, the website you used, the resource title and form, i.e. web page, blog.

Remember when recording textbook sources of information used to include the author's name, the title of the book, the name of the publisher, the place where it was published and the year of the publication.

The Act also established Monitor as the health sector's regulator for health care with responsibility for regulating all NHS-funded services in England. The importance of ensuring all care and support provided is of the highest quality is one of the key principles of this Act. This led to the Care Quality Commission, the independent regulator of adult social care in England improving its systems for inspecting care and support services to ensure that individuals do not experience any serious failures, i.e. such as those experienced at the Mid Staffordshire NHS Foundation Trust, where between January 2005 and March 2009 up to 1,200 patients died.

The Care Act 2014

The Care Act aims to make care and support clearer and fairer. It is underpinned by the 'well-being' principle that takes into account the physical, mental and emotional well-being of individuals who require care and support and their carers. It aims to empower individuals to be in control of their care and support. It also states that services must prevent, reduce or delay the need for care and support for all individuals. For example, if an older individual requires assistance with care, shopping or household tasks then they have a right to be supported to access the care and support they require and be provided with a range of options that meet their individual needs and preferences.

Command word activity

Summarise (AC3.1)

Produce an information handout that sums up how the Care Act 2014 relates to individuals who access services and their carers.

Take it further

For more information on the Care Act, you will find it useful to access Skills for Care's resources: http://www.skillsforcare.org.uk/Standards-legislation/Care-Act/Care-Act.aspx

In addition to legislation there are **codes of practice** (also referred to as codes of conduct), relating to equality, diversity, inclusion and discrimination:

Code of Conduct for Health care Support Workers and Adult Social Care Workers in England

This Code is overseen by **Skills for Health** and **Skills for Care** and includes the following Principles, that is, to:

- be accountable for your actions or omissions
- promote and uphold the privacy, dignity, rights, health and well-being of individuals who use health, care and support services and their carers at all times
- work together with your colleagues to ensure the delivery of high-quality, safe and compassionate health care, care and support
- communicate openly and effectively to promote the health, safety and well-being of people who use health, care and support services and their carers
- respect a person's right to confidentiality
- be committed to continuing professional development to improve the quality of health care, care and support
- promote equality, diversity and inclusion.

 Key terms

Codes of practice set out the standards or values that care practitioners must follow to provide high-quality, safe, compassionate and effective care and support

Skills for Health a not-for-profit organisation whose role is to inform policy and raise standards in the health sector

Skills for Care a not-for-profit organisation whose role is to inform policy and raise standards in the adult social care sector

Command word activity

Summarise (AC3.1)

Sum up in 60 seconds how the Code of Conduct for Health care Support Workers and Adult Social Care Workers in England benefits individuals who access services and their carers.

Take it further

For more information you can access the Code of Conduct for Health care Support Workers and Adult Social Care Workers in England from here: **http://www.skillsforcare.org.uk/Documents/ Standards-legislation/Code-of-Conduct/Code- of-Conduct.pdf**

Mental Capacity Code of Practice

The Mental Capacity Code of Practice supports the Mental Capacity Act 2005. It provides guidance on how the five Key Principles of the Mental Capacity Act 2005 should be applied.

Take it further

For more information you can access the Mental Capacity Code of Practice from here: **https://www. gov.uk/government/uploads/system/uploads/ attachment_data/file/497253/Mental-capacity- act-code-of-practice.pdf**

Command word activity

Summarise (AC 3.1)

Produce an information booklet for individuals and their carers about how their rights are promoted through legislation and codes of practice relevant to equality, diversity, inclusion and discrimination:

- a summary of current and relevant legislation and codes of practice relating to equality, diversity, inclusion and discrimination. A summary means that you need to provide an account that includes the main points about relevant legislation and codes of practice.

Check your understanding

1. Give two examples of legislation relating to inclusive practice in health and social care settings
2. Define the meaning of a 'code of practice'.
3. Give two examples of codes of practice relating to inclusive practice in health and social care settings.

LO4: Understand the role of the health and social care practitioner in relation to inclusive practice

4.1 Evaluate the role of the health and social care practitioner in meeting individuals' needs through inclusive practice

Inclusive practice

Inclusive practice is about ensuring that individuals are included and involved in all aspects of life and that they are not excluded or discriminated against because of their differences. Inclusion also links with equality and diversity as it involves recognising individuals' differences and treating them fairly.

The role of the health and social care practitioner

All workers in health and social care have a professional duty of care to ensure that individuals are supported to live their lives as they want to and are in control. Legislation and codes of practice also require health and social care practitioners to support inclusive practice. They require care practitioners to work in the best interests of the individual they care for and support.

Factors that enable inclusive practice

The role of the health and social care practitioner is underpinned by the following principles that enable inclusive working practices:

Activity

Inclusion and the health and social care practitioner (AC 4.1)

Refer back to the case scenario about Lee, a health care assistant working in individuals' own homes in the community that you read about in AC 2.2 and answer the following questions:

1. How could Lee adapt his working practices in this situation to work in an inclusive way?
2. What might be the impact of Lee working inclusively?

1. **Promoting individuals' rights** – practitioners must promote and maintain individuals' rights, i.e. to independence, dignity, privacy, choice, respect, safety, not be discriminated against and accept their differences as unique characteristics of who they are.

2. **Choice** – practitioners must enable individuals to make their own choices within their abilities. For this to be effective individuals need to be able to have accurate information and suitable to their needs, i.e. in a format that can be understood.

3. **Dignity** – practitioners must promote individuals' dignity at all times by respecting their unique preferences, their right to privacy and not to be humiliated.

4. **Culture and personal beliefs** – practitioners must respect individuals' cultures and personal beliefs. The starting point involves getting to know the individual, finding out about their culture, their beliefs and how they prefer to practise them. The next step is to take into account these differences in all aspects of their care and support. Empowering an individual to practise their culture and beliefs will make them feel valued and respected.

5. **Protecting from danger, harm and abuse** – practitioners have a duty to safeguard individuals from danger, harm and abuse and to raise any concerns they have if they believe that an individual's safety or care or dignity is at risk; this is known as whistleblowing. Being trained in how to recognise signs of abuse and knowing the policies and procedures available in organisations for the actions to take will ensure that the potential for abuse occurring is significantly reduced.

6. **Effective communication** – good communication between practitioners and the individuals who access care and support and others is important for the building of positive relationships where everyone feels that they can have open and honest communications and mutual trust and respect are the basis.

7. **Individual care** – care and support that focuses on the individual, their strengths, abilities, unique preferences and differences will enable the individual to feel in control of their care and support. Individual care involves personalising all services provided to the individual while being able to manage any risks identified safely.

8. **Confidentiality** – practitioners have a duty of care to maintain individuals' confidentiality and doing so is an integral part of high-quality care. They must also be aware of when confidentiality must be broken and how to do this without affecting the trust developed with individuals.

9. **Anti-discrimination** – practitioners must not tolerate any discriminatory practices or behaviours; these must always be challenged. It is also important that practitioners are aware of how to ensure that their own personal beliefs and values do not influence the care and support they provide to individuals and that they also educate and mentor others. Developing an organisational culture where this is the case will promote and enable inclusive practice.

Challenges to inclusive practice

Inclusive practice is not without its challenges. As you have already learned, valuing people's individuality and encouraging individuals to express their views increases their self-esteem and confidence. This may in turn mean that individuals make choices and decisions that are in conflict with health and social care practitioners' duty to care. It is important that dilemmas and tensions that may arise do not prevent individuals and practitioners from working together to ensure that individuals have access to the same opportunities as everyone else, including the right to make mistakes and take risks.

Practitioners must use their empathy and communication skills to ensure that they listen to individuals, hear what they are saying, understand what they mean and then adapt their working practices to meet individuals' needs.

Take it further

For more information on the roles and responsibilities of health and social care practitioners you will find it useful to read Unit HSC CM8 (LO4).

Command word activity

Evaluate (AC 4.1)

Imagine you are a care practitioner in a health and social care setting. Write a reflective diary of how you meet the needs of individuals that you provide care and support to through inclusive practice and then evaluate your effectiveness in doing so:

- an evaluation of the health and social care practitioner's role in meeting individuals' needs through inclusive practice. An evaluation means that you need to consider several arguments and come to a conclusion about their success.

Check your understanding

1. Define the term inclusion.
2. What are the benefits of health and social care practitioners working in inclusive working practices?
3. How can health and social care practitioners show respect for individuals' cultures and beliefs?
4. Why is effective communication important to inclusive practice?
5. What is the meaning of individual care and how does it impact on individuals?

Read about it

Age UK (2011) 'Delivering the Equality Duty, Age Matters in public services', London: Age UK

Butt, J. (2006) 'SCIE Race equality discussion paper 03: Are we there yet?' Identifying the characteristics of social care organisations that successfully promote diversity, Social Care Institute for Excellence

Care Quality Commission (2015) 'Equal measures: equality information report' for 2014, Care Quality Commission

INVOLVE (2012) 'Diversity and inclusion: What's it about and why is it important for public involvement in research?', Involve

Morris, C., Ferreiro Peteiro, M. and Collier, F. (2015) Level 3 Health and Social Care Diploma, London: Hodder Education

Websites

Care Quality Commission – (guidance for providers of health and social care services) www.cqc.org.uk

Equality and Human Rights Commission – (information about the Equality Act 2010, Human Rights Act 1998 and on equality, diversity and rights)

www.equalityhumanrights.com

Government Equalities Office – (information about equality legislation and policy) www.gov.uk/government/organisations/government-equalities-office

Skills for Care – (information and resources about the Care Act 2014, Codes of Conduct for care practitioners) www.skillsforcare.org.uk

Skills for Health – (information and resources about the Code of Conduct for care practitioners) www.skillsforhealth.org.uk

MIND – (information and resources about the Mental Capacity Act 2005 and its accompanying Code of Practice)

www.mind.org.uk

Rethink Mental Illness - (information and resources about the Mental Capacity Act 2005 and its accompanying Code of Practice)

www.rethink.org

Unit HSC CM1: How will I be graded?

The table below shows what the learner must do to achieve each grading criterion. Learners must achieve all the criteria for a grade to be awarded (i.e. criteria D1 to D3 must be achieved to pass this unit assessment at grade D). A higher grade may not be awarded before a lower grade has been achieved in full, although component criteria of a higher grade may have been achieved.

		Assessment grading criteria	Assessment of learning/What you need to show
D1	1.1	Define the terms: ● equality ● diversity ● inclusion ● discrimination	Provide information to define each of the following terms: ● equality ● diversity ● inclusion ● discrimination
D2	3.1	Summarise legislation and codes of practice relating to equality, diversity, inclusion and discrimination.	Information must relate to equality, diversity, inclusion and discrimination to summarise: ● current and relevant legislation ● more than one relevant code of practice.
D3		Show evidence of reading or use of sources.	There should be evidence of learners' reading or use of sources. Learners must use a minimum of two traceable references. Learners must include an accurate reference list (bibliography) at the end of the assessment task.
C1	1.2	Explain how rights are promoted in health and social care services.	Explain how rights of individuals are promoted in health and social care services.
C2	2.1	Explain how to promote equality and support diversity.	Provide information to explain a range of ways that equality and diversity can be promoted in health and social care.
C3		Show evidence of reading or use of sources with referencing relevant to the explanations. Good use of vocabulary and grammar.	Use of referencing should show evidence of reading or use of sources. Vocabulary and grammar should be appropriate and accurate for purposes.
B1	1.3	Discuss ethical dilemmas that may arise when balancing individual rights and duty of care.	Discussion must focus on more than one ethical dilemma to demonstrate: ● understanding of ethical dilemmas ● conflicts that may arise when balancing individual rights and duty of care ● consideration from more than one perspective.
B2	2.3	Explain how to support others in promoting equality and rights.	Explanation must demonstrate a range of ways that others can be supported to promote equality and rights.
B3		Show evidence of reading or use of sources. Referencing supports discussion or explanation.	Use of reading or use of sources should be shown through a range of relevant referencing. Referencing should be used appropriately to support discussion or explanation.
A1	2.2	Describe how to challenge those not working inclusively in a way that promotes change.	Provide detailed information to describe ways to effectively challenge practitioners to work inclusively.

		Assessment grading criteria	Assessment of learning/What you need to show
A2		Show evidence of wider background reading or use of sources. Referencing supports discussion and analysis.	Wider background reading should be evident or a wide range of source material should be used. Referencing should support discussion and analysis.
A*1	4.1	Evaluate the role of the health and social care practitioner in meeting individuals' needs through inclusive practice.	Evaluation of the practitioner's role in meeting individual needs through inclusive practice must demonstrate understanding of: ● inclusive practice ● practitioner's role/responsibility when supporting inclusive practice ● factors that enable inclusive practice ● challenges to inclusive practice. Valid judgements must be included to support the evaluation.
A*2		Show evidence of a range of background reading or use of sources used selectively.	Learners should show the ability to consider or explore relevant issues which contribute to the evaluation. An extensive range of background reading or use of sources should be used selectively and cited appropriately.
Current legislation as relevant to Home Nation			

HSC CM2
Human Growth and Development

Learning outcomes

LO1: Understand the key elements of development across human lifespan

1.1 Identify the life stages of human development

1.2 Describe social, emotional, cognitive and physical developments within each life stage

LO2: Understand theories of human growth and development

2.1 Describe theories of human growth and development

LO3: Understand significant life events within each stage of human development

3.1 Explain significant life events that can occur within each stage of human development

3.2 Analyse the impact that significant life events have on individuals

About this unit

The aim of this unit is to provide knowledge and understanding of human growth and development through the human lifespan. It will explore changes across the lifespan and theories of human growth and development. Finally, it will explain some of the significant life events and the potential impact these can have on individuals. This unit has relevance to health and social care in that practitioners work with people of all ages. In addition, health and social care practitioners need to be aware of the impact of life events on the individual they are caring for, their family and the impact that change within the wider family may have on the individual.

LO1: Understand the key elements of development across human lifespan

1.1 Identify the life stages of human development

The human lifespan consists of different life stages. These are shown in Figure 2.1.

We continue to develop through each life stage. Development can be considered in physical, cognitive, emotional and social aspects. Development progresses sequentially through simple to increasingly complex actions, for example a child will walk before they can run or jump.

1.2 Describe social, emotional, cognitive and physical developments within each life stage

Physical development concerns how the body develops, such as growing taller or developing muscles groups. A 'motor skill' is the control of muscles and movement. Gross motor skills involve the use of larger muscle groups, which lead to the development of skills such as walking or running. Fine motor skills involve the use of small muscles groups used for accurate and precise movement such as writing, or using a knife and fork.

Cognitive development is the growth of thinking and intellectual skills. This includes: memory, both short term and long term; understanding and comprehension, such as understanding numbers and shapes; language development, such as being able to understand and speak increasing complexities of language; creativity, such as engaging in imaginary play; and problem-solving skills, which progress as an individual develops, for example from being able to complete jigsaws to putting together arguments for assignments.

Emotional development is the growth and maturation of feelings, and how to express them, learning to manage and deal with emotions, displaying them appropriately as we grow and develop. This is about both one's own feelings as well as other's feelings and being able to express these in an appropriate manner. For example, infants will often express their emotions by crying or getting angry, displaying 'temper tantrums'. As children get older, they are able to express these feelings in other ways such as through talking. Attachment, or the emotional bond between a child and their primary caregivers, is also part of emotional development.

Social development is about learning skills to be able to develop relationships with others and be part of a group such as having friends. To be part of a group and have relationships, individuals must learn the values and skills needed to be able to relate to other people.

Key terms

Physical development how the body develops such as growing taller, or developing muscle groups

Cognitive development relates to thinking and intellectual development

---

Take it further

See Unit HSC CM6, Section 3.1 for more details on attachment theory.

Infancy 0–2 → Childhood 3–10 → Adolescence 11–17 → Early adulthood 18–29 → Middle adulthood 30–60 → Late adulthood 60+

Figure 2.1 The key stages of human life

Key terms

Emotional development is the development and expression of feelings

Social development is about learning skills to be able to develop relationships with others and be part of a group

Key terms

Holistic development Considering all aspects of development, not just one aspect

Reflex an automatic response to something

Although development is often discussed in these areas, they are interlinked. This is known as **holistic development**. For example a 7 year old writing a story with a pen requires cognitive skills to communicate language, and creativity and emotional development to imagine the feeling of the characters. It also requires physical development, with fine motor skills in holding and controlling the pen. Although there are norms, which refer to sequences of development that is expected, it is important to remember that everyone grows and develops at different rates. One child may learn to walk earlier than another, but that child may develop speech before other children. There can be big variations between these developments. There are, however, normal age ranges when babies are children are expected to accomplish some tasks, such as being able to walk by the age of two. Where this does not happen, then further assessment may be required.

Infancy (0–2 years)

In their first two years of life, infants go through a period of rapid growth and development. Newborn babies can demonstrate a number of **reflexes**:

1. Swallowing and sucking reflex where they will suck and swallow anything in their mouths
2. Rooting reflex where the baby will turn their head towards the touch if the side of their cheek is gently stroked
3. Moro reflex is present when a baby feels as if he or she is falling. The baby will spread out their arms, open the hands and then bring them back over the body as if trying to catch hold of something
4. Stepping or walking reflex; when a baby is held upright and tilting slightly forward the baby will use forward stepping movements.

Physical, cognitive, emotional and social development

Table 2.1 illustrates some of the skills that are developed throughout infancy.

Table 2.1 Skills developed by stage of infancy

Stage	Type of development	Skills developed
	Physical	
Newborn 12 weeks 6–9 months 9–12 months 12–18 months 18 months– 2 years		Requires support to lift head Keeps head and chest up while on stomach (supine); kicks legs First teeth; sitting; rolling; crawling Fine pincer grip; cruising; walking Climbing; kneeling; sitting to standing; climb stairs with support Can run and climb stairs one at a time
	Cognitive	
Newborn		Respond to noise and other sounds Starts showing an interest in their surroundings such as following people with their eyes or looking round
6 months		Will understand the meaning of some words such as 'up' or 'down', 'bye bye' and make gestures to demonstrate

Stage	Type of development	Skills developed
9 months		Recognises familiar pictures and faces Language is starting to develop, such as using monosyllables
1 year		Language will progress from imitation of adult sounds, to understanding words, to saying a few words Will use trial and error methods to learn about objects
18 months		Able to recognise parts of their body and point to them on themselves and others Respond to commands, for example 'where's the dog?' Will know their own name and the number of words they can use will increase
2 years		Further increase in word use and they will often talk to themselves Will name objects and what they are doing Speak around 200 words
Emotional		
Newborn babies		Demonstrate happiness often when they are being cared for, for example if they are in the bath or being cuddled
6 months 1 year 18 months 2 years		Will turn immediately when they hear their main carer's voice Can recognise emotions in others and copy that (although does not mean they are experiencing that emotion) May demonstrate temper tantrums as they learn to express and experience emotions Can begin to express how they are feeling Beginning to develop independence Will often request their main carer and demonstrate a strong attachment by clinging to them
Social		
Newborn		When being fed, they will demonstrate engagement with the carer and will often fix their eyes as this occurs Babies start to smile from about 4 to 6 weeks
By 1 year		Will learn to offer toys to others or become wary of strangers
18 months		Will remember where objects are; eager to be independent
2 years		Often engage in role play (such as having a doll who is a baby and putting this baby to bed) May engage in solitary play; types of play may be influenced by cultural factors; children may copy and role play adults

Key term

Culture the beliefs, customs, ways of thinking and behaving of groups in society

Command word activity

Describe (AC 1.2)

Create a booklet aimed at new parents that describes the changes they can expect to see through infancy.

Childhood (3–10 years)

Table 2.2 illustrates some of the skills that are developed throughout childhood.

Table 2.2 Skills developed by stage of childhood

Stage	Type of development	Skills developed
	Physical	
4 years		Ride a tricycle and walk backwards Control a pencil with a thumb and two fingers
5 years		Increased agility and shows good balance Can kick and throw a large ball Has control over implements such as paint brushes
6 years		Gaining strength and agility Can skip Writing becomes more co-ordinated
7 years		Can hop on either leg Has good fine motor skills so can colour inside lines and cut using a line as a guide
	Cognitive	
3 years		Will increase in development of language and understanding Will ask lots of questions to help develop understanding Remember songs and rhymes Will understand concepts of time Most children are toilet trained in the day, although some may still have occasions when this does not happen. It can take longer for children to be toilet trained through the night
4 years		Can count to 20; solve problems
5 years		Can begin to understand abstract problems such as talking about something that has happened or is going to happen Shows an interest in reading and writing
6 years		Begins to understand concepts such as time and distance Can talk with increasing fluency and confidence
7 years		Can express themselves Perform simple calculations As the child gets older, they will be able to read more complex stories and use this language in their writing
	Emotional	
3 years		Enjoys being helpful and will often tidy up or copy tasks that adults are doing Shows affection for younger siblings
4 years		Will try to work out right and wrong
5 years		Many children can show sympathy for friends who are hurt and care for their pets
6 years		Develops concepts of forgiveness and fairness; develops in self-confidence
7 years		Many children have a clear sense of right and wrong
	Social	
3 years		Will like to be with other children and is willing to share toys Makes friends Likes to be independent and will demonstrate this in dressing and undressing themselves Understands the concept of turn-taking
4 years		Independent; can wash and dry their hands; dress and undress Engages in imaginative play
5 years		Can enjoy team games and understand rules of games
6 years		Chooses friends because of their interests or personality
7 years		Takes part in increasingly complex play. As children develop they will display loyalty to a group and will often have a best friend that shares similar interests

Adolescence (11–17 years)

This period of time is marked with rapid changes in all aspects of development.

Physical development

Physical development in this age group is often referred to as puberty.

Puberty is the name given to the period of time where a child's body develops and they turn into an adult. According to the NHS, the current average age for commencement of puberty in girls is 11 years and 12 years in boys.

Table 2.3 demonstrates some of the physical developments in boys and girls.

Table 2.3 Some of the physical developments in boys and girls

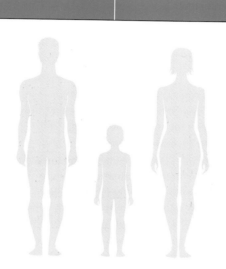

Figure 2.2 Changes to girls and boys in puberty

Boys	Girls
Testicles and penis grow. Growth of pubic hair. Changes in voice as it gets permanently deeper (known as 'voice breaks'). Possible acne. Growth spurt; boys will become taller and more muscular. Facial hair begins to grow. Increase in body sweat as sweat glands become larger and more active.	Increase in genital growth; ovaries, uterus and vagina. Breast development occurs, which is often the first sign of puberty. Breasts continue to grow and change in shape over the first 4 years of puberty. The body changes in size and shape as the girl grows taller and the hips widen. The commencement of menstruating known as the menarche. This will be irregular at first. Growth of pubic hair. Increase in body sweat as sweat glands become larger and more active.

Take it further

Read about young people and mental health and well-being on the Young Minds Website http://www.youngminds.org.uk/about

Emotional development

Adolescents are able to think about others and understand a different perspective. They can develop their own **culture** and values, which may be in conflict with their main carers. They can also experience wide emotional swings and tiredness due to the influence of hormones. These can be difficult for adolescents to manage themselves and for those around them and, as a result, they can often feel misunderstood. Individuals may also feel self-conscious about their own appearance. It can be a stressful period with exams and anxiety about their future. Individuals may require additional support to manage the extra stress in this life stage. According to the Young Minds charity, the proportion of individuals reporting that they frequently feel anxious or depressed has doubled in the last 30 years, from 1 in 30 to 2 in 30 for boys, and 1 in 10 to 2 in 10 for girls.

Cognitive development

Adolescents are able to process increasingly complex information and abstract thought. They can reason and derive conclusions. Their knowledge increases and memory functions efficiently. This lifespan stage also sees individuals undergoing public examinations in GCSEs and A-Levels. Many decisions are made during this time that can influence later life.

Social development

This period of development often sees adolescents becoming increasingly independent from their parents. This can be seen in gaining employment and having their own money, or being able to go to places on their own. Young people in this age group will continue to develop their own set of values and friends will often share similar interests and values.

Activity

Aaron is 15 years old. He has begun puberty and is feeling anxious about this, along with the pressure of revising for school exams. Identify five key messages of support that you would offer him through the changes in this period.

Early adulthood (18-29 years)

Adulthood is the longest period of the lifespan, and although development still occurs, it is not as rapid as in earlier stages.

Physical development

Within this time period adults reach physical maturity and major change in physical performance and development. Most adults reach their physical peak before the age of 30 years. This can be seen in many athletes who will retire from competitive activity early in this life stage. Creating a healthy lifestyle of diet and exercise can help in this period.

Females may become pregnant in this life stage and the body changes during pregnancy, both externally and internally, to adjust to the requirements of the foetus and newborn baby.

Take it further

Research using the NHS website http://www.nhs.uk/Tools/Pages/Pregnancy.aspx or other sources and describe the changes to mother and foetus throughout the pregnancy and factors that can help a woman to have a healthy pregnancy.

Cognitive development

Adults continue to learn throughout this period of their lives. They may develop new skills for a job and acquire new knowledge, and this may be through formal or informal learning. The majority of adults work throughout this stage of their life, earning a living and often focus on establishing their careers.

Emotional development

Work changes can cause stress as expectations of a career and the reality can be different. The challenge of balancing work demands and family life can be difficult to manage. Individuals may form lifelong partnerships, or may find this does not happen for them, or partnerships may break down. All of these situations can cause emotional changes as adults attempt to manage the situation. Adults will form attachments with partners and their own children. These can be influenced by an adult's own experience.

Social development

Social relationships may change in this life stage. Many adults remain friends with people from school, especially if they share similar cultures. Adults may form friendships with people in similar situations, such as their work, or, if they have children, with other parents who have children of the same age. The pattern of activities undertaken with friends may change.

Middle adulthood (30–60 years)

Physical development

For many people, middle adulthood is a time of declining physical skills. There are a number of physical signs and changes in appearance. For example, the skin begins to lose fat and collagen; hair can become thinner and greyer. Internally adults tend to lose muscle length and strength along with bone density. Vision and hearing can decline. **Stress and genetics** (see page 29 for definition) can have an impact upon the rate and intensity of these changes.

Menopause occurs from early to middle adulthood. This is when the ovaries stop producing an egg each month. Women may have various symptoms which can vary in intensity. These include hot flushes, night sweats, mood swings and reduced libido due to the reduction of oestrogen levels.

Emotional development

This period often sees an attempt to balance work and relationships with changes in ageing. Relationships can change in this life stage and parents may see their children growing up and leaving home. This can be a major transition and source of sadness along with pride for some parents. Going through menopause can create

sadness as loss of the ability to have children signifies a major role change in individuals.

Cognitive development

There may be career changes as people assess their lives and decide about balancing family and work. Many adults carry on learning through this period, although there may be some decline in cognitive functions such as memory and problem solving.

Social development

Relationships may continue through from early adulthood into this life stage. These might have begun in school, work or areas with mutual interests such as a club or, as parents, through their children. Adults may split their time between living their own lives and caring for children, with many getting involved in caring for grandchildren. Focusing on these areas may limit social activity. Friendships continue to be important.

Later adulthood (60 years upwards)

Physical development

A gradual physical decline accompanies ageing. There is a continual decline in physical well-being from middle adulthood along with a decline in mobility. **Sensory** functions such as seeing and hearing can decline. There can be a reduction in the ability to absorb nutrients and this can lead to an increase in the risk of being unwell. Many of the body systems such as cardiovascular or musculoskeletal can decline in older age and conditions such as arthritis may present.

Activity

Research one of the following: dementia, arthritis, coronary heart disease or COPD. Outline the condition, along with a description of the causes and treatment methods. Is there any way to prevent the condition or minimise the severity?

Cognitive development

Many adults in this age group carry on learning and some take up new skills. There is an increased risk of dementia during this life stage, which is a progressive disease that affects normal brain functioning. There is evidence that continuing to use cognitive skills can help to maintain healthy functioning in adulthood.

Emotional development

The changes of ageing along with loss of parents, friends or a partner can lead to a decrease in self-esteem and self-confidence. Older people can find tasks harder to complete, which can also impact upon this. It can be difficult to adjust to a change in role, such as retirement, and some may need support throughout this process.

Social development

Throughout the process of ageing people may also experience ageism where employers or colleagues view older people in a negative stereotypical way and believe they do not have the mental cognition to work. Retirement can provide an opportunity to take up new skills and experiences, although in some cases people may struggle with not having work as a focus for their social relationships.

Command word activity

Identify (AC 1.1)

Pauline is 82 years old and married to Amos. They married at 21 years of age and had three children Greg, Brian and Kathryn and now have eight grandchildren. Pauline worked in a large NHS hospital as a medical secretary until her retirement.

Create a large timeline using some wallpaper or similar. Annotate it with examples of development that have occurred throughout her lifespan.

Check your understanding

1. Identify all six life stages.
2. Briefly define the differences between physical, cognitive, emotional and social development.
3. Give an example of each type of development: physical, cognitive, emotional and social.
4. Outline the similarities and differences in puberty for boys and girls.
5. Explain the term holistic development with examples of development from three of the life stages.

LO2: Understand theories of human growth and development

2.1 Describe theories of human growth and development

There are many theories of human growth and development from different perspectives. It is a broad area exploring how individuals change as they grow from birth through child and adolescence into adulthood. Psychologists often separate development into specific areas of physical, cognitive and social or emotional development. Psychology tries to explain every aspect of development for example how children learn to respond to emotions, how they make friends and how we learn to think. These are helpful to understand this development and how we can support individuals to grow and develop. Different factors can influence development, some of these are genetic and some are from the environment, or a combination of both of these. This is known as the nature/nurture debate.

Take it further

Read about the nature/ nurture debate in Unit HSC CM6, Section 2.

Key term

Genetic the characteristics such as the physical, behaviour or medical conditions that are inherited from parents

Cognitive theory

Cognitive theory is the study of the mind focusing on learning, attention, reasoning, and language. Many consider that the brain can be understood as a computing system. The three psychologists within this field are Piaget, Vygotsky, and Kohlberg.

Piaget

Piaget suggested that children pass through a number of stages in their cognitive development. The stages are fixed and named sensorimotor, preoperational thinking, concrete operation and formal operational. Children initially explore the world through their senses and as they get older, they are able to develop understanding of complex information and abstract thought.

Take it further

Read about Piaget's Stages of Cognitive Development in Unit HSC CM6, Section 3.1.

Vygotsky

Vygotsky emphasised the importance of people around the child and the social group. He devised a term called the **Zone of Proximal Development**. Vygotsky stated that there is a difference between the development a child can achieve independently and the development a child can achieve with guidance. There is a balance between activities the child will find too easy and those that they will find too hard.

The role of the health and social care practitioner is to assist them at a level appropriate for that child. For example, if a child is reading and comes across a word they do not understand, then methods such as breaking the word down into phonics, or discussing what is happening in the story can help the child to identify the word for themselves. Telling the child the word would not help their development.

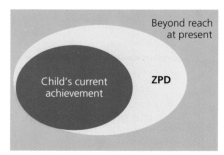

Figure 2.3 Zone of Proximal Development

 Key term

Zone of proximal development this describes tasks that the child cannot complete by themselves, but can be completed with the help or assistance of adults

Vygotsky researched the importance of language and education. He considered that children use language to communicate and to solve tasks. This is demonstrated as children will often verbalise a commentary on what is happening around them. Eventually, this becomes internal speech and their thoughts. Vygotsky identifies language as a key factor in the development of cognitive ability.

Activity

Using the information given in LO1, or your own knowledge, identify a skill that a child learns to develop. For example, tying shoe laces. How do adults help the child to learn these skills?

Kohlberg

Kohlberg focused on moral development and built on Piaget's stages of development, so his is considered to be a cognitive approach to the development of morality (Gibbs 2013). He devised a number of dilemmas and a series of questions to explore to which subjects would respond. He concluded that there were three levels of moral development and six stages. Kohlberg argued that individuals go through the stages in a hierarchical order. See Table 2.4.

Command word activity

Evidence (AC 2.1)

Research Kohlberg's theory, including the 'Heinz dilemma', one of the scenarios that he used to demonstrate his theory. How might a child, going through each of the six stages above, respond differently to the dilemma at each stage? Identify other factors that may influence the child's response.

When carrying out your research, ensure you use a range of resources. Keep an accurate record of the sources you have used. Use specific references to your research when responding to the question.

Table 2.4 Kohlberg's stages of development

Level	Stages	Description
1. Preconventional In this stage the judgement of the child is based on those they see as authority close by	1. Punishment and obedience 2. Individualism and exchange	People must be good to avoid being punished Children realise that there is more than one viewpoint, but follow rules
2. Conventional The rules and norms of the group become the basis of moral judgements	3. Mutual interpersonal relationships 4. Maintaining social law and order	Children want to be good to gain approval of others and so it becomes important The child becomes aware of wider rules in society, but still feel they must follow the law
3. Post conventional An individual will make choices and make judgements based on what concerns a specific individual or group	5. Social contract and individual rights 6. Universal ethical	Individuals realise that values may change according to different situations (although rules should generally be followed) This will only apply to a small number of adults These follow self-chosen ethics to work out what is right or wrong

Humanist theories

Humanists explore psychology by looking at the whole person. Maslow is one psychologist that uses this perspective. Maslow was interested in exploring the theory of motivation and how this links to human behaviour. His hierarchy of needs is frequently displayed as a pyramid with basic needs at the lower level of the hierarchy and progressing towards the higher ends.

Physiological needs are basic needs that are required for survival and include water, air and sleep. Maslow placed these needs at the bottom of his hierarchy as he felt that these are the most important. Without these, individuals will not be able to physically survive. Maslow considered that once basic needs are met, then security is next with a requirement for employment and safety in the environment. The third level includes social needs such as love, belonging and acceptance into a social group. After these three levels, self-esteem becomes increasingly important as well as the need to respect others, or accomplish goals or tasks, such as doing well at school or

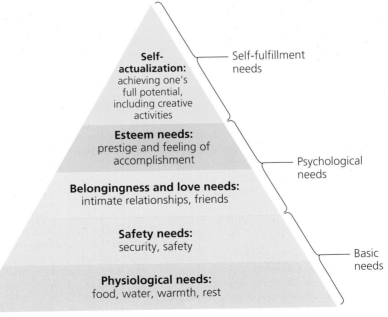

Figure 2.4 Maslow's hierarchy of needs

in a hobby. The last level of self-actualisation is the highest level of need and is concerned with personal growth and fulfilling potential.

Maslow's hierarchy is useful for demonstrating how we can develop into healthy individuals. Maslow has been criticised for only using a small number of individuals when researching self-actualisation and for stating that individuals have to move through all the stages, mastering each before achieving the next.

Classroom discussion (AC 2.1)

Discuss Maslow's hierarchy of needs. Do you agree with Maslow and the order of the stages? Are there any other needs you would add into the hierarchy? Do you feel it is possible for all individuals to reach the higher levels of the pyramid?

Activity

Choose two of Erikson's life stages and identify a fictional character that may be in each of these life stages. Create a profile of the individual, describing the typical behaviour and characteristics they are displaying from that stage and then consider whether they have had a positive or negative outcome

Learning/conditioning

Some psychologists considered we develop through learning observable behaviour and the environment. Skinner is one such psychologist. He considered the important factor is how rewards and punishments shape behaviour and therefore how behaviour can be modified to improve behaviour. Skinner introduced and evaluated the importance of reinforcement which can strengthen behaviour, whereas behaviour that is not reinforced is weakened and not likely to be repeated. This can be identified in human behaviour; for example, if a child is praised for doing something such as getting themselves dressed, they are more likely to repeat this behaviour.

Psychosocial

Erikson theorised that development occurs through completing a series of stages. For each one there are two possible outcomes. If the individual completes the stage successfully, they will have a healthy personality and be able to interact with other people. If an individual does not complete the stage successfully, then this will explain how someone may behave or feel in later life and can cause problems in later life. The stages are as given in Table 2.5.

Table 2.5 Erikson's stages of development

Stage	Description	Positive outcome	Negative outcome
1. Trust vs Mistrust	*Between birth and 1 year* The infant learns the world is good and can be trusted, or bad and cannot meet his or her needs	The infant develops a sense of trust and in adulthood believes that challenges can be resolved	An inability to trust with possible anxiety, insecurities and mistrust in the world
2. Autonomy vs Shame	*1–3 years* Children begin to develop their independence such as choosing what to play with. Toilet training is a vital part of this process as a child learns to control their own body functions	A child will become confident and secure in their own ability. They often say no	If children are criticised, then they learn self-doubt and will feel shame and that they are inadequate. Later, as an adult they may criticise themselves and feel they have less of an ability than they actually do
3. Initiative vs Guilt	*3–6 years* Children assert themselves and develop their own sense of autonomy. They plan games and initiate activities	Successful outcomes lead to an ability to lead others and they are secure in their decisions and plans	If a child is punished or receives a persistent negative reaction for expressing these ideas, then they develop a sense of guilt and may lack self-initiative

Stage	Description	Positive outcome	Negative outcome
4. Industry vs Inferiority	*6 years to puberty* Children develop pride in what they have accomplished	Successful completion will lead to confidence and an ability to achieve goals	A child will feel less worthy and will lack motivation in adulthood to achieve. They may often compare themselves to others
5. Identity vs Role Confusion	*12 –18 years* Children are becoming more independent and decide about career goals, and relationships	Security and forming their own identity	There may be role confusion and drifting in later life
6. Intimacy vs Isolation	*Young adulthood* The adult will develop an intimate relationship or if does not do so will become isolated	Exploring relationships leading to longer term commitments. Success in this stage will lead to comfortable relationships and a sense of commitment	If someone does not develop intimacy and commitment they may experience isolation, loneliness and possibly depression
7. Generativity vs Stagnation	*Mature Adulthood late 20s to 50s* Follows on from developing values and close relationships. The adult will pass on what they have learned, have a family and help the next generation	Individuals will feel they are contributing to society	Individuals may feel unproductive or uninvolved in the world
8. Ego Integrity vs Despair	*50s and beyond* People in this life stage will look back on their life	Successful completion means looking back with very few regrets and generally feeling satisfied	They may feel that their life has been wasted and may experience regrets

Take it further

We explore Erikson's theory further in Unit HSC CM6, Section 3.1.

Activity (AC 2.1)

Some children might have a reward chart for good behaviour or for completing an activity, such as putting their toys away. After doing the task they are given a sticker or star. When a certain number of tasks have been completed, the child is given a treat or reward.

1. Describe how Skinner may explain the reward chart as a way of reinforcing behaviour.
2. Explain one strength of using a reward chart and one possible weakness.

Social learning

Bandura

Bandura stated that behaviour is learned and role models are therefore essentially important. This can be seen in children copying the behaviour of their parents, for example wearing adults' shoes for fun. Behaviour is more likely to be repeated if there has been reinforcement. This can be a positive reinforcement such as rewarding a behaviour, or a negative reinforcement, which requires a behaviour change to stop the negative experience. Children will have a range of role models that they may relate to and may imitate or copy their behaviour. In an early years setting, workers should act as role models, for example in the language used and how staff interact with each other. This approach can also be useful in treating addictions, either by modelling non-addictive behaviour or being exposed to someone who is receiving negative consequences of the behaviour (for example being in prison).

Activity

Identify role models that children may have. Do these influence behaviour or values in a positive or negative way? Evaluate the concept of a role model in influencing behaviour by considering how the role model influences behaviour and what may stop the influence. Consider other factors in a child's life that may influence them. Is there anything that makes one influence stronger than another?

Classroom discussion (AC 2.1)

Compare and contrast theories of development. Consider whether these theories break down the development into sequential stages and the duration of life time the stages cover, the influences on development such as genes or environment and any weaknesses of these theories.

Command word activity

Describe (AC 2.1)

Create an information poster which lists the different life stages. At each stage, list the relevant theorists of human growth and development that link to that life stage, and give a brief description of their theory.

Check your understanding

1. Identify the basic physiological needs in Maslow's hierarchy of needs.
2. Identify the theorists that use stages of development as part of their theories.
3. Outline the role of reinforcement in Skinner's theory.
4. Identify two stages of Erikson's theory.
5. Explain Kohlberg's theory.

LO3: Understand significant life events within each stage of human development

3.1 Explain significant life events that can occur within each stage of human development

3.2 Analyse the impact that significant life events have on individuals

Life events are stages or milestones that occur during a human's life. Each event is likely to have an effect, sometimes short term and sometimes long term. It can affect different aspects of development, that is, physical, cognitive, emotional and social.

This section is important to understanding the impact that events may have on the reason why you are working with the individual. For example, a health promotion nurse may try to encourage an individual to give up smoking, but he or she may be going through a divorce or coping with the death of a close relative or friend, which may mean that the nurse will need to change the priorities of working or the way in which health promotion is carried out.

Feeding

The establishment of feeding is a key life event; the infant at this stage learns to trust that his or her basic needs will be met. Feeding also is part of the development process, leading to an increase in independence as the child learns to feed themselves. In addition to learning to trust the carer, healthy eating and diet can lead to a healthy lifestyle for the child and healthy eating habits in later life.

Toilet training

Toilet training will happen at the child's own pace. It is important that this age group is given consistent and calm guidance and encouragement. A child gains independence and responsibility at this stage and, as such, it's a major life event. It can aid self-control and self-confidence which can

Activity (AC 3.1)

Create an information leaflet on toilet training on strategies used to help children learn toilet training. Describe the benefits of toilet training for both the child and the parents. Outline how this links to Erikson's theory

be positively influenced by a successful toilet training experience. Conversely, a child who does not achieve the skill quickly may find that they feel shame and doubt their own abilities, leading to a lack of confidence. Parents have an important role here as success can lead to feelings of competence or doubt (this links to Erikson's theory of Autonomy versus Shame).

Starting nursery or school

Often the first time a child is left for a period of time without their parents is when they start nursery. It can be a source of stress for both children and their parents. Children may experience a feeling of separation from parents or other carers and this itself can be a source of anxiety.

In this new environment, infants and children learn new skills and new tasks and develop new relationships with other children and other adults. They will learn how to interact with others and practise important skills to help their social development, such as turn-taking. It can be daunting for the child, especially as they will be meeting so many new children and adults. There may be some difficult situations along the way in establishing friendships, and children's self-esteem and self-concept can be affected if they compare themselves with others.

As children enter secondary school, a big change occurs from having one main teacher to subject-specific teachers. There is then the added pressure of public examinations and making decisions about their future. Some children may have a negative experience within school and experience bullying.

Take it further

Research how parents and health and social care practitioners can support children when starting school.

Case scenario: Kate

Kate is 14 years old and attends secondary school. A group of other students created a fake social media account and used this to contact people in the school to insult them. Kate became upset about this and tried to tell people that it was not her who had contacted them, but they did not believe her. Kate become lonely at school as none of the other students would talk to her and began to make up symptoms of illness to stay away from school. When this was investigated one of the members of the group that had created the account explained how they did not want to do it, but had felt pressurised from other members in the group to help create the account.

1. Identify the types of bullying that occurred.
2. Describe the potential impact of the bullying on Kate and the other students that have been contacted.
3. Explain why the member of the group may have felt pressure to join in with the bullying.

Bullying

Bullying can take place in different settings including schools. It can happen at different ages and in different ways. Examples include cyber bullying or physical bullying. It often has a major impact upon self-esteem and confidence, causing anxiety and worry. This in turn can impact upon concentration on subjects, and some individuals may not want to attend school. This can have long-lasting impacts on attainment and impact upon choices after school has finished.

Birth of a sibling

The arrival of a new brother or sister can have a major impact upon a family. It is likely to change the dynamics of the family. The older child's emotions may vary. They may feel happy as they have someone to play with or care for, or be proud with extra responsibility and a new role as the 'big sister / brother'. They may feel that the individual is taking over their role in the family and may experience feelings of jealousy if they feel that their parents are giving more attention to the new sibling than themselves. In some circumstances, it can cause older children to regress in their own development such as by experiencing disturbed sleep or they may no longer have control of their bladder and bowels despite being 'toilet trained'.

Parenthood

Having a child is another major life event that may occur in adulthood. Parents acquire many new skills in learning how to look after the new baby. It can be a sociable experience, for example by meeting other parents in the same situation; on the other hand it can be an isolating one, for example if parents lose touch with their other friends. Parenthood is a bonding experience between parents and children. Parents will lose their free time and their lives will not be as flexible as previously. It can be emotionally draining, as parents will not sleep as well in the early stages. They may also feel some anxiety as they worry about their child. Some mothers may also experience post-natal depression in the first year after the birth of a child.

Command word activity

Explain (AC 3.1)

Create a pamphlet aimed at new parents. It should explain the challenges and benefits of parenthood, and explain how a new sibling can affect the family dynamics.

Leaving home

Leaving home is a big step for an individual and a very significant life event. Many young people do this as they go off to university; some may remain in the family home until later in their lives. This can have a number of impacts. An individual learns to be independent, resilient and resourceful. However, learning to manage day-to-day tasks such as cooking and cleaning, household finances and budgeting to pay bills, buy food and have money for social occasions can be very challenging. Some people find it difficult to do this and may end up in debt. They may miss their families and their previous life, which can have an emotional impact. Families will miss the individual and parents may have 'empty nest syndrome' where they feel grief and loneliness when the children leave home.

Employment

A person's first job often occurs within the adolescent life stage. The UK Commission for Employment and Skills reports that 40 per cent of teenagers have a job in the UK, combining working with education. According to the Office of National Statistics, in the population as a whole, there are 31.77 million people in work.

Employment creates responsibilities, as employees have to follow the policies and procedures of the workplace, along with fulfilling their job role requirements. An employee will learn new skills and this achievement can be a positive source of self-esteem and feelings of accomplishment. Employment provides individuals with an opportunity to meet people with similar views to themselves. Successfully managing stress can have a positive impact upon an individual's resilience and ability to cope. However, employment can also be a source of stress and difficulties for an individual. It may be that they struggle with money or have difficulty separating work and family life. Some people may be disappointed that they do not get promotion or are unable to take up other opportunities, which can have a negative impact on self-esteem.

Some people opt to be self-employed and work for themselves rather than an employer. Some people find this a more positive experience as they can set their own hours and may have more control over their work / life balance. It may also mean that someone can work in an area that they really enjoy. However, it may cause additional pressure as some of the in-work benefits such as sick pay or annual leave do not exist. An individual may struggle to make their business work from a financial perspective, or they may miss the social aspects of work, such as conversations with colleagues, if they are running their business alone.

Redundancy

When a business or workplace needs to reduce their workforce, it may be that the job role or employee is no longer needed. This must be done in a legal and fair way, but redundancy has obvious financial implications for individuals, mainly the loss of a regular income. It can create a loss of self-esteem and identity which can be difficult for the person to overcome as they have gone from being employed to being unemployed. The individual may have a number of feelings such as shock, anger, sadness, and a loss of confidence. It can create difficulties within relationships due to extra financial pressures or adjusting to the new roles in the household. It can, however, be a beneficial experience, especially if the individual did not enjoy their job. It can be an opportunity to retrain or move to a different area.

Marriage

The legal union of two people is a big step in a relationship. Some people live together or 'cohabit' without being married. This can provide a good source of security for the individuals and the benefits of having someone who cares and loves them can increase feelings of self-esteem. The sharing of finances can help reduce anxiety and increase the resources available to both. However, marriage can be difficult to begin with as people adjust to the new roles and learn to accommodate someone else, especially if a couple has not previously cohabited.

Marriage can sometimes result in divorce, which is the legal dissolution of the marriage. Divorce is a difficult process, and although there may be an overwhelming sense of relief if the marriage was a source of unhappiness, it can have a number of impacts. Financially, learning to adjust to less of an income and the resulting complications of sorting new housing can have an impact. Learning to adjust to a new role as someone who is divorced can also be difficult. The impact on any children can be especially difficult. They may feel a sense of loss, and disruption if they need to move to a different house or school. They may even feel guilty, believing that it's their fault or something they have done, and many children hold on to a wish that their parents may get back together.

Moving home

This may occur at any age in the life stage. It can be a source of a fresh start and having time to begin again. It may provide an opportunity to take up new jobs or gain promotion. However, it can also be a source of stress for individuals, as finding out where to go or where facilities are can be difficult, as is making new friends. There is a wealth of research stating that adults who have good social networks have a lower risk of disease and depression.

Activity (AC 3.1)

Brian and his daughter have moved to a new area for Brian's work. They are now further away from Pauline and Brian's brother Greg and their family. Identify the effect that this change may have on Brian, his daughter and Pauline.

Loss of partner, parent or friend

In life, people will experience the loss of a partner, parents, close friend or child. Grief is a response to loss and has a number of impacts. People will feel a range of emotions such as anger, shock, guilt, sadness or a feeling of hopelessness. Grief can have a wide range of effects: for instance someone may feel overwhelming exhaustion or be unable to sit still. It can have physical effects too such as loss of appetite or eating too much. An individual may even experience aches and pains. It can cause anxiety or it may affect sleep and relationships with others. Different individuals will cope with loss in a range of ways.

Age-related and chronic medical conditions

Individuals may be born with medical conditions or they may develop these throughout their

lifespan. If a condition lasts longer than three months, it is known as a **chronic condition**.

As individuals get older, the incidences of certain conditions increase. Some examples of these conditions are dementia, cardiovascular disease or osteoarthritis.

All of these chronic conditions can have an impact upon different aspects of development. Individuals may experience pain and discomfort and they may need to attend regular hospital appointments. Some conditions can be degenerative and get progressively worse over time. This can affect cognitive development with individuals needing to miss time off school or work.

As a condition progresses, individuals may need to change their job. This can cause a change in self-esteem and self-concept as the individual adjusts to the effects of their condition. It can cause additional financial pressures as they may not be able to work and contribute to the family income. There can be additional caring responsibilities for another family member, which can cause additional emotional pressures.

 Key term

Chronic condition a condition such as a health condition or disease that lasts longer than three months

Activity (AC 3.1)

Read this letter from Amos to his friend Cecil

Dear Cecil,

I'm not writing with good news really. You know Pauline my wife has been unwell for a while, well she passed over last week. It was very peaceful in the end and I'm thankful that we were able to have her at home like she wished. I know she was ill for so long and that there was nothing they could do, but I miss her so much. I feel guilty that I could not do more.

I find myself laying an extra place at the table for dinner, and going to turn on the TV for programs that she watches thinking she's there, but of course she's not. I find that I cannot sleep or I sleep all the time. I can't eat very well. I'm scared about how I am going to carry

on without her, we'd been together so long.

What am I going to do Cecil? Is this normal?

Best Wishes

Amos

1. Research support groups in your local area that can assist individuals who are experiencing grief and loss.
2. How are they contacted? What support do they offer?
3. Then write a reply to Amos explaining grief and groups and organisations that may be able to help him. Revisiting HSC CM6, Section 3 may also help with this activity.

Activity

Choose a chronic, long-term health condition and conduct some research. Identify the health promotion activities that help support people with this condition. Evaluate the extent to which these activities are effective.

Check your understanding

1. Identify three major life changes that can occur in adulthood.
2. Outline how toilet training can impact upon an infant.
3. Describe how employment can have positive and negative effects.
4. Identify and explain the impact of one age-related medical condition on development.

Command word activity (AC 3.1)

Explain

Using the case study of Pauline in Section 1.1 add information to your timeline, which explains two significant life events that have occurred in her lifespan.

Analyse

Using more than one theoretical perspective, analyse the impact that life events may have had on Pauline.

Command word activity (AC 3.2)

Evidence

Using the life events that impacted upon Pauline, you have analysed, consider how these impact upon other members of the family. Create a spider diagram with Pauline and the chosen life event in the middle.

Then identify all other members of the family who may be affected. For each member of the family, identify a quote or reference from books or websites that explain, the impact this can have.

Case scenario: Marina Chapman

Marina Chapman spent around five years of her early life living in the jungles of Colombia with no human contact. She describes spending much of this with the monkeys in the jungle until being found by hunters. With the monkeys she learned how to acquire food from them and where to drink water. When she was found, she had no human language and did not walk; she mobilised by crawling. She has since said she missed human contact.

1. Outline how this case study can help understand physical, cognitive and social development.
2. Consider the impact of social deprivation on holistic development. Apply theoretical perspectives to support your response.

Read about it

Boyd, D. and Bee, H. (2015) *Lifespan Development*, England: Pearson

Gibbs, J. (2013) *Moral Development and Reality: Beyond The Theories Of Kohlberg, Hoffman, & Haidt*, Oxford: Oxford University Press

Hattenstone, S. (2013) 'Was Marina Chapman really brought up by monkeys?' *The Guardian*, Saturday 13 April 2013.

Santrock, J. (2013) *Life-span Development*, Texas: McGraw Hill

Vygotsky, L. (1986) *Thought and Language*, 2nd edition, Cambridge, MA: MIT Press

Websites

NHS (2016) Stages of Puberty accessed from http://www.nhs.uk/Livewell/puberty/Pages/puberty-signs.aspx

ONS (2016) UK Labour Market September 2016 Retrieved from http://www.ons.gov.uk/employmentandlabourmarket/peopleinwork/employmentandemployeetypes/bulletins/uklabourmarket/september2016#main-points-for-may-to-july-2016

YoungMinds (2016) Mental Health Statistics retrieved from http://www.youngminds.org.uk/training_services/policy/mental_health_statistics

Unit HSC CM2: How will I be graded?

The table below shows what the learner must do to achieve each grading criterion. Learners must achieve all the criteria for a grade to be awarded (i.e. criteria D1 to D3 must be achieved to pass this unit assessment at grade D). A higher grade may not be awarded before a lower grade has been achieved in full, although component criteria of a higher grade may have been achieved.

Grade	Assessment criteria number	Assessment criteria	Assessment of learning / What you need to show
D1	1.1	Identify the life stages of human development.	Provide information to identify the life stages of human development.
D2		Show evidence of reading or use of sources.	There should be evidence of learners' reading or use of sources. Learners must use a minimum of two traceable references to support the discussion.
C1	1.2	Describe social, emotional, cognitive and physical developments within each life stage.	Refer to the life stages identified for D1 to describe developments that may take place during each stage, in relation to: ● social development ● emotional development ● cognitive development ● physical development.
C2		Show evidence of reading or use of sources with referencing relevant to the descriptions. Good use of vocabulary and grammar.	Use of referencing should show evidence of reading or use of sources. Vocabulary and grammar should be appropriate and accurate for purpose.
B1	2.1.	Describe theories of human growth and development.	Information must focus on human growth and development to describe more than one relevant theory which may include: ● cognitive theory ● psychosocial theory ● humanist theory ● social learning theory.
B2		Show evidence of reading or use of sources. Referencing supports discussion.	Use of reading or use of sources should be shown through a range of relevant referencing. Referencing should be used appropriately to support description.
A1	3.1.	Explain significant life events that can occur within each stage of human development.	Refer to the life stages identified for D1 to provide a detailed explanation of more than one significant life event that may take place at each stage.
A2		Show evidence of wider background reading or use of sources. Referencing supports the explanation.	Wider background reading should be evident or a wide range of sources material should be used. Referencing supports the explanation.
A*1	3.2.	Analyse the impact that significant life events have on individuals.	Provide detailed information to analyse the impact that significant life events may have on individuals. Information must be given from more than one perspective to support the analysis.
A*2		Show evidence of a range of background reading or use of sources used selectively.	Learners should show the ability to consider or explore relevant issues which contribute to the evaluation. An extensive range of background reading or use of sources should be used selectively and cited appropriately.

HSC CM3
Safeguarding in Health and Social Care

Learning Outcomes

LO1: Understand safeguarding

1.1 Explain what is meant by safeguarding

1.2 Explain how safeguarding:
- keeps individuals safe
- values individuals' needs
- protects individuals

1.3 Explain how health and social care practitioners can take steps to safeguard themselves

LO2: Understand how to safeguard individuals in relation to legislation, policies and procedures

2.1 Summarise current legislation in relation to safeguarding

2.2 Describe the relationship between legislation, policy and procedure

2.3 Identify policies and procedures in relation to safeguarding

LO3: Understand factors that may contribute to an individual being vulnerable to harm or abuse

3.1 Explain factors that may contribute to an individual being vulnerable to harm or abuse

LO4: Know signs, symptoms, indicators and behaviours that may cause concern

4.1 Describe signs, symptoms, indicators and behaviours that may cause concern relating to:
- neglect
- self-neglect
- physical abuse
- emotional abuse
- sexual abuse
- domestic abuse
- financial abuse
- institutional abuse
- bullying

LO5: Understand the lines of reporting and responsibility in relation to the safeguarding, protection and welfare of individuals

5.1 Describe the lines of reporting and responsibility in relation to safeguarding, protection and welfare

5.2 Explain the boundaries of confidentiality in relation to the safeguarding, protection and welfare of individuals

LO6: Understand the role and responsibilities of the health and social care practitioner in relation to safeguarding individuals

6.1 Evaluate the role and responsibilities of the health and social care practitioner in relation to safeguarding individuals

About this unit

Safeguarding in health and social care involves not only protecting individuals' health, well-being and development, but also valuing their unique needs and promoting their human rights; that is to live free from potential and actual danger, maltreatment, harm, abuse and neglect. Safeguarding is an essential part of the role of a health and social care practitioner and the provision of safe, high-quality and effective care.

In this unit you will find out about the meaning of safeguarding in health and social care, including how health and social care practitioners can safeguard individuals and themselves. Understanding the current safeguarding legislation that exists as well as how this underpins work settings' policies and procedures will help you to further develop your understanding of how safeguarding is put into practice.

Individuals in health and social care may be more vulnerable to danger, harm, abuse and neglect than others; understanding the factors that may contribute to an individual's vulnerability as well as recognising the signs, symptoms, indicators and behaviours that may cause concern will help with their protection. You will also learn more about the health and social care practitioner's role and responsibilities in relation to safeguarding for reporting causes for concern and maintaining boundaries of confidentiality when doing so.

LO1: Understand safeguarding

1.1 Explain what is meant by 'safeguarding'

Safeguarding children and adults who access health and social care services is fundamental to providing high-quality care and support.

Safeguarding of children involves:

- protection from maltreatment
- prevention of the impairment of promotion of their health and development
- ensuring they are provided with safe and effective care
- enabling all children to have the best outcomes in life.

Legislation identifies that safeguarding adults means 'protecting an adult's right to live in safety, free from abuse and neglect'. The Care Act 2014 recognises that this cannot be achieved by organisations and health and social care practitioners working in isolation; instead, they must work together to prevent individuals from being placed in danger or experiencing harm, abuse and neglect. At the same time, it is crucial that individuals' health, well-being and rights are promoted and that their individual needs, wishes, preferences and abilities to understand the risks associated with their personal circumstances are taken into account.

Take it further

Current legislation on safeguarding can be found at **www.gov.uk**. For more information on the Care Act 2014, you will also find it useful to read LO2 in this unit; Unit HSC CM8 (LO1); Unit HSC DM1 (LO1); and Unit HSC DM2 (LO1).

The safeguarding of children is underpinned by the following two principles:

1. **Safeguarding is everyone's responsibility:** everyone who works with children has a responsibility to keep them safe, e.g. by identifying and raising their concerns, working closely with other professionals and services, ensuring they are aware of their own role in safeguarding as well as those of others.

2. **A child-centred approach:** the services that provide care and support must put the interests, needs and views of the children first, e.g. by listening to children, taking what they express or say seriously, working with them to decide how to meet their needs.

The safeguarding of adults is underpinned by the following six principles:

1. **Empowerment:** providing individuals with support to make their own **informed choices and decisions** (see p. 44 for definition) in relation to what they would like to see happen as the result of the safeguarding process, e.g. by supporting individuals to understand the

risks, benefits and possible options open to them and encouraging them to consider these.

2. **Prevention:** equipping individuals with the knowledge and understanding of what danger, harm, abuse and neglect are, e.g. providing individuals with information in a format that they can understand, i.e. verbal, written, pictorial about what danger, harm, abuse and neglect are, the actions to take as well as the support that is available if these happen.

3. **Proportionality:** ensuring all safeguarding decisions made in relation to individuals are appropriate to the level of risk identified, e.g. reassuring individuals that everyone is working in their **'best interests'** and that action will only be taken when needed (see p. 44 for definition).

4. Protection: providing individuals with support and representation during the safeguarding process when required, e.g. providing information to individuals in relation to how to report abuse in a format they can understand, providing reassurance when individuals have concerns and/or report abuse.

5. **Partnership:** working in partnership, i.e. with individuals, their families, friends and advocates, health and social care practitioners, other professionals, across different services and organisations, e.g. by maintaining the individual at the centre of all partnership working, providing continuity and consistency of care and support.

6. **Accountability:** being willing to accept responsibility and account for one's actions, e.g. being clear about how to work together to protect individuals, getting to know the individuals and all those involved in their lives.

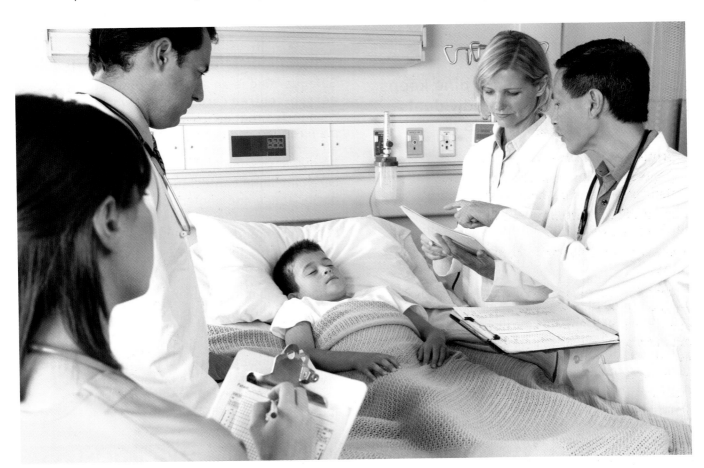

Figure 3.1 Working together to protect individuals

Key terms

Informed choices and decisions relates to having all the necessary information including the options available to make choices and decisions

Best interests relates to taking into account an individual's circumstances and preferences before making a decision or choice for the individual

Command word activity

Explain (AC1.1)

Work in pairs to agree on how individuals in health and social care settings are safeguarded.

Draw up two separate lists, with examples of health and social care practitioners 1) safeguarding individuals; and 2) not safeguarding individuals. Discuss the reasons for including these examples in each column. Then agree on the meaning of safeguarding in a health and social care context.

1.2 Explain how safeguarding keeps individuals safe, values individuals' needs, protects individuals

Keeping individuals safe

As you already know, safeguarding involves organisations and health and social care practitioners working together to prevent individuals from being harmed and, by sharing information about individuals' care and support needs, reduce the risk of them being harmed, abused or neglected.

Safeguarding also involves supporting individuals to make their own choices and decisions and managing any risks associated with these so that they can be empowered to take personal responsibility for their own safety and well-being. For example, if an individual who is prone to falls wants to go out for a walk in the uneven garden then it is for the individual to decide whether doing so may mean that they are likely to fall and cause themselves harm. In this way, the individual becomes an **active participant** in their own safeguarding and in the promotion of their safety.

Activity (AC1.2)

The White Paper, 'Equity and Excellence: Liberating the NHS', 2010 set out the Government's vision of an NHS where patients and the public come first and where 'no decision about me, without me' becomes the standard for day-to-day working practice.

Research the meaning of this slogan and how it is linked to keeping individuals who access health and social care services safe.

Take it further

You can access a copy of the White Paper, 'Equity and Excellence: Liberating the NHS', 2010 from this web link:

https://www.gov.uk/government/uploads/system/uploads/attachment_data/file/213823/dh_117794.pdf

Valuing individuals' needs

Safeguarding is an approach that values **person-centred care**; a way of working that recognises that an individual's unique needs, preferences and views must be the focus of all care and support that is planned for and provided. Placing individuals in control of their care can significantly reduce the likelihood of harm, abuse and neglect because individuals will have a good understanding of what high-quality care and support involves and be aware of their rights to be kept safe and free from harm, abuse or neglect.

Empowering individuals in this way will also mean that they would be more independent and more likely to share their concerns if their needs were not being valued and respected; again, this can reduce their risk of being harmed. You will learn more about the factors that increase individuals' vulnerability to being harmed or abused later on, in LO3 of this unit.

Classroom discussion (AC 1.2)

Discuss what person-centred care means and how it relates to safeguarding.

Take it further

Additional information, including a video clip can be accessed from the Royal College of Nursing's, First Steps for Health Care Assistants resource: 'What person-centred care means':

http://rcnhca.org.uk/sample-page/what-person-centred-care-means/

Protecting individuals

Safeguarding also protects individuals from danger, harm, abuse and neglect. Under the Care Act 2014 each local authority is required to take the lead in protecting individuals from abuse by:

- overseeing and coordinating the safeguarding of individuals
- investigating if an individual is experiencing or is at risk of harm, abuse or neglect
- deciding the action that must be taken to prevent the individual being at risk or in danger of harm, abuse or neglect
- establishing a **Safeguarding Adults Board**
- ensuring individuals have representation when they require it during the safeguarding process
- working in partnership with all of its members.

Take it further

For more information on protection in relation to safeguarding you will find it useful to read Unit HSC DM2 (LO1).

Key terms

Active participant relates to an individual being actively involved in all aspects of their life, care and support

Person-centred care relates to an individual being in control of their care and support

Safeguarding Adults Board where different health and social care sectors and agencies work together to help and safeguard adults with care and support needs

1.3 Explain how health and social care practitioners can take steps to safeguard themselves

Health and social care practitioners are not only responsible for safeguarding the individuals they work with but they also have a duty to protect themselves from being accused of behaving unprofessionally or suspected of causing harm or abuse towards the individuals they provide care and support to.

This means that all health and social care practitioners must follow their work setting's **agreed ways of working** (see p. 45 for definition) as well as the Code of Conduct for Healthcare Support Workers and Adult Social Care Workers in England that states how they must not cause harm to an individual's health and well-being and must never abuse, harm, neglect or exploit the individuals who access health and social care services, individuals' carers and others who they work with.

For example, a community support worker who is supporting an individual to prepare their lunch safely at home must ensure that a risk assessment has been undertaken prior to the activity taking place including the measures that have been agreed and put in place to eliminate any risks to the individual such as a fall or a cut or from the activity itself such as a fire. The full risk assessment including the controls in place must then be documented clearly so that should an incident occur during the activity then the health and social care practitioner can show that they had taken into account the individual's safety and had done their upmost to protect the individual while promoting their rights to independence.

Take it further

You can access the Code of Conduct for Healthcare Support Worker's and Adult Social Care Workers in England from this web link: **http://www.skillsforhealth.org.uk/standards/item/217-code-of-conduct**

Key term

Agreed ways of working relates to the working practices that are followed in a work setting, including policies and procedures

Having a good awareness of what safeguarding is, including understanding how the six principles that you learned about earlier on underpin and influence day-to-day working practices is another way that health and social care practitioners can protect themselves. For example, by taking responsibility for one's own actions and being clear about the reasons behind these (the accountability principle) or by ensuring that individuals' 'best interests' are always taken into account during the safeguarding process (the proportionality principle).

To safeguard themselves health and social care practitioners must act fairly at all times when working with individuals and recognise individuals' unique needs. They must not put themselves in any situations that are unsafe or have the potential to cause danger or harm to themselves.

Read through the Case scenario: Taking risks and answer the questions that follow.

Command word activity

Explain (AC 1.1, 1.2, 1.3)

Produce an illustrated information leaflet for volunteers working with children and adults who have learning disabilities that explains what safeguarding is and what it involves. Your information leaflet must include an explanation of:

1. The term safeguarding: you need to provide a clear account of your understanding of the meaning of this term in a health and social care context.
2. The role of safeguarding: you need to provide a clear account with a detailed examination of how safeguarding promotes the safety, needs and protection of individuals.
3. How health and social care practitioners can safeguard themselves: you need to provide a clear account that sets out the different ways and their purposes in relation to health and social care practitioners safeguarding themselves.

Check your understanding

1. What is the meaning of safeguarding adults?
2. Can you name the two principles that underpin the safeguarding of children?
3. Can you give two examples of how safeguarding protects individuals?
4. Can you give two examples of how health and social care practitioners can safeguard themselves when providing support to individuals?

Case scenario: Taking risks (AC 1.3, 5.1, 5.2, 6.1)

Jeremy is a mental health support worker to a young adult, Michael, who lives in a flat on his own. He provides support with day-to-day activities such as cooking, household cleaning and shopping. Part of Michael's plan of support, states that two support workers must always be present when supporting Michael with shopping as he can become very anxious when outside his home.

When Jeremy arrives, Michael tells him that he does not want to clean his room and the kitchen today, as previously planned, but instead would prefer to go shopping. Jeremy explains to Michael that because he is working on his own today, he is unable to

support him with going out as two support workers must always be present. Michael begins to get very agitated and starts pacing up and down the room.

Jeremy decides that if he takes Michael out to get some fresh air that he may calm down a little and suggests that they both go shopping together. He tries to phone his supervisor to tell him about the change of plan, but as he can't get through on the phone he decides to go shopping anyway.

1. Discuss Jeremy's decision and any subsequent consequences for Jeremy and Michael.
2. What advice do you think Jeremy's supervisor would have given him and why?

LO2: Understand how to safeguard individuals in relation to legislation, policies and procedures

2.1 Summarise current legislation in relation to safeguarding

There are a number of different pieces of legislation in England that are relevant to the safeguarding of both children and adults. As you will have already learned, developing a good knowledge of these is a good way for health and social care practitioners to safeguard themselves and the individuals they work with.

A proposed piece of legislation by the Government is called a bill. To become law, a bill must be approved by both the Members of Parliament in the House of Commons and the Peers in the House of Lords.

Table 3.1 provides information about the current legislation in England, in relation to safeguarding.

Table 3.1 Current UK safeguarding legislation

Legislation	How it relates to safeguarding
Care Act 2014	Relates to adults, i.e. individuals who are 18 and over and have care and support needs. It requires local authorities to promote individuals' well-being and safeguard them from abuse and neglect. The Act defines the meanings of abuse and neglect, how local authorities must take the lead in ensuring individuals' safety and how different organisations can work together to keep individuals safe, including the development of clear safeguarding policies and procedures. It also established the role of safeguarding adult boards and ensured that individuals have access to representation such as **advocacy** during the safeguarding process.
Children Act 1989	Requires local authorities to make enquiries if there are concerns that a child is or could be at risk of harm to safeguard and protect the child's welfare. It also placed a duty on all services and organisations to assist and provide information to child protection enquiries when required.
Children Act 2004	Requires local authorities to work together with their partners, i.e. district councils, the police, the probation service, youth offending teams and **clinical commissioning groups** to promote the well-being of children in relation to their physical and emotional health and well-being, protection from harm and neglect, education, training and recreation, making a positive contribution to society, social and economic well-being. It also established Local Safeguarding Children Boards that are responsible for investigating and reviewing all the deaths of children in their area.
Data Protection Act 1998	Gives rights to individuals over the use of their personal data/information by others in order to reduce the risk of individuals' data not remaining secure and therefore placing individuals at a higher risk of being abused. It gives individuals rights in relation to any personal data/information held by others about them such as the rights of the individual to: access their information; prevent the use of their information by others to cause harm; and ensure data held about them is accurate and up to date.
Equality Act 2010	Protects and safeguards individuals against unfair treatment or discrimination on the grounds of them having 'protected characteristics'. The protected characteristics are: age, disability, gender reassignment, marriage and civil partnership, pregnancy and maternity, race, religion or belief, sex, and sexual orientation.
Health and Social Care Act 2012	Promotes the working in partnership of health, social care and other services to improve the quality and the effectiveness of the care and support provided to individuals. It established CCGs and **health and well-being boards** to oversee the provision of services in each local area. CCGs are responsible for safeguarding both children and adults who access health and social care services, i.e. including responding to abuse and neglect that takes place, undertaking enquiries or reviews of services where abuse or neglect has taken place.

Legislation	How it relates to safeguarding
Human Rights Act 1998	Gives rights to every individual who lives in the UK that are based on respect, freedom, equality, dignity and fairness. They include the right not to be tortured or cruelly treated as well as the right to life and to live independently.
Mental Capacity Act 2005	Empowers and safeguards individuals who are unable to make choices and decisions for themselves because they lack the capacity to do so due to, for example, an illness or a disability. It is based on five key principles: always assume that individuals are able to make their own decisions; never assume that they are not able to; provide support to individuals so that they can make their own choices and decisions; respect individuals' rights to make decisions that others may not agree with; if an individual lacks capacity then decisions made on their behalf must always be in the individual's best interests only and must be the least restrictive option, i.e. the option that gives the individual as much freedom as possible.
Safeguarding Vulnerable Groups Act 2006	Protects and safeguards individuals from harm or risk of harm by setting up the vetting and barring scheme that prevents people who are not suitable to work with children and adults from doing so. It established the Independent Safeguarding Authority (ISA) which later merged with the Criminal Records Bureau (CRB) to become the **Disclosure and Barring Service (DBS)**.

It is important that health and social care practitioners are aware of all updates and changes made to legislation for their own continuing professional development; this involves time proofing their knowledge against existing legislation to ensure they are aware of any developments that arise for example, by referencing the Government's website: www.gov.uk

Take it further

For more information on continuing professional development in health and social care you can access Unit HSC CM9 (LO1).

Key terms

Advocacy supporting an individual to express their views and interests when they are unable to do so themselves

Clinical commissioning groups organisations that are responsible for the provision of NHS services in England

Health and well-being boards where health and social care organisations work together to improve the health and well-being of the people living in the local area they are responsible for

Disclosure and Barring Service a service that makes background checks for organisations, on people who want to work with children and adults

Command word activity

Summarise (AC 2.1)

Produce a poster of the main laws in England in relation to safeguarding. For each piece of legislation ensure you include its main characteristics. Once completed, show your poster to a partner and sum up why these safeguarding laws are important.

Take it further

You can find out more about relevant legislation in relation to the safeguarding and protection of children and young people and adults in HSC DM2.

2.2 Describe the relationship between legislation, policy and procedure

Legislation in relation to safeguarding individuals is the basis of all policies and procedures that are developed, but what are the differences between legislation, policy and procedure and how do they link together? Read through Table 3.2 that sets out their key meanings.

Table 3.2 Comparison of legislation, policy and procedure

Legislation	Policy	Procedure
Laws are guided by current government policy	Policies can be national and local	Procedures can be national and local
Laws include the standards and principles that are required to be followed	Policies set out an organisation's systems and how it plans to meet its legal requirements. Policies state what an organisation hopes to achieve, i.e. their aims	Procedures set out how an organisation is meeting its legal requirements. Procedures state the methods that will be used by an organisation to achieve their aims
If laws are not followed, then the consequence could be court prosecutions for those responsible	Policies are not law but they can include guidance for those using them so that they are adhered to. Not following policies may result in individuals and others being harmed, damage to an organisation's reputation, dismissal from a job role	Procedures are not law but they can include guidance for those using them so that they are adhered to. Not following procedures may result in individuals and others being harmed, damage to an organisation's reputation, dismissal from a job role

 Classroom discussion (AC 2.2)

For one chosen health and social care setting, discuss the impact that the Care Act 2014 will have had on its safeguarding policy and procedures. How are the three interlinked?

You may find it useful to speak to health and social care practitioners who work with children and/or young people about how safeguarding legislation impacts on their day-to-day agreed ways of working.

Command word activity

Describe (AC 2.2)

Identify one example of a national policy and procedure that is relevant to health and social care and find out about the legislation that underpins it; it may be one or more pieces of legislation. Then, working in pairs, give a verbal account of the characteristics that are common to all of them.

Take it further

You can find out more about the differences and the relationship between legislation, policies and procedures in HSC CM8 (LO1).

2.3 Identify policies and procedures in relation to safeguarding

All individuals who access health and social care services have a right to have their well-being promoted, to have their needs valued, to be kept safe, and to be protected from potential and actual danger, harm, abuse and neglect. For this reason, services have in place policies and procedures that relate specifically to safeguarding.

Having policies and procedures in place in relation to safeguarding is also a requirement under the Care Act 2014 for organisations and services working with adults who are at risk.

A safeguarding policy sets out, in the form of a statement, an organisation's or service's commitment to safeguarding individuals. A safeguarding procedure usually accompanies this and sets out what the organisation or service will do to safeguard individuals, including how all concerns will be responded to. These policies and procedures are based on current safeguarding legislation, local and national guidance in relation to safeguarding. Figure 3.2 below includes some examples of safeguarding policies and procedures that children and adult health and social care settings have in place:

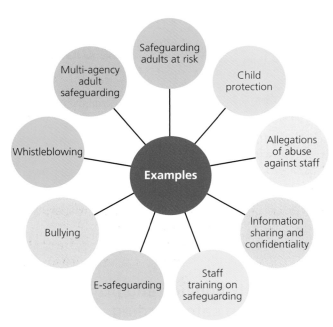

Figure 3.2 Safeguarding policies and procedures in health and social care

Although safeguarding policies and procedures will vary between different health and social care settings they will all include the following:

1. A statement of purpose: i.e. the organisation's commitment to ensuring that at all times individuals' well-being will be promoted, harm prevented and all safeguarding concerns responded to

2. Clearly defined safeguarding roles and responsibilities: i.e. roles and responsibilities of service provider, manager, carer, volunteer

3. Details of the reporting actions to take when there are safeguarding concerns: i.e. when an abuse incident is witnessed, when an incident is reported to another person, who to report to internally and how, when to report externally and how

4. Contact details for referrals including telephone numbers, in and out of office hours: i.e. when reporting concerns to an on-call manager for the service, the local authority's safeguarding contact, the Care Quality Commission's contact for reporting, the duty social worker, the police

5. Details of the recording actions to take when there are safeguarding concerns i.e. recording forms, when and how to complete them, the information that is required

6. Internal and external sources of advice and information: i.e. the internal designated person for safeguarding, the service's policies and procedures, the local authority's policies and procedures and websites of useful organisations, support services available for individuals, their families, staff involved in the safeguarding process

7. Details of multi-agency communication: i.e. how the service works with other agencies to safeguard individuals and promote their well-being

8. Details of the use of advocacy: i.e. who will represent individuals' best interests, who to go to when health and social care practitioners and services can't agree on the action to take in relation to a safeguarding concern

9. Details of how the policy will be reviewed: i.e. to be kept up to date and effective, an annual review as a minimum, more regular updates and reviews to learn from safeguarding incidents that have occurred either in the service or in the local area

There are also national safeguarding policies in place that are produced by the UK Government and other organisations that can provide health and social care services with additional guidance and support. For example:

● Prevention in Safeguarding (Social Care Institute of Excellence, 2011) in relation to empowering individuals and preventing harm

● Safeguarding Children and Young People (The Charity Commission, 2014) in relation to safeguarding procedures and systems

● Making Safeguarding Personal –a toolkit for responses (Local Government Association, 2015) in relation to best practice when responding to concerns.

Command word activity

Identify (AC 2.3)

For a chosen health or social care setting, research one example of a safeguarding policy or procedure. How does the policy safeguard individuals?

You can use the internet to conduct your research or you can speak with the manager of the setting to find out more information.

Activity (AC 2.1, 2.2, 2.3)

Produce a short presentation that shows your knowledge and understanding of current and relevant safeguarding legislation, policies and procedures. Your presentation must include:

- a summary of current legislation in relation to safeguarding. A summary means that you need to put into your own words the main points about what you learned in relation to safeguarding legislation including the Health and Social Care Act 2012, the Care Act 2014 and other relevant legislation.
- a description of the relationship between legislation, policy and procedures. A description means that you need to give an account that includes all the relevant characteristics of the relationship between legislation, policy and procedure in the context of safeguarding in health and social care.
- identified safeguarding policies and procedures. Identifying policies and procedures means that you must include a list of relevant safeguarding policies and procedures that are specific to safeguarding.

✔ Check your understanding

1. Describe how the Mental Capacity Act 2005 safeguards individuals.
2. Why is the Health and Social Care Act 2012 relevant to safeguarding?
3. What is the difference between a policy and a procedure?
4. Explain the purpose of a safeguarding policy.
5. Can you give two examples of what a safeguarding procedure must include?

LO3: Understand factors that may contribute to an individual being vulnerable to harm or abuse

3.1 Explain factors that may contribute to an individual being vulnerable to harm or abuse

Safeguarding individuals involves being aware of the different factors that may increase an individual's vulnerability to harm or abuse so that the necessary actions can be taken to prevent the individual being harmed.

Environmental factors

The health and social care setting could contribute to an individual being vulnerable to harm or abuse if, for example, it is in a remote location where few people visit or where the individual lives on their own as this can make it easier for an individual to be harmed without anyone noticing.

A service where there is a lack of training, support and monitoring of staff can also increase the likelihood of individuals being harmed and/or abused. For example, if a nursing home that provides care to individuals who have dementia does not train staff in how to meet these individuals' needs then staff may work in a way that does not promote their well-being or value their needs. This in turn may lead to individuals challenging staff which can then impact on staff's stress levels and may lead them to getting frustrated with individuals.

If staff who work in a nursery feel that they are not supported by management or have excessive workloads they may not carry out their roles in a professional manner, which in turn may lead to the children being placed in unnecessary danger or being harmed. Similarly, no or little monitoring of staff in health and social care settings can lead to poor working practices and individuals therefore being made more vulnerable to harm or abuse.

Individual factors

Individuals with care and support needs can by the very nature of their needs be more vulnerable to harm or abuse. If an individual depends on health and social care practitioners for support with day-to-day living then they may be less likely to report any concerns they have about their treatment because they may be worried that the service that they need will be withdrawn or that the staff involved may lose their jobs.

Individuals who have, for example, specific communication difficulties because of an illness or disability may be more vulnerable to harm or abuse because they may find it difficult to communicate what has happened to them.

Similarly, individuals who have specific conditions such as dementia or mental health needs may also be at higher risk of being harmed or abused. An individual with dementia may have difficulty remembering events and therefore may be targeted by an abuser who knows that the individual will be unlikely to be able to recall what has happened to them or tell anyone about it. An individual with mental health needs may have associated behaviours with their condition that can be difficult to manage and therefore have the potential to cause additional pressure and stress to the staff that provide their care and support. An individual who is frail or has poor mobility may be unable to defend themselves or move away quickly if they are being harmed or abused.

Command word activity

Explain (AC3.1)

Research an example that has been reported in the media of a child or an adult that has been harmed or abused while accessing health or social care services. Discuss in pairs the factors that may have made the individual more vulnerable to being harmed or abused.

You can use the internet or the newspapers as sources of information on cases and inquiries that have been reported in the media.

Activity (AC 3.1)

Produce an information brief to share with newly qualified health and social care practitioners about the factors to be aware of that may contribute to an individual becoming vulnerable to harm or abuse. You could use as an example the case you researched in the previous activity.

Your information brief must include an explanation of the factors that may contribute to an individual being vulnerable to harm or abuse. An explanation means that you need to provide a clear account of your understanding of the different and relevant factors that may contribute.

Check your understanding

1. Why is it important for health and social care practitioners to be aware of the factors that can make individuals more vulnerable to harm or abuse?
2. Can you name two environmental factors that may contribute to an individual being harmed or abused?
3. Can you name two individual factors that may contribute to an individual being harmed or abused?
4. Why can individuals who have communication difficulties be more vulnerable to being harmed or abused?
5. Why can individuals who have high care and support needs be more vulnerable to being harmed or abused?

LO4: Know signs, symptoms, indicators and behaviours that may cause concern

4.1 Describe signs, symptoms, indicators and behaviours that may cause concern

Health and social care practitioners can only safeguard and protect individuals if they are able to recognise the signs, symptoms, indicators and behaviours that may cause concern over an individual's well-being or safety. It is also important to remember that individuals may experience one type of abuse or several types of abuse at the same time or at different times. Similarly, abuse may occur on just one occasion or on several occasions.

It is also important to remember that because all individuals are unique, the way they may experience abuse or harm will also be unique which means that all individuals will not necessarily show the same signs, symptoms, indicators and behaviours. The most effective way that health and social care practitioners can safeguard individuals' rights and protect them from harm or abuse is to spend time getting to know the individual so that any unusual changes they do show, however small, are noticed immediately.

The ten types of abuse and neglect identified in the Care Act 2014 are: physical, sexual, psychological,

discriminatory, rganisational, domestic violence, modern slavery, financial and material, neglect and acts of omission and self-neglect. Modern slavery includes human trafficking and domestic servitude, and discriminatory abuse includes unfair treatment of individuals that is based on their protected characteristics as well as verbal abuse and harassment. Table 3.3 includes examples of the main types of abuse and their commonly associated signs, symptoms, indicators and behaviours that may cause concern (see p. xx for information on bullying):

> ## 🔑 Key terms
>
> **Signs** are outwardly visible to others, e.g. bruises
> **Symptoms** are experienced by individuals, e.g. feeling upset, angry, alone
> **Indicators** are the signs and symptoms shown
> **Behaviours** physical and emotional acts, e.g. screaming, self-harm

Table 3.3 Signs, symptoms, indicators and behaviours relating to abuse

Type of abuse	Signs, symptoms, indicators and behaviours
Neglect: a failure of others to meet an individual's needs, e.g. not providing food, access to medical care	*Signs and symptoms*: malnutrition, dehydration, bedsores, unhygienic living conditions, feeling confused, low in mood *Indicators and behaviours*: listlessness, being withdrawn
Self-neglect: a failure of an individual to meet their own needs, e.g. poor personal hygiene, not eating or drinking, not taking prescribed medication	*Signs and symptoms*: malnutrition, dehydration, weight loss, not wearing clean clothes, feeling confused, low in mood *Indicators and behaviours*: listlessness, being withdrawn
Physical abuse: unwanted contact leading to injuries or pain, e.g. hitting, pushing, biting, restraining an individual incorrectly	*Signs and symptoms*: bruises, pressure marks, broken bones, burns, being in pain and discomfort, being anxious and fearful *Indicators and behaviours*: flinching in the presence of the abuser, getting angry and upset, wearing long-sleeved clothing/jackets in hot weather to cover up
Emotional abuse: actions that make an individual feel worthless and humiliated e.g. threats, controlling, harassment, isolation, withdrawal of services	*Signs and symptoms*: anxiety, disturbed sleep, inability to eat, feeling unwell *Indicators and behaviours*: little confidence, getting upset, low self-esteem
Sexual abuse: unwanted sexual contact and involvement in sexual activities and relationships e.g. rape, sexual harassment, subjection to pornography	*Signs and symptoms*: e.g. pain and bruises around the thighs, breasts and genital area, unexplained bleeding *Indicators and behaviours*: sexually transmitted infections, inability to take part in physical activities due to pain or discomfort
Domestic abuse: threatening behaviour, violence or abuse between individuals who are related e.g. honour-based violence, emotional abuse, physical abuse	*Signs and symptoms*: these can include any of the signs and symptoms of the other types of abuse identified in this table. *Indicators and behaviours:* these can include any of the signs and symptoms of the other types of abuse identified in this table

Type of abuse	Signs, symptoms, indicators and behaviours
Financial abuse: the unauthorised use of a person's property, money or possessions e.g. theft, fraud in relation to financial transactions, wills, property	*Signs and symptoms*: no money, large withdrawals of money, not being able to pay bills, feeling anxious *Indicators and behaviours*: not wishing to spend money on day-to-day essentials such as food, valuable items disappearing
Institutional abuse: the focus of the service on the needs of the organisation and its staff rather than on the needs of the individuals who access the service e.g. no provision made available to meet individuals' needs, rigid routines and systems	*Signs and symptoms*: poor care standards, lack of choice and individuality, low self-esteem *Indicators and behaviours*: inadequate staffing, a lack of positive responses to individuals' needs

Command word activity

Describe (AC 4.1)

Produce a factsheet that includes information about five types of abuse, their associated signs, symptoms, indicators and behaviours. Your factsheet must include: a description of the signs, symptoms, indicators and behaviours that may give cause for concern for five types of abuse. A description means that you need to give an account that includes all the relevant characteristics of the five types of abuse, including the signs, symptoms, indicators and behaviours related to each type.

Check your understanding

1. Why is it important for health and social care practitioners to be able to recognise when an individual is being harmed or abused?
2. What are the consequences of health and social care practitioners not knowing about the signs, symptoms, indicators and behaviours associated with abuse types?
3. What is the meaning of institutional abuse?
4. Define self-neglect.
5. What are the likely indicators and behaviours of the following types of abuse: domestic and financial?

LO5: Understand the lines of reporting and responsibility in relation to the safeguarding, protection and welfare of individuals

5.1 Describe the lines of reporting and responsibility in relation to safeguarding, protection and welfare

Health and social care practitioners need to know what to do if they suspect, witness or hear that an individual has been harmed or abused. Safeguarding is everyone's responsibility and similarly every health and social care practitioner is responsible for taking action; ignoring their own or others' concerns or doing nothing is never an option. It is also their responsibility to take the correct actions in different situations; for example, in relation to knowing who to report to, i.e. your manager; understanding the actions to take when it may not be appropriate to report to that person, i.e. if the concerns raised are about your manager; and knowing what steps to take if you do not feel that your concerns have been taken seriously, i.e. whistleblowing – reporting it to senior management, the Care Quality Commission, the police, the local authority's adult care team or children and families department.

Reporting

If you witness, are told about or hear about an individual that gives you cause for concern you must report this immediately. If you are a health and social care practitioner you must follow your work setting's safeguarding procedure for reporting i.e. to your team leader, manager.

The manager of the service will then ensure that the individual at risk is safeguarded and that they have been informed of the actions that will be taken.

The manager will also need to notify the relevant authorities such as the Care Quality Commission and the police.

Responsibility

The person reporting the concern must safeguard the individual at risk from any further danger, harm or abuse.

It is also important that no one else is placed in any danger.

Medical care may need to be arranged for the individual if injured or in pain; in an emergency situation you or a qualified colleague will need to call for help, i.e. police and/or ambulance may be required.

Ensure you preserve any available evidence by recording the incident; ensure you also record the actions you have taken to safeguard the individual.

Follow your work setting's agreed ways of working for reporting the incident.

Figure 3.3 Reporting to safeguard individuals

Take it further

You can find out more about the actions to take if harm or abuse is suspected and/or disclosed for children and young people and adults in HSC DM2(LO2).

5.2 Explain the boundaries of confidentiality in relation to the safeguarding, protection and welfare of individuals

Maintaining individuals' confidentiality in health and social care settings helps to encourage the building of trust and mutual respectful working relationships. At the same time, sharing information among health and social care practitioners for the purposes of safeguarding, protection and the welfare of individuals is essential for ensuring safe, effective care and preventing individuals from being harmed. It is important therefore for health and social care practitioners to understand what information can and can't be shared and what information is classed as confidential; including when an individual's wishes to keep their information confidential may not be able to be maintained, i.e. if they or others are at risk of being harmed.

Confidential information refers to information that is of a personal or sensitive nature and that is not available in the public domain. All information-sharing in health and social care is guided by the **Caldicott Principles** (see p. 56 for definition) and in 2013 these were revised to take into account the boundaries of confidentiality in relation to safeguarding:

The revised Caldicott Principles are as follows:

1. Justify the purpose(s). The use and purpose of all confidential information within or from an organisation should be clearly documented and reviewed by an appropriate **guardian** (see p. 56 for definition).

2. Don't use personal confidential data unless it is absolutely necessary. Personal confidential data should not be included unless it is essential.

3. Use the minimum necessary personal confidential data. Only use personal confidential data where it is considered to be essential.

4. Access to personal confidential data should be on a strict need-to-know basis. Only those individuals who need access to personal confidential data should have access to it.

Key terms

Caldicott Principles a set of standards aimed at improving information handling in health and social care from a review commissioned by the Chief Medical Officer of England

Guardian the lead person for safeguarding an individual's confidential information

5. Everyone with access to personal confidential data should be aware of their responsibilities. All those handling personal confidential data must be made fully aware of their responsibilities to respect confidentiality.

6. Comply with the law. Every use of personal confidential data must comply with legal requirements.

7. The duty to share information can be as important as the duty to protect individuals' confidentiality. Health and social care professionals should have the confidence to share information in the best interests of individuals and they should be supported to do so by the policies of their employers, regulators and professional bodies.

When individuals or others are at risk of being harmed or abused then it may be necessary for health and social care practitioners to share confidential information with others to prevent any further harm or abuse from taking place and to fulfil their responsibilities to protect individuals and promote their welfare.

Command word activity

Describe (AC 5.1, 5.2)

For one health or social care setting research the reporting procedures for safeguarding, including maintaining confidentiality. Discuss your findings with a partner. Your findings must include a description of the lines of reporting and responsibility in relation to safeguarding, protection and welfare.

A description means that you need to give an account that includes the relevant characteristics of reporting and responsibility in relation to safeguarding.

Command word activity

Explain (AC 5.1, 5.2)

For one health or social care setting research the procedures for safeguarding, including maintaining confidentiality. Discuss your findings with a partner. Your findings must include an explanation of the boundaries of confidentiality.

An explanation means that you need to produce a clear account of your understanding of confidentiality and how and why it applies to safeguarding, protection and welfare

Check your understanding

1. Whose responsibility is safeguarding? Why?
2. Name two actions a health and social care practitioner must take in relation to reporting their concerns about an individual being harmed or abused.
3. Describe two responsibilities health and social care practitioners have when safeguarding individuals at risk of being harmed.
4. Define the term confidentiality.
5. Why is confidentiality important in safeguarding?

LO6: Understand the role and responsibilities of the health and social care practitioner in relation to safeguarding individuals

6.1 Evaluate the role and responsibilities of the health and social care practitioner in relation to safeguarding individuals

All health and social care practitioners have a duty to keep individuals safe, value their needs and protect their well-being. To be able to safeguard individuals effectively they must:

Work with the requirements of the current legislation; this involves keeping up to date with all legislation that is relevant to safeguarding through participating in training, learning and development. It includes understanding how the legislation is relevant to their day-to-day role and responsibilities.

Follow policies, procedures and lines of reporting; this involves reading and understanding their work setting's policies and procedures and seeking advice from relevant people such as their managers if they are unsure or do not understand any aspect of these. Health and social care practitioners must also ensure that they know how to report causes for concern about individuals and what to do in different circumstances that may arise.

Maintaining own role in relation to others; this involves being aware of others' roles and responsibilities but also being committed to working together with others to safeguard individuals.

The extent of roles and responsibilities in relation to safeguarding individuals; this involves health and social care practitioners understanding the limits of their roles and responsibilities including the boundaries of confidentiality that apply and must be respected.

Take it further

You can find out more about the roles and responsibilities of the health and social care practitioner in HSC DM2 (LO2).

Command word activity

Evaluate(AC 6.1)

Produce a profile of a health or social care practitioner that includes their role and responsibilities in relation to safeguarding individuals from their own perspective and that of their manager.

Your profile must include an evaluation of the role and responsibilities of the health and social care practitioner in relation to safeguarding.

An evaluation means that you need to make a judgement that takes into account more than one perspective and uses available research and evidence.

Figure 3.4 Safeguarding in health and social care

Command word activity

Evidence (AC6.1)

Keep a referencing diary to show that you've read widely and researched the roles and responsibilities of the health and social care practitioner in relation to safeguarding

Use the Harvard referencing system to produce an easy-to-follow list of all the sources of information that you've read and referred to that may include

work settings' policies and procedures and articles.

Remember when recording articles used to include the author's name, the year of publication, the title of the article, the title of the publication and the page number.

Record the range of sources you've referenced in your referencing diary as you read them; use them selectively and cite them appropriately.

Check your understanding

1. Name two requirements of a health and social care practitioner's role in relation to safeguarding individuals.
2. Describe how legislative requirements underpin the role and responsibilities of health and social

care practitioners in relation to safeguarding individuals.
3. Give two examples of how health and social care practitioners can work in partnership with others. Why is this relevant to safeguarding?

Read about it

DOH (2016) 'Care and Support Statutory Guidance, Section 14.7, Adult safeguarding – what it is and why it matters', DOH

HM Government (2015)'Working together to safeguard children. A guide to inter-agency working to safeguard and promote the welfare of children'

Lindon, J. (2008) *Safeguarding Children and Young People: 0-18 Years: Child Protection 0-18 Years,* London: Hodder Arnold Publication

Morris, C., FerreiroPeteiro, M. and Collier, F. (2015) *Level 3 Health and Social Care Diploma*, London: Hodder Education

SCIE (2015) 'At a glance 69: Adult safeguarding: Types and indicators of abuse', Social Care Institute for Excellence.

Ward, H. and Davies, C. (2011) *Safeguarding Children Across Services: Messages from Research*, London and Philadelphia: Jessica Kingsley Publishers.

Websites

Abuse Survivors – (information and support for survivors of abuse)
www.abuse-survivors.org.uk

Care Quality Commission – (guidance for providers of health and social care services)
www.cqc.org.uk

SCIE– (adult safeguarding resources)
www.scie.org.uk

Skills for Care – (information and resources about the Care Act 2014, Codes of Conduct for care practitioners)
www.skillsforcare.org.uk

Skills for Health – (information and resources about the Code of Conduct for care practitioners)
www.skillsforhealth.org.uk

MIND – (information and resources about the Mental Capacity Act 2005 and its accompanying Code of Practice)
www.mind.org.uk

NSPCC – (information and resources about safeguarding children and young people)
www.nspcc.org.uk

UK Government – (information and policies on safeguarding children and adults)
www.gov.uk

Unit HSC CM3: How will I be graded?

The table below shows what the learner must do to achieve each grading criterion. Learners must achieve all the criteria for a grade to be awarded

(i.e. criteria D1 to D3 must be achieved to pass this unit assessment at grade D). A higher grade may not be awarded before a lower grade has been achieved in full, although component criteria of a higher grade may have been achieved.

		Assessment grading criteria	Assessment of learning/What you need to show
D1	1.1	Explain what is meant by 'safeguarding'.	The explanation of safeguarding must: • show accurate understanding of the meaning of safeguarding • relate safeguarding to the context of health and social care.
D2	2.1	Summarise current legislation in relation to safeguarding.	Provide a summary of current legislation in relation to safeguarding such as: • Health and Social Care Act 2012 • Care Act 2014 • Other relevant legislation
D3	2.2	Describe the relationship between legislation, policy and procedure.	The description must provide evidence of understanding of the relationship between legislation, policy and procedure.
D4	2.3	Identify policies and procedures in relation to safeguarding.	Knowledge of policies and procedures relating to safeguarding must be shown. Policies and procedures identified must be shown as relevant in the context of safeguarding and not generic to health and social care.
D5		Show evidence of reading or use of sources.	There should be evidence of learners' reading or use of sources. Learners must use a minimum of two traceable references to support the discussion.
C1	4.1	Describe signs, symptoms, indicators and behaviours that may cause concern.	Select 5 of the types of abuse. For each type of abuse, a correct description of the signs, symptoms, indicators and behaviours which may cause concern must be given.
C2	5.1	Describe the lines of reporting and responsibility in relation to safeguarding protection and welfare.	More than one aspect of lines of reporting and responsibility must be considered in the description.
C3		Show evidence of reading or use of sources with referencing relevant to the description. Good use of vocabulary and grammar.	Use of referencing should show evidence of reading or use of sources. Vocabulary and grammar should be appropriate and accurate for purposes.
B1	3.1	Explain factors that may contribute to an individual being vulnerable to harm or abuse.	More than one factor must be explained. The explanation must demonstrate: • an understanding of relevant factors • the contribution of these factors to an individual becoming vulnerable to harm or abuse.
B2	1.3	Explain how health and social care practitioners can take steps to safeguard themselves.	Provide a detailed explanation of more than one way that health and social care practitioners can safeguard themselves; each way must be clearly different and show understanding of key issues relevant to own safeguarding.
B3	1.2	Explain the role of safeguarding.	A detailed explanation of the role of safeguarding must demonstrate an analytical approach to the safety, needs and protection of individuals.

		Assessment grading criteria	Assessment of learning/What you need to show
B4		Show evidence of reading or use of sources. Referencing supports the explanation.	Use of reading or use of sources should be shown through a range of relevant referencing. Referencing should be used appropriately to support the explanation.
A1	5.2	Explain the boundaries of confidentiality in relation to the safeguarding, protection and welfare of individuals.	The boundaries of confidentiality must be explained in depth to show: • understanding of the boundaries of confidentiality • the application of the boundaries of confidentiality to safeguarding, protection and welfare.
A2		Show evidence of wider background reading or use of sources. Referencing supports the explanation.	Wider background reading should be evident or a wide range of source material should be used.
A*1	6.1	Evaluate the role and responsibilities of the health and social care practitioner in relation to safeguarding individuals	Evaluate to address the role and responsibilities of the health and social care practitioner from more than one perspective to include: • working with the requirements of current legislation (D1) • following policies, procedures and lines of reporting (D3, B1) • maintaining own role in relation to others (B2, A1) • the extent of roles and responsibilities in relation to safeguarding individuals.
A*2		Show evidence of a range of background reading or use of sources used selectively.	Learners should show the ability to consider or explore relevant issues which contribute to the explanation. An extensive range of background reading or use of sources should be used selectively and cited appropriately.
Current legislation as relevant to Home Nation			

HSC CM4
Communication in Health and Social Care

Learning outcomes

LO1: Understand communication channels in health and social care settings

1.1 Explain the use of communication in health and social care settings

1.2 Explain the impact of communication on service delivery outcomes

LO2: Understand how to support communication

2.1 Outline theories of communication

2.2 Describe communication and language needs and preferences of individuals

2.3 Explain factors that influence communication and interactions

2.4 Explain how barriers to communication can be overcome

2.5 Explain how to communicate to meet the needs of others

2.6 Explain how to access additional support or services to enable individuals to communicate effectively

LO3: Understand legislation, policies, procedures and codes of practice relating to information management

3.1 Explain the meaning of the term confidentiality

3.2 Summarise legislation, policies, procedures and codes of practice relating to the management of information

3.3 Explain the potential tension between maintaining confidentiality and the need to disclose information

LO4: Understand how to work in line with legislation, policies, procedures and codes of practice relating to information management

4.1 Describe how to ensure the security of data when accessing and storing records

4.2 Describe how to ensure the security of data when sharing information

4.3 Explain how to maintain records

About this unit

The aim of this unit is to provide knowledge and understanding of communication and data management in health and social care. Both are essential skills for anyone working in health and social care. Communication skills are used many times every day in health and social care settings, in different forms and between different people. They are essential in building good working relationships with colleagues and individuals who are being cared for.

This unit will explore the specific needs that some individuals may have, such as using sign language or pictures to communicate. Organisations and individuals who provide additional support will also be explored. Sometimes, barriers exist that stop effective communication and these, along with ways in which barriers can be overcome, will be examined. Finally, this unit aims to provide an understanding of how data management is essential to ensure the safe use and security of information of the individuals within our care.

LO1: Understand communication channels in health and social care settings

Communication is an essential part of everyday life. It is a two-way process where information is exchanged and understood. Although essential in everyday life, good communication has an increased significance in health and social care settings, where we are communicating with people who are vulnerable. We communicate in many different ways through what we say and how we speak, gestures we use, body language and how we may dress. Within health and social care effective communication is essential. This section explores how communication is used and the impact that positive or negative communication may have on individuals, family members, carers, practitioners and colleagues as well as the organisation's partnerships with other agencies/services.

 Key term

Communication channel the method or way that communication is transferred

Activity (AC 1.1)

Choose two health and social care settings. For each setting, identify the interactions that may occur between individuals and outline the purpose of such interaction. These interactions may be between practitioners, between practitioners and individuals and between individuals.

1.1 Explain the use of communication in health and social care settings

A range of people communicate within health and social care. This could be within teams of nurses to each other, between different organisations such as a hospital ward discharging an individual to a nursing home, or an individual such as a doctor talking to a patient. Communication methods vary and may occur for different reasons. Some examples are shown in Table 4.1.

Table 4.1 Reasons for communication

Reason for communication	Explanation	Example from health and social care
Offer reassurance	To help someone feel less anxious or discuss concerns about a situation.	An anaesthetist may discuss the procedure with a patient who will have a general anaesthetic.
Express feelings and/or concerns	To explain an individual's state of mind such as if they are feeling anxious or pleased. There may also be worries or issues that may be troubling an individual.	A new resident explains that they are feeling sad and anxious about moving into a care home.
Inform	To give instructions or directions.	A nurse provides a patient with information about head injuries after a fall.
Guide	Someone shows someone how to get somewhere or how to do something.	A qualified nurse assists a student on how to complete falls documentation to assess the risk of a fall and strategies implemented to reduce the risk of a fall occurring.
Form/build relationships	Build trust and respect. This also meets the needs that many individuals have for company and companionship.	A social worker builds a trusting relationship with a young person leaving care.
Socialise / interact	To get to know the people you are communicating with in an informal manner.	A team has a coffee morning and chat.

Reason for communication	Explanation	Example from health and social care
Ask questions	To gain information.	A carer questions a social worker about a procedure for assessment for themselves and respite care.
Build self-esteem	To build own self-esteem through forming relationships with others or to encourage an individual to increase their own self-esteem.	A children's centre worker encourages and praises a child in modelling positive behaviour.
Support	To give assistance or help someone in a situation.	An **advocate** may communicate in a multi-disciplinary meeting offering support to an individual with learning disabilities to communicate their view.
Enable choice	To give individual's options about something.	For example giving an individual with learning disabilities two pictures of different dinners to choose from.

Key term

Advocate is an independent person who will speak on behalf of an individual

Command word activity

Explain (AC 1.1)

Identify all the reasons for communication that occur within your placement. Ensure that you do not mention names or any other identifiable detail. Explain the type of communication used, along with who communicates and the reason.

Methods of communication

There are a range of communication methods, all to do with how information is conveyed. These include verbal communication which is to do with speaking or talking but it also includes the differences in how someone speaks, such as the tone, pitch and volume as well as the vocabulary that is used. These can alter the meaning and reason of the message being conveyed.

Effective listening is needed to ensure that the purpose of communication is completed.

Non-verbal communication is done with body language. This can include facial expressions, gestures, eye contact, body positions and even how someone is dressed. This is a powerful aspect of communication with much of what is being said communicated in this manner.

Activity

Identify the feelings from each of the individual's faces shown in Figure 4.1. Outline two reasons why non-verbal communication can help to understand what an individual is trying to communicate.

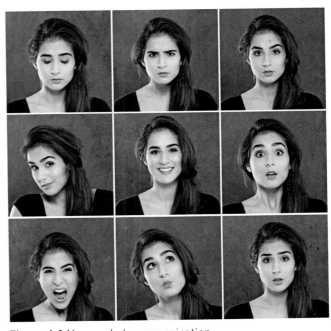

Figure 4.1 Non-verbal communication

Types of communication, range of people who need to communicate with each other and different reasons for communicating

Communication can be *written*; this may be in the form of care plans or patient notes, for example, and may be handwritten or on a computer. *Electronic communication* is increasingly common and can include emails or data submitted such as electronic blood pressure or monitoring machines. Communication aids may be technological or the use of pictures. Technology, for example speech-generating devices or voice-operated communication aids are electronic devices that enable the individual to select messages which are then spoken out loud. The messages can be letters, words, a phrase or a sentence used alone or in combination. Pictures are also used as a communication aid. This may include using a picture, for example, of a drink to communicate a need, or using pictures to demonstrate a step-by-step procedure.

Communication may also occur on a one-to-one basis or in a group. Both use different skills. One-to-one communication is where two individuals are having a conversation, for example a GP talking to a patient. It can also be within a group such as a team meeting with each person taking a turn. Communicating in a group means individuals will have to ensure they take it in turns to speak and listen to everyone within the group.

Interactions may be formal or informal depending on the reason for the communication and who it may be with. An individual may use different methods of communication with the same people depending upon the situation. For example, two colleagues may have an informal conversation when they arrive at work or on a break, but a formalised **handover** when discussing patient care.

Activity

Compare the similarities and differences in communication skills required for communicating in a one-to-one situation, group situations, written and electronic forms.

Key term

Handover passing information needed to continue the care of an individual from one member of staff to another

Activity

Using the picture shown in Figure 4.2, identify the types of communication occurring. Is it written, verbal or non-verbal? Is it formal or informal?

Explain the importance of each type of communication.

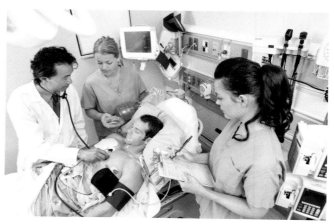

Figure 4.2 Types of communication

1.2 Explain the impact of communication on service delivery outcomes

Key term

Ombudsman an official body appointed to explore unresolved complaints about public bodies in organisations

The impact on the individuals

In 2014, the **Ombudsman Service** cited poor communication as one of the top three reasons for complaints. Communication can therefore have a significant impact in many different ways.

Effective communication is essential when communicating with patients and service users. It can reassure individuals that they are being listened to, their views valued and respected. This will help them feel at ease and in control of their lives and care. Without effective communication, patients or service users will be unable to communicate their needs, wishes or concerns. Good communication can mean that questions about treatments or procedures can be properly answered and the patient can then fully consent.

Individuals, family members, carers

Communication should always value the individual you are looking after. A nurse on a surgical ward, for example, may look after many patients who are having similar procedures every day. For that nurse, this procedure may be fairly routine. For the individual it may be overwhelming. The nurse must ensure that they listen to the patient and their concern without appearing unsympathetic or uncaring. Lack of communication means people may become isolated. This in itself can have negative effects on health and well-being. Not meeting needs for individuals with speech difficulties, for example, can cause depression and isolation.

Family members and carers will be worried about their relatives, and so the health care practitioner has a key role in reassuring and listening to their concerns. This can be a source of frustration for family members as the health care practitioners are bound by confidentiality and cannot fully discuss their patient's case, creating a barrier to communication. Families will have questions and often advocate on behalf of the patient. The role of the health care practitioner is to facilitate and listen to concerns and respond. However, it is the person in their care who remains central to their role.

Practitioners and colleagues

Health and social care workers do not work in isolation. Partnerships with other practitioners and colleagues and other organisations are vitally important. A team that works together well can have a tremendous effect on each team member and patient outcomes. People feel supported; they can discuss their opinions and ideas and are respected within their team. There will be consistency and continuity in care given and confidence from staff in their delivery.

Communication is key to effective working. Many people require 24 hour care and, therefore at some point, this care will be 'handed over' to the next team. Lack of communication here can have severe implications for the person being looked after, with their needs not being met. This in turn can lower the morale of the staff team who may feel they are not doing their job to their best ability.

The organisation and partnerships

Effective communication can have positive outcomes for the health and social care organisation. As stated earlier, many complaints that are made about organisations are to do with a lack of communication taking place between individuals or their families and the service being provided. An organisation can acquire a good or poor reputation on this basis. Individual and partnership organisations have a choice over which service to use and this in turn can have implications for the running of the organisations. Staff have a choice over where to work, so may choose organisations that have better reputations. Effective communication can ensure that services are run more efficiently so boosting staff morale, leading to higher productivity and higher performance.

Command word activity

Evidence (AC 1.2)

Create a presentation along with supportive information in note format to explain the impact of communication in delivering care aimed at senior care workers. You need to include the impact on these groups: individuals, practitioners, the organisation and partnerships with other agencies. Follow this plan in creating your presentation:

1. Define the group.
2. Give two examples of how poor communication may affect that group (e.g. not understanding the care they are receiving, and care not being consistent between organisations).
3. Give two examples of how good communication can have a positive impact upon that group (e.g. individual feels they are being valued which may increase their self-esteem).
4. For each of the examples try to expand on your statement of the impact by using phrases such as 'this means that ...' or 'this is important because ...'.
5. Use different sources of information to support your answer such as information gained from the activity, exploring serious case reviews, statistics, publications such as *Nursing Times* or patient voices, such as those from the website **http://www.patientvoices.org.uk/stories.htm**. Ensure you keep an accurate record of all sources used for each piece of information.

Key term

CQC (Care Quality Commission) responsible for monitoring, inspecting and regulating health and social care services

Check your understanding

1. Identify three people that a resident in a nursing home may communicate with in one day, the reasons for the interaction and whether it is formal or informal.
2. Define both verbal and non-verbal communication.
3. Outline why non-verbal communication is so important.
4. Explain the positive impact communication can have on a patient or service user.
5. Explain the negative impact communication can have on an organisation.

LO2: Understand how to support communication

2.1 Outline theories of communication

This section will explore two theories of communication: Argyle's theory of communication and Tuckman's stages of group development. Theories are helpful as they can enable health and social care practitioners to understand what is occurring, along with a tool to aid effective communication.

Argyle's communication cycle

Argyle believed that effective interpersonal communication was a skill that needed to be learned. He developed the concept of a cycle where messages are sent, received and understood. Although the purpose of the communication may be different (such as asking a question or conveying a need) this cycle can be helpful in health and social care as many individuals may be vulnerable to being misunderstood. This cycle can help health and social care practitioners to understand how communication works and how effective communication can therefore be promoted. The barriers to communication discussed in AC 2.4 below stop this cycle occurring and therefore action should be taken to reduce or remove these barriers. This process is as follows:

1. An idea or concept that one individual wishes to convey occurs.

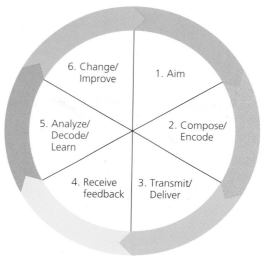

Figure 4.3 Argyle's communication cycle

2. Message coded: this is when the individual decides how the communication is going to be sent. This may be verbally or non-verbally.

3. Message sent: the message is conveyed to another person. This may be written and signed or sent in some other format.

4. Message received: the message is received by another person or people. This could be by hearing the message or reading it.

5. Message decoded: the person who receives the message makes sense of this. This can cause problems as it may be misinterpreted (for example, body language).

6. Message understood: the message is understood in the way it is intended (this may be demonstrated by feedback, an appropriate question or paraphrasing).

For example, a patient may be discussing a concern they have about an operation with a staff nurse. See Table 4.2

Key term

Active listening a method of listening to build rapport, trust and mutual understanding of the message that is being communicated

Tuckman's theory of group development

There are numerous examples of when communication occurs within a group situation. This can be a short-term group that changes rapidly, for example a staff handover at the start of a shift or a longer term group such as a staff team. This theory on group development is helpful as it provides insight into how groups develop. Tuckman (1965) wrote an influential article describing the stages of group development. He considered that groups went through a process of orientation, conflict, cohesion and being ready for functioning. For communication to be effective in group situations, group cohesion is important. The stages are as shown in Table 4.3.

Table 4.2 A discussion between a patient and a nurse

An idea or concept:	The patient has the feeling of anxiety and decides to communicate this to the nurse
Message coded:	The patient requests to talk to the nurse and decides what and how to communicate the feeling of anxiety
Message sent:	The patient verbally tells the nurse: 'I am really anxious about my operation, I am scared that something will happen to me under the anaesthetic'
Message received:	The nurse listens to the patient, using **active listening** skills and ensuring that any barriers to effective communication are reduced
Message decoded:	The nurse processes the concerns that the patient has and may demonstrate this in body language or expression, such as showing empathy
Message understood:	The nurse checks they have understood the individual, for example by saying 'I understand that you are really anxious about your operation. Your main concern is the anaesthetic. Is that right?'

Group stage	Description
Forming	This is the initial stage of group development. Individuals may be unsure of their role and so may ask lots of questions of the leader. There will be little coherence of aims of the group. Individuals often want to be accepted by others so there will be little conflict.
Storming	Within this stage, there may be evidence of role and responsibilities, although teams may not be able to make decisions effectively.
Norming	Within this stage, there is agreement and roles and responsibilities of people are clear. People within the team are committed.
Performing	In this section, the team are able to have a shared vision and idea of what and how the task is going to be achieved.

Command word activity

Outline (AC 2.1)

Think back to a conversation that has taken place. It can be from any setting, e.g. a class team activity or a conversation or group activity with friends. Outline the communication cycle within that conversation or the stages of Tuckman's group development.

2.2 Describe communication and language needs and preferences of individuals

Each individual will have a range of needs and preferences that they may use to communicate. Figure 4.4 illustrates some of the methods used to meet these.

Figure 4.4 Individuals may have different needs or preferences

Speech and language therapists

Speech and language therapists (sometimes referred to as SALT) are professionals who work with individuals (both children and adults) who have difficulties with communication, eating, drinking or swallowing. These professionals can help individuals in a range of settings such as hospitals, schools, own homes and prisons.

There may be many reasons why someone needs assistance, for example, they have a stammer, learning disabilities, throat cancer, or had a stroke. Speech and language therapists will offer support and advice for individuals who may find it difficult to make themselves understood or have problems with understanding or using language. They will also offer support and advice to professionals such as care staff or doctors. An individual will generally be referred to a speech and language therapist via a GP or hospital inpatient services.

Interpreting services

An individual who speaks a different language may use an interpreter. This can be face to face or over the phone. Some may also use online services. The interpreter will facilitate discussions to ensure the individual who speaks a different language can be fully involved, understands completely what is being said to them, and is able to get across their own meaning.

Translation services

Translation services are very similar to those provided by interpreters. Translators tend to focus on converting written material into a different language. For example, an individual may need a care plan or referral form translated.

Advocacy services

An advocate is someone who is normally not a friend or family member and will be independent. Their role, according to the NHS, is to help people who are vulnerable in society and need assistance to access information, be involved in decisions, explore choices, define and promote their rights and responsibilities and speak out about issues.

Information and communication technology (ICT)

ICT is a general term that includes a range of communication devices. Individuals may find this helpful and use these to learn about their health.

This can increase self-management of their condition. There are many examples of the use of technology in health. One example is the Big White Wall, a digital support and recovery service aimed at individuals who are stressed or anxious, feeling low or not coping. The Big White Wall also provides a number of support courses that help individuals to manage their condition. There are many other digital or online services that provide support, information and advice on medical conditions.

Command word activity

Describe (AC 2.2)

There are numerous ICT devices available to support individuals with their communication. Choose a health condition that affects communication and describe the needs and preferences of someone with that condition. What support is there available? Present your information as a resource that practitioners could utilise.

Take it further

See **www.bigwhitewall.com**

Augmentative and alternative communication methods

These are a range of methods that can help people with disabilities to communicate with others. They may produce text and can be a simple or sophisticated system. Methods sometimes use different items of technology such as mobiles or laptops. These methods include speech-generating devices, for example, which speak a message when a button is pressed. Not all augmentative communication methods use technology. Some other examples include the use of a symbol for an object or activity, or a photograph.

Makaton

Makaton is a language that uses signs and symbols to help people to communicate

meaningfully and effectively. It supports the use of gestures and pictures to help develop the use of spoken language. Using the combination of signs, symbols and speech, it helps to ensure individuals can share and communicate their feelings and thoughts. It also helps individuals to be enabled to take part in choices over activities. For example, individuals in residential care homes can communicate preferred activities such as whether they would like to swim, horse ride or walk. Makaton can help to support inclusive practice.

Objects of reference

Objects of reference are another means of communication using objects that represent something. They can be used to communicate objects or activities. The objects can be a miniature version of the item, for example a small computer mouse for a computer activity. Or a different object that has a meaning linked with what is being communicated such as a shoe for going for a walk. The objects should be tactile so that individuals with sensory difficulties can utilise this method.

Picture exchange communication system (PECS)

This is a non-verbal communication system that uses symbols and pictures to aid communication. The individual using the system will carry the pictures they use and approach another person, giving them a picture of what they would like or need, such as a picture of a drink of squash. The individual initiates the conversation with the person honouring the request. This system can be developed further and thoughts and feelings can be communicated or questions answered using the picture system. See Figure 4.5.

Each individual may communicate in a different way. As part of person-centred planning, it is important to ensure that the communication

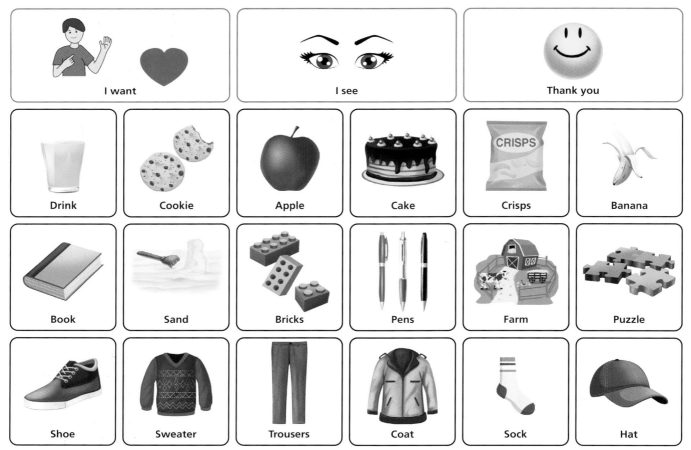

Figure 4.5 An example of a picture exchange system

method meets their specific individual need to ensure that they are fully involved and able to communicate their needs and preference.

2.3 Explain factors that influence communication and interactions

Each individual is different and a health and social care practitioner will encounter many individuals who have different needs and personal preferences. In addition, the professional's working priorities may impact on communication. It is important to establish these on an individual basis and not assume that because an individual has a particular condition or need they will communicate in a specific way. This section covers some examples of communication needs and preferences that may create a barrier to effective communication.

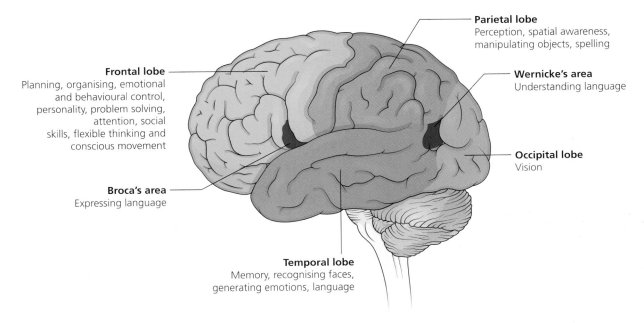

Parietal lobe
Perception, spatial awareness, manipulating objects, spelling

Frontal lobe
Planning, organising, emotional and behavioural control, personality, problem solving, attention, social skills, flexible thinking and conscious movement

Wernicke's area
Understanding language

Broca's area
Expressing language

Occipital lobe
Vision

Temporal lobe
Memory, recognising faces, generating emotions, language

Figure 4.6 There are particular areas of the brain that are activated when using speech and language.

Medical conditions

There are a number of medical conditions that can affect language. People with the condition of **aphasia** or **dysphasia** may make errors in the words used (known as expressive aphasia). This could be using the wrong word, or sound or putting the words together in the wrong way. Aphasia may also affect written communication or understanding language (known as receptive aphasia). Common causes of aphasia and dysphasia are stroke or brain injury.

Other speech disorders include dysarthria which is difficulty speaking caused by the muscles of speech. Speech might be slow or weak or unco-ordinated. Individuals may only be able to use short phrases or single words. This may be developmental due to brain changes before or after birth such as cerebral palsy, or acquired, for example from a stroke.

Another example is dementia. As dementia progresses, and affects the parts of the brain that control language, an individual with dementia will have difficulties with communication. It can display itself as not finding the right words or using a related word. The speech may not make sense or the response may be inaccurate or inappropriate.

Health or medical conditions such as pain can pose a significant barrier. People may become distracted as a result or have other priorities and therefore feel that they cannot concentrate on the communication. Individuals may also tell a professional that they 'feel fine' when they are experiencing high levels of pain. Individuals may also find it hard to discuss their health or medical condition which can impact upon the interaction. This could be for a number of reasons; for example, someone may be embarrassed about having a sexually transmitted disease or may be scared that a lump is cancerous and ignore the signs.

 Key term

Aphasia and dysphasia are conditions where the part of the brain responsible for language is affected

Command word activity

Explain (AC 2.3)

Identify health conditions using the NHS Choices site at www.nhs.uk. Create a factsheet explaining how the medical condition potentially impacts upon communication and how the health and social care practitioner could overcome any barriers to communication.

Language

An individual may not use English as their first language. If someone is on holiday or has recently moved to the country, they may know specific words or phrases, but not always the terminology for medical conditions. Even if they do have the right words, they may not feel comfortable using these. People can also use language in different ways, such as using words that have particular meanings for them.

A dialect is a form of language that varies depending on an area or a social group. The use of dialects can also cause language problems. Although two people may speak the same language, differences in dialect can make it difficult for individuals to understand or interpret what is being said. For example, a bread roll can be a bap, barm cake, cob or batch. Where there are differences such as these, an individual in care might not be able to communicate their need or preference.

Terminology used in a communication can act as a barrier as it may not be fully understood by the recipient. Medical professionals should also be clear with the language they are using. A doctor may tell a patient 'they have a positive diagnosis for cancer'. The patient may think that as the doctor has said it was positive, this meant it was good news. The doctor would actually mean that the tests had a positive indication of cancer, meaning the individual did in fact have cancer.

Acronyms (a word or name made up of the initial letters in a phrase or a word) should be avoided as the individual may not understand what these are, but also as different acronyms may have different interpretations. CCU for example could be coronary care unit or critical care unit. PT can mean part-time, patient or physiotherapist. If, for example, a health care professional has been told to discuss something with 'the PT', they may misinterpret this and think they have been told to discuss with the physiotherapist, when they were actually meant to talk to the patient.

The medical profession sometimes uses complex words, expressions or jargon to explain medical issues. They may also communicate using medical words such as 'syncope' for fainting or 'epistaxis' for nose bleed. This can cause anxiety with patients not knowing what has happened to them or thinking their condition is extremely serious. It is therefore better to avoid jargon and use everyday language when speaking to individuals.

Personal factors

Personal factors can affect communication. There is a link between how an individual feels – such as how confident they feel in the situation, or if they are anxious about something – and how the communication occurs.

Attitudes from both the health and social care professional or the individual may impact communication. There may be lack of motivation or desire to communicate, therefore presenting a significant barrier. This can lead to someone being unwilling to explore different ideas and this can prove frustrating. Anger can affect someone's communication skills as they have difficulty in accepting and listening to what is being said. Pride may be a barrier, for example individuals may feel they do not need help and therefore will not be as receptive to what a professional is saying. It is not just the attitudes of the individual or patient to consider; for example, a negative attitude from a member of staff will have a significant impact as the individual they are interacting with will feel they are not valued.

Anxiety has a negative impact on communication skills as someone may be preoccupied by those thoughts and therefore not receptive to communication.

Activity

Explain how a patient who has been admitted for being unwell, may find it difficult to ask doctors to explain their medical condition. What might be the role of the nurse or nursing assistant looking after this patient in this situation? Outline the impact that this would have on the individual and the medical professional.

Confidence can be a barrier as an individual may not have the confidence to ask questions about issues that may be of concern to them or to say that they do not understand what is being said to them. The power balance within the interaction may not be equal; for example, someone may hold a medical person in a higher regard and feel intimidated by their presence.

Different abilities and disabilities

Sensory abilities, such as hearing and sight, may also affect both verbal and non-verbal communication. A person with a hearing impairment or a visual impairment may require help in receiving or understanding communication. It is important to remember that people can have very different levels of impairment; for example, someone who is profoundly deaf will require a different approach to someone who is in the early stages of losing their hearing.

Some individuals such as those with autism, a developmental condition can find it difficult to interpret verbal and/or non-verbal communication, such as facial expression or tone of voice. For instance, sarcasm may be taken in a literal manner, or an abstract saying such as 'Jump up on this chair for me' (meaning to sit on it) could be interpreted as being asked to literally jump on the chair. Some individuals may not speak at all or have limited speech, and some may display 'echolalia' where they repeat what the other individual has just said.

Individuals with learning disabilities do not have one way of communicating. The British Institute of Learning Disabilities (BILD) states that between 50 and 90 per cent of individuals have communication difficulties. The individual may not understand everything that is said to them, and may often respond in a way they think you want them to respond. Dyslexia is a condition that can affect communication. Many people assume that this is just difficulty in communicating written language. However, an individual with dyslexia may also have difficulties with verbal

language, following a conversation or expressing their own views.

Other factors

Alcohol and drugs can cause disorientation, confusion and affect an individual's ability to communicate effectively. Alcohol is rapidly absorbed into the blood stream which affects the brain, causing slurred speech. This in combination with a loss of inhibitions can have a negative effect, with individuals displaying aggressive and irrational behaviour, and even hallucinations. Estimates suggest that 1.2 million violent incidents are linked to alcohol misuse, NHS 2015.

The age of the person can affect communication. The complexity of language used for a child, will be different to that for an adult, and this is altered to help their understanding. It is important to not appear patronising and many older children who have a long-term condition such as cystic fibrosis or diabetes will have more knowledge and understanding of the condition than may be perceived. Non-verbal cues can be extremely useful with young children who often express themselves through playing.

Professional priorities can affect communication. For example, a health and social care professional may have two patients: Patient 1 wishes to discuss their medical concerns, and Patient 2 has a serious condition that is deteriorating and requires immediate medical attention. The responsibility of that professional may be to prioritise, managing the condition of the deteriorating Patient 2. In this situation, Patient 1 would not have immediate access to the information they are seeking and may feel that they are being ignored or neglected. The professional priority of assisting Patient 2 who is deteriorating therefore impacts upon the opportunity to communicate with Patient 1. It should be remembered, however, that communication is always important and failure to communicate may have serious implications for individuals.

2.4 Explain how barriers to communication can be overcome

Effective communication is very important in health and social care settings. Barriers to communication can be reduced or eliminated by a number of different methods. Always ensure that those you are caring for are treated as individuals. Health and social care practitioners should not make assumptions about how someone may communicate.

Sensory barriers

If an individual has a sensory impairment then speaking slowly and not shouting can assist. Ensure the person can see your face and the light is suitable. Sign language or braille can also be used.

Cognitive barriers

Cognitive barriers can be reduced by removing distractions, and communicating ideas one at a time. Be aware of how language can be misinterpreted. Communicating with individuals with dementia can be helped by speaking clearly and using short sentences. Non-verbal communication and gestures can be helpful. All practitioners should ensure they allow time for the individual to respond. As dementia progresses and the effects on the brain increase, yes or no questions can be beneficial. For example, ask the individual 'would you like some water' rather than 'what would you like to drink?' The use of non-verbal expression is also helpful; so too is approaching the person from the front, introducing yourself.

Language skills

If there are language issues then it is important to use translation and interpreting services; it would be best practice to use an independent person rather than a family member. This is so the individual does not feel unintentional pressure or feel influenced to make a decision. Speech and language therapists are important members of the multi-disciplinary team

Take it further
Further details can be found in AC 2.3.

and can provide advice and guidance about communication methods. Details on their role can be found in AC 2.2. This is especially useful in relation to aphasia and other conditions that affect communication.

Environmental barriers

Environmental barriers can be a hindrance, for example when it is too noisy or too dark. This means that people may not hear or pick up on non-verbal communications, which can affect the quality and meaning of communication.

Noisy situations can present an environmental barrier as it will stop both interpretation and communication of a message. This can be reduced by using quieter spaces, and taking steps to reduce noise where possible such as closing windows or doors. Lighting should be adjusted to meet the needs of the individual.

Command word activity
Explain (AC 2.3, 2.4)
Identify possible environmental barriers in a health and social care setting and explain the effect they can have on interactions. Explain for that setting how these can be overcome.

The need for privacy or a lack of it can present a barrier to communication. An individual will not feel relaxed in the interaction if there is a chance that others can overhear. This includes hospital wards with many interactions occurring behind an individual's curtain on the ward. Although a closed curtain promotes privacy, it does not provide a sound barrier and the individual may feel embarrassed or inhibited from voicing concerns or asking questions. Taking individuals to a separate location can help to overcome this situation.

Some individuals may experience a state of high arousal – a state of mind that can be caused by different situations or sensations, including reactions to stress and anxiety and too much stimulation in the environment. For example, many people with autism have sensory sensitivity and are unable to ignore or block out background sounds. These then become overbearing and impact on effective communication. These can be overcome by being aware of the needs of the individual, along with being aware of the influence of the background and removing unnecessary sounds.

Social barriers

Social barriers are another group of possible barriers that may occur in health and social care situations. They may include cultural differences, language differences, physical gestures, interpersonal skills, and the proximity of health and social care practitioners.

Culture refers to customs that communities of people adopt. In different cultures, language and words used can vary. The word 'hot', for example, can mean hot in terms of body temperature or 'hot' can mean stolen or desirable. Misunderstandings can occur as a result.

Physical gestures and facial expressions can also lend themselves to different interpretations. For example, some people may smile when they are embarrassed as well as happy. In some cultures eye contact can be seen as rude. To overcome this, knowledge and understanding of the individual is important: by understanding the culture, but also by asking and not assuming. Information about these differences should be recorded on the care plan if available.

Proximity (distance) can affect communication too. Being too far away can mean that communication is too hard to understand; being too close means that an individual may feel that their personal space is invaded and therefore they are not at ease for communicating. Often,

individuals who are more comfortable with each other will stand closer together. Those that are angry or aggressive will often be at a level of eye-to-eye contact. Being aware of personal space and eye contact, and sitting at an angle to the individual, for example, can help to overcome this barrier and make an individual feel more comfortable.

Interpersonal skills that are either excellent or poor will have a bearing on effective communication. How someone sits can facilitate communication and being in a SOLER position can help facilitate interaction. SOLER is an acronym standing for:

Sit squarely

Open posture

Lean towards the individual

Eye contact

Relax.

Touch can be reassuring and convey concern and affection; however, this can also be a barrier as there may be cultural or other issues around the use of touch which means it should not be used without checking how this would be perceived by the individual.

Activity

Practice the SOLER position and then see if you can identify it being used in your placement.

2.5 Explain how to communicate to meet the needs of others

To meet the needs of others, it is essential to first identify how they wish to communicate and their preferred method. Consistency between all members of staff is important and training may need to be provided to ensure this is achieved. A health and social care practitioner should ensure that they give enough time for the person to listen and respond, and check that they have understood. A good awareness of non-verbal communication is important to pick up on any visual clues about the interaction. A health and social care practitioner should always be honest if they do not understand what is being said to them, rather than make a guess.

2.6 Explain how to access additional support or services to enable individuals to communicate effectively

There are a number of sources of additional support to enable effective communication. For all of these sources, policies and procedures should be followed which can offer access and support as to how to access these services.

Advocacy services

An advocacy service will offer independent support on behalf of an individual. This may be with or without the individual being present. They will represent the wishes, needs and preferences of the patient or service user. For instance, it may be necessary to speak for someone in situations where the individual feels they cannot, or to write letters on their behalf. There are a number of organisations that offer these services such as the British Institute of Learning Disabilities, MIND, Mencap or SEAP (Support, Empower, Advocate, Promote). These can be contacted directly through the organisation and can be contacted by the individual themselves

or via referral from a health and social care practitioner.

Key term

NHS Trust an organisation within the NHS that has specific responsibility for a geographical locality

Speech and language therapists

For information on speech and language therapists, see AC 2.2 above.

Translation and interpretations services

An independent person can be useful for translating or interpreting what an individual is saying, for example if they speak a different language. Family members should not be used as they may unintentionally lead an individual to say something they did not mean or may not translate exactly what is being said. The individual may also wish to communicate about something privately. These services can be accessed face to face or via telephone. A range of companies exist which can provide these services. Individuals may also be employed in this role in larger **NHS Trusts**.

Specialist equipment

Specialist equipment can also be useful. Hearing aids and hearing loops are frequently used. Some

Take it further

Remind yourself of communication needs and preferences in AC 2.2.

Figure 4.7 An example of specialist communication equipment

technological examples are discussed in AC 1.1, Methods of communication. Other examples include a communication passport which is an individual specific book which aims to provide those that come into contact with individuals an overview of their needs and individual wishes. Phones can be used as a technology aid to help facilitate communication. This will be through, for example, a phone that can type, 'speak', hear or read a message. Some communication aids use a computer to facilitate communication. The computer stores a variety of messages, which are then selected by the individual using the system. The chosen message is then displayed on a screen. All of these aids will generally be accessed via a speech and language therapist or at a specialist centre.

Support from others

Support for communication can also come from other people. This may be the individual's family or friends. They may be able to provide guidance on techniques and the individual's preferred methods or suggest meanings of phrases or words that an individual may use that are difficult to understand. For example, a child may have a specific name for part of their body or an object that provides comfort for them.

Command word activity

Explain (AC 2.6)

Create a fact file of local services available to offer support to enable individuals to communicate effectively. Explain how these services assist individuals to communicate effectively and ensure you include information on how these can be accessed.

✓ Check your understanding

1. Define a barrier to communication.
2. Identify three examples of factors that can influence effective communication and interaction.
3. Give two ways in which barriers to communication can be overcome.
4. Outline the role of a speech and language therapist.
5. Name one organisation that can help with communication and explain how they can be accessed.

LO3: Understand legislation, policies, procedures and codes of practice relating to information management

Every day, a health and social care practitioner will come into contact with data. It is extremely important this information is managed correctly. This section will explore the legislation that governs information management.

3.1 Explain the meaning of the term confidentiality

Confidentiality is about protecting personal information. Information includes names, date of birth, age, gender and medical history. Confidentiality exists to protect the data of individuals. Every day, health and social care practitioners come into contact with information that is confidential, for example, from what they are told by individuals, information sheets about who they are going to be looking after in hospital, from what they are told by individuals or information sheets about who they are going to be looking after in a hospital or nursery. Data protection laws ensure that individuals are kept informed of how their information is stored so they can choose how and whether it is used. If a practitioner were to breach the confidentiality of an individual or share their information without permission, there could be serious consequences such as the individual feeling that they cannot trust the practitioner or service, putting the individual at risk. There may be consequences for health and social care practitioners for breaking policies and procedures. This may include disciplinary action or the health and social care organisation could be found to have broken the law.

 Key term

Confidentiality means keeping information private. It is a legal obligation under the Data Protection Act 1998 and as a health and social care professional you must follow it.

 Classroom discussion (AC 3.1)

Milly is a busy community care worker. She is given a piece of paper each day detailing her visits. One day she drops this on the way into the house of one of the individuals she is looking after.

As a class discuss:

1. What type of information may be on Milly's sheet.
2. Why it is important to keep this information confidential.
3. The possible consequences for the individuals named on the sheet, Milly and the organisation she works for.
4. How this situation could have been prevented and what measures could have been taken to reduce the risk if the sheet is found.

3.2 Summarise legislation, policies, procedures and codes of practice relating to the management of information

There are a number of pieces of **legislation**, **policies**, **procedures** and codes of practice that link to security of data. These are summarised in Table 4.4.

Table 4.4 Summary of key legislation

Legislation	Summary	How this may apply to data management practice
Care Act 2014	Replaced and reformed a number of previous laws. Set out new responsibilities for local authorities and promotes new rights for carers and service users. An emphasis on well-being, prevention, integration of services and information advice and advocacy. Establishes Health Research Authority which protects and promotes the interests of the public but facilitates patient information for purposes beyond direct patient care.	All organisations should have arrangements in place for sharing information between each other.
Data Protection Act 1998	Principles of the Act: Data and information should: be processed fairly and lawfully be obtained for a specific purpose be adequate, relevant and not excessive not be kept longer than necessary for the purpose(s) be handled in a way that protects people's rights have measures taken to protect its loss, destruction or damage so it is kept securely not be transferred outside of the European Economic Area unless there is adequate level of protection and rights.	Have legitimate reasons for collecting data. Only collect information that is sufficient for what is required. Ensure data taken is accurate and the source is clear. Store data in a secure way. Securely delete information no longer needed or required to be retained.

Legislation	Summary	How this may apply to data management practice
Human Rights Act 1998	Sets out a number of rights (called articles) that everyone is entitled to. All public bodies (for example hospitals) must respect and protect human rights.	Article 8: Gives everyone the right to respect for private and family life. This includes not sharing personal data.
Common Law duty of Confidentiality	Although not written in one document like other Acts, there are a number of 'judge made' laws or precedents (previous court decisions that are legally binding) set.	It is accepted that if information is given in circumstances with a duty of confidence, it cannot be disclosed without the provider's consent. Consent must be obtained (unless there is a legal reason it is not required) before disclosing information.

Key terms

Legislation laws made by the government which must be followed. Legislation includes Acts of Parliament as well as Regulations

Policy is a statement of how an organisation works. This is normally linked to legislation. Examples include Confidentiality Policy and Health and Safety Policy

Procedures are a step-by-step guide of how to complete a task or implement a policy

Caldicott Guardian

A Caldicott Guardian is a senior person in an organisation who is responsible for protecting the confidentiality of patient and service-user information. They are also responsible for enabling appropriate information-sharing. This will apply to all NHS Trusts and they will give advice and write policies to do with confidentiality.

Codes of practice

Codes of practice are job specific and present the professional standards expected to be upheld by the professional. These professionals include nurses, midwives, social workers, doctors, physiotherapists and occupational therapists. If an individual does not follow that code then it will bring their suitability for the job into question. Here is an example of a code of practice concerning privacy and confidentiality. It states nurses and midwifes must:

5.1 respect a person's right to privacy in all aspects of their care

5.2 make sure that people are informed about how and why information is used and shared by those who will be providing care

5.3 respect that a person's right to privacy and confidentiality continues after they have died

5.4 share necessary information with other healthcare professionals and agencies only when the interests of patient safety and public protection override the need for confidentiality, and

5.5 share with people, their families and their carers, as far as the law allows, the information they want or need to know about their health, care and ongoing treatment sensitively and in a way they can understand.

Source: Nursing and Midwifery Council Code of Practice, Section 5 (NMC 2016)

Here is an example of a code of practice for paramedics regarding confidentiality:

7 understand the importance of and be able to maintain confidentiality

7.1 be aware of the limits of the concept of confidentiality

7.2 understand the principles of information governance and be aware of the safe and effective use of health and social care information

7.3 be able to recognise and respond appropriately to situations where it is necessary to share information to safeguard service users or the wider public

Source: Section 7 Health Care Professional Council Code of Practice

Command word activity

Summarise (AC 3.2)

1. When next at placement, or when you can research, ask for a copy of the Confidentiality Policy and procedure and Data Protection Policy and procedure.
2. Identify any links to at least two pieces of legislation. Summarise the relevant legislation, policies and procedures.

 Key terms

Disclosure to report or reveal information that is often sensitive or confidential

Serious case review an enquiry into the death or serious injury of a child or vulnerable adult where abuse or neglect is known or thought to be a factor

Duty of care an obligation to ensure the safety and well-being of others. This is a legal requirement under legislation such as The Care Act (2014) under codes of practice such as the NMC Code

Policies and procedures

All organisations will have policies and procedures around sharing information. Examples include Data Protection Policy, Confidentiality Policy and Information Sharing Policy. These will reflect the relevant legislation and must be followed by all staff in that organisation.

3.3 Explain the potential tension between maintaining confidentiality and the need to disclose information

Tensions may arise when there is a need to disclose information. Patients and service users have a right to have their information kept confidential. Patients generally have the right to the use and disclosure of confidential information. There are certain exceptions where **disclosure** is required, such as in situations where there is a risk of abuse or neglect. If a health and social care practitioner has concerns about the safety and well-being of someone in their care (such as where they have disclosed abuse) then this must be shared in adherence with policy and procedures in the setting. This is to meet current legislative requirements and also to protect the individual. Failure to disclose information can have detrimental impacts for the well-being of vulnerable individuals. Numerous **serious case reviews** have mentioned a lack of communication and sharing information as a factor contributing to systematic failures and leading to serious harm. A tension arises as the right to confidentiality and the need to disclose are in conflict. This

may be exacerbated or worsen as the patient or service user may not want the information to be shared.

Health and social care workers have a **duty of care** and the well-being of the patient or service user is paramount. Information can be kept confidential and only shared on a need-to-know basis, for example with the safeguarding officer. A 'need-to-know' basis means that information should only be shared with those who would be unable to do their job properly without the relevant knowledge. It may involve revealing only the minimum amount of information required about an individual – only the bare facts they need at that time, in that situation, and nothing more. Therefore that same information should be kept confidential from others, including relatives and other colleagues, who do not need to be aware of the information. Policy and procedures of the setting should be followed and will provide information on who to disclose to and in what format, and guidance on what to include or not.

Take it further

Read about legislation and safeguarding in HSC CM3 (LO2) and HSC DM2, Section 1.1.

You can view the reports arising from serious case reviews on the internet, for example on the NSPCC website.

Case scenario (AC 3.3)

Aaron is a staff nurse and arrives for his 7.30 a.m. day shift. He, along with his student nurse, listens to the bedside handover given by a member of staff and reads the documentation given from Gemma on one of their patients, John.

John who is 46 years old has learning disabilities and is in hospital recovering from an operation. He is being treated in a side room. His brother is his main carer and comes to the ward to assist with personal care for John and discusses his care with the medical team. During their shift, they observe that John has developed a rash that may be infectious. John says that they are not allowed to tell anyone as he does not want any other hospital staff or his brother to know.

1. Outline one reason why John might not want anyone to know about his medical condition.
2. Identify John's rights.
3. Identify Aaron's responsibilities to John, his brother, other patients and staff.
4. Outline and justify the action Aaron should take.

Command word activity

Explain (AC 3.3)

The need to safeguard individuals is an example of potential tension between maintaining confidentiality and the need to disclose information. Read about safeguarding in HSC CM3: Safeguarding in health and social care, Section 1.1 and 5.2; and HSC DM2: Protection of children, young people and adults in health and social care, Section 2.2.

Explain the rights of individuals to have their private information kept confidential in health and social care settings. What are the responsibilities of health and social care practitioners if a disclosure is made? Explain why this may create a tension between confidentiality and disclosing information.

LO4: Understand how to work in line with legislation, policies, procedures and codes of practice relating to information management

This section explores the practicalities of complying with information management. All organisations must follow the principles of legislation that relate to information management. These include the Data Protection Act 1998, The Human Rights Act 1998 and the Care Act 2014. Further information on these pieces of legislation can be found in Table 4.2.

4.1 Describe how to ensure security of data when accessing and storing records

Policy and procedures

All staff working in a health and social care setting will come into contact with information. Staff will follow the policy and procedures of their organisation, and this will include a Confidentiality Policy.

A number of records have to be kept for a legally specified period of time. Maternity records for example are kept for 25 years after the birth of the last child, adult social care records for 8 years (although these differ for different types of records).

Check your understanding

1. What is confidentiality?
2. Identify two pieces of information you may have about a patient that should be kept confidential.
3. Outline two pieces of legislation that protect personal data.
4. What is meant by the term need-to-know basis?
5. Why might there be tension when there is the need to disclose information?

Storing records, accessing records and storing information

Records that are paper based should be stored correctly to protect the confidentiality of the information contained within the documents and to prevent damage or records being destroyed. The facility for storage must be secure and environmentally safe. They must be protected by security systems and all staff members must be aware of the measures in place and comply with these. This will ensure that records are kept safely and can be accessed when needed. When taken out of storage, they must be returned as soon as possible and not left on desks.

Data and records on a computer should be password protected and access only given to staff that need this information. Passwords should be secret, but you should be able to remember them so you do not have to write them down. Passwords longer than eight characters are more difficult to crack but should still be changed regularly. They should never be shared between colleagues and staff must always ensure they log off when they have finished on the computer. Staff should only access information that they are required to know, for example staff should not use their access to look up family and friends' medical records.

4.2 Describe how to ensure the security of data when sharing information

There are occasions when information may need to be shared. Shared information should only be in the best interests of the patient or service user, and it may be that the whole record does not need to be shared. In some circumstances the objective of sharing information could be achieved by anonymising the data. If the data needs to be shared then consideration should be given to which method to use. There are methods of promoting the privacy of information, for example password protecting documents or sending the personal details such as name, date of birth in a separate document to the rest of the details. If information is sent by email, then the sender should be double-checked prior to sending. External emails can be encrypted to maintain confidentiality. If information is to be shared over the phone, then consideration should be given to privacy and the sender of the information should check that the receiver is in a private area to be able to receive the information.

4.3 Explain how to maintain records

Numerous records are kept within health and social care settings, all of which have a purpose and may be read by a number of different people. Examples include nursing notes, care plans, medication records, food diaries, fluid balance charts intake (such as drinks or IV fluids) and output (such as urine or vomit) and pressure ulcer risk assessments. These assessments help to determine how likely an individual is to develop a pressure ulcer, along with actions that can be implemented to reduce the risk.

Records are a key source of communication between staff as colleagues taking over the care of an individual will rely on that information. This helps to ensure seamless quality of care. Records provide a safeguard to demonstrate interventions and care for a patient or service user. As a health and social care professional, it is impossible to remember in detail the care provided for every single patient for years. Clear and accurate documentation is therefore essential. Health and social care practitioners cannot assume that someone will know that you have carried out a task. It is generally assumed that 'if it is not recorded, it has not been done'.

It is important that records are maintained in the following ways:

1. They should be legible, factual and contain true, unambiguous, clear and accurate information. If the patient or service user reports anything such as how they are feeling, then this should go in quotation marks.

2. Any decision made should have a reason or evidence.

3. Notes should be dated, timed and signed and the name of the author printed alongside (initials should be avoided as there could be more than one person with the same initials).

4. Records should not be accessed or written in public places and staff should be vigilant for signs of unauthorised access.

5. In nursing, service user notes, jargon or phrases that can be speculated about or are offensive should be avoided. It is poor practice to write that a patient has 'been difficult' or 'played up'.

6. Notes should be written as soon as possible.

7. Each organisation will have their own agreed format of using records and this should be followed to ensure consistency.

8. Abbreviations should generally be avoided as these can mean different things in different settings; for example, CCU can be a Critical Care Unit or a Coronary Care Unit.

9. Actions taken should be reviewed for effectiveness. For example if a patient reported pain relief and was administered pain medication, has this worked?

10. Records should not be falsified and should be written in agreement with the individual.

Activity

Look at the following record. Identify any positives or room for improvement on this record.

Nursing Notes. Date: 10.01.16 Time: 16:20

Bob has been happy all shift. He ate one bowl of cereal and a cup of tea. He played Scrabble with another patient. He spoke to his mum on the phone. RJ

Command word activity

Explain (AC 4.3)

Explain how to maintain good records and why it is important to do so. Suggest measures that can be implemented to promote good documentation keeping.

✔ Check your understanding

1. Evaluate one role of the health and social care practitioner in maintaining records.
2. Identify two records kept in health and social care settings and where these records will be stored.
3. Explain two factors that can help to store electronic resources.
4. Explain one reason why keeping records is important.

Read about it

Argyle, M. (1972) *The Psychology of Interpersonal Communication*, Harmondsworth: Pelican

HCPC (2014) *Paramedics Standards of Proficiency*, London: HCPC

Tuckman, B. (1965) 'Developmental sequences in small groups', *Psychological Bulletin*, 63(6), pp. 384–99

Websites

Bridge School (2010) *Speech Generating Devices*. Accessed from https://www.bridgeschool.org/transition/multimodal/sgd.php

HRA *Our Committees*. Accessed from http://www.hra.nhs.uk/about-the-hra/our-committees/section-251/

ICO *Guide to Data Protection*. Accessed from https://ico.org.uk/for-organisations/guide-to-data-protection/principle-6-rights/

NHS (2015a) *How Long Should Medical Records be Kept For*? Accessed from http://www.nhs.uk/chq/Pages/1889.aspx?CategoryID=68&SubCategoryID=160

NHS (2015b) *Advocacy Services*. Accessed from http://www.nhs.uk/conditions/social-care-and-support-guide/pages/advocacy-services.aspx on 28.09.2016

NHS (2015c) *Alcohol Misuse-Risks*. Accessed from http://www.nhs.uk/Conditions/Alcohol-misuse/Pages/Risks.aspx on 28.09.2016

PECS (2016) *Picture Exchange Communication Systems*. Accessed from http://www.pecs-unitedkingdom.com/

SCIE (2015) *The Care Act 2014*. Accessed from http://www.scie.org.uk/care-act-2014/

Unit HSC CM4: How will I be graded?

The table below shows what the learner must do to achieve each grading criterion. Learners must achieve all the criteria for a grade to be awarded (i.e. criteria D1 to D3 must be achieved to pass this unit assessment at grade D). A higher grade may not be awarded before a lower grade has been achieved in full, although component criteria of a higher grade may have been achieved.

Grade	Assessment criteria number	Assessment criteria	Assessment of learning / What you need to show
D1	1.1	Explain the use of communication in health and social care settings.	Provide information to explain ● types of communication used in health and social care settings, ● a range of people who need to communicate, between each other, ● different reasons for communicating in health and social care settings.
D2	2.1	Outline theories of communication.	Outline more than one relevant theory of communication.
D3	3.1	Explain the meaning of the term confidentiality.	Provide information that defines the term confidentiality that: ● shows accurate understanding of the term, ● relates to the context of health and social care.
D4	3.2	Summarise legislation, policies, procedures and codes of practice relating to the management of information.	Information must focus on management of information and summarise: ● relevant legislation, ● more than one relevant policy, ● more than one relevant procedure more than one relevant code of practice.

Grade	Assessment criteria number	Assessment criteria	Assessment of learning / What you need to show
D5		Show evidence of reading or use of sources.	There should be evidence of learners' reading or use of sources. Learners must use a minimum of two traceable references.
C1	2.2. 2.5	Describe communication and language needs and preferences of individuals. Explain how to communicate to meet the needs of others.	Information must focus on effective communication to show: ● a range of language needs, that individuals may have a ● range of preferences, that individuals may have preferences ● how to communicate to meet the needs of others.
C2	4.1. 4.2	Describe how to ensure the security of data when accessing and storing records. Describe how to ensure the security of data when sharing information.	Information must show understanding of how security of data can be maintained when: ● storing records, ● accessing records, ● sharing information.
C3	4.3	Explain how to maintain records.	Links to C2. Provide an explanation to demonstrate how records must be maintained.
C4		Show evidence of reading or use of sources with referencing relevant to the explanations. Good use of vocabulary and grammar.	Use of referencing should show evidence of reading or use of sources. Vocabulary and grammar should be appropriate and accurate for purpose.
B1	2.3. 2.4	Explain factors that influence communication and interactions. Explain how barriers to communication can be overcome.	Explain how to communicate to meet the needs of others and consider: ● the factors which influence communication and interactions between others ● barriers to effective communication and how these can be overcome.
B2	2.6	Explain how to access additional support or services to enable individuals to communicate effectively.	Explanation must show knowledge and understanding of: ● a range of additional support services, ● how to access additional support services, ● support that the services offer to enable individuals to communicate effectively.
B3		Show evidence of reading or use of sources. Referencing supports the explanation.	Use of reading or use of sources should be shown through a range of relevant referencing. Referencing should be used appropriately to support view or explanation.
A1	3.3	Explain the potential tension between maintaining confidentiality and the need to disclose information.	Explanation must focus on confidentiality to demonstrate detailed understanding of: ● the need to maintain confidentiality, ● the potential tension between maintaining confidentiality and disclosing information, ● the need to disclose information.
A2		Show evidence of wider background reading or use of sources. Referencing supports the explanation.	Wider background reading should be evident or a wide range of sources material should be used.

Grade	Assessment criteria number	Assessment criteria	Assessment of learning / What you need to show
A*1	1.2	Explain the impact of communication on service delivery outcomes.	Provide a detailed explanation of the impact of effective and ineffective communication in relation to: ● individuals, family members, carers ● practitioners and colleagues ● the organisation partnerships with other agencies/services.
A*2		Show evidence of a range of background reading or use of sources used selectively.	Learners should show the ability to consider or explore relevant issues which contribute to the explanation. An extensive range of background reading or use of sources should be used selectively and cited appropriately.

Current legislation as relevant to Home Nation

HSC CM5
Infection Prevention and Control in Health and Social Care

Learning outcomes

LO1: Understand types of biological organisms that cause disease

1.1 Describe types of microbiological organisms that cause disease

LO2: Understand the features of vector borne disease

2.1 Explain the features of vector borne disease

LO3: Understand transmission of disease

3.1 Describe how pathogenic microorganisms are transmitted

3.2 Explain why individuals may be more vulnerable to infection

3.3 Describe the body's defence mechanisms against infection

3.4 Explain how to break the chain of infection

LO4: Understand methods of microorganism control

4.1 Explain methods of microorganism control in relation to:
- sterilisation
- disinfection
- pasteurisation
- sanitation
- asepsis

LO5: Understand precautions to be taken to reduce the spread of infection in a health or social care setting

5.1 Explain the importance of personal hygiene and attire in relation to infection control

5.2 Explain the correct hand washing technique

5.3 Explain the use ofpersonal protective equipment

5.4 Explain the process of safe waste disposal for:
- body fluids
- linen
- sharps and equipment

LO6: Be able to minimise the spread of infection

6.1 Use the correct hand washing technique

6.2 Use personal protective equipment

6.3 Dispose of waste safely

LO7: Understand how infectious diseases can be controlled and treated by medication

7.1 Evaluate the use of drugs to control and treat infectious disease

7.2 Explain how antimicrobial resistance occurs

Learning outcomes

LO8: Understand the requirements of RIDDOR and COSHH in relation to infection prevention and control

8.1 Explain the requirements of RIDDOR in relation to infection prevention and control

8.2 Explain the requirements of COSHH in relation to infection prevention and control

LO9: Understand the role and responsibilities of the health and social care practitioner in relation to infection prevention and control

9.1 Analyse the role and responsibilities of the health and social care practitioner in relation to infection prevention and control

About this unit

Infection control is a major issue in health and social care. Failure to do so has many detrimental impacts. This unit aims to provide knowledge and understanding of infection prevention and control in health and social care. It explores diseases, the microorganisms that cause these and the features of vector borne disease.

Many individuals who use health and social care services are vulnerable to infection and this unit will explore the reasons why and precautions that must be taken to reduce and prevent the spread of infection. Issues such as antimicrobial resistance will be discussed and the evaluation of drugs to control and treat infectious disease. The requirements under legislation in relation to infection prevention and control will be explored and an analysis of the role and responsibilities of the health and social care practitioner in preventing the spread of infection.

LO1: Understand types of biological organisms that can cause disease

A microorganism is a living organism. However, these are so small they can only be seen by a microscope. Bacteria, viruses, fungi and protozoa are all examples. Microorganisms that cause disease are **pathogenic**. Some diseases can be caused by more than one pathogen. Meningitis, an infection of the tissue that surrounds the brain, is one example. This may be caused by several types of bacteria or viruses.

 Key term

Pathogenic is a medical term that describes any microorganism that can cause disease

1.1 Describe types of microbiological organisms that cause disease

Bacteria

Bacteria are small, single-celled organisms. They are found almost everywhere and while many are **non-pathogenic** and therefore harmless, performing a necessary function in the body such as those in the intestines, which aid digestion, a number can cause significant and serious diseases. 'Bad' bacteria can affect humans as they can cause disease by infecting individuals or they can cause food spoilage. On the human body are flora (bacteria and organisms) which can be either normal – always present and do not cause a disease – or transient – opportunistic flora that cause disease.

 Key term

Non-pathogenic a term to describe microorganisms that do not cause disease

Structure

Bacteria do not have a nucleus; but they do have DNA, a cell wall and membrane. Some have a flagellum, which is a tail that helps it to move along. Bacteria cause pathogenic disease by releasing harmful toxins.

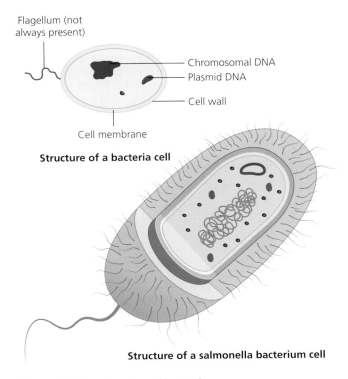

Flagellum (not always present)

Chromosomal DNA

Plasmid DNA

Cell wall

Cell membrane

Structure of a bacteria cell

Structure of a salmonella bacterium cell

Figure 5.1 The structure of bacteria

Bacteria come in different shapes. *Cocci* are oval shaped; *bacilli* are rod and spiral shaped.

Life cycle

Bacteria reproduce through a process called **binary fusion**. The bacterium (one single cell of bacteria) divides into two identical cells. Each contains the exact same DNA. These two cells then each divide into two to make four, the four then further divide. If the conditions are optimal for growth then this can occur every 20 minutes.

Key term

Binary fusion a form of cell division that results in the cell dividing into two identical parts, each being able to grow to the original size

Activity

Work out how many bacteria will be present from two bacteria if division occurs every 20 minutes for 1 hour.

Bacterial requirements for growth

In order to survive and thrive, bacteria require an environment that contains nutrients and water, as a high percentage of the bacteria consists of water. Some bacteria are aerobic, which means they require oxygen to survive, and some are anaerobic, which means they do not require oxygen.

Some bacteria create spores. These are capable of withstanding some negative physical and chemical conditions, which means they are difficult to destroy. These **spores** then become active when conditions are right.

The effect of temperature on bacteria

Bacteria grow and reproduce more quickly when they are warm. When bacteria are cold, for example between 0°C and 5°C bacteria (fridge temperature), they grow more slowly. Very cold temperatures, below -18°C, will render the bacteria dormant but not kill the microorganism. Extreme high temperature will kill bacteria. Different bacteria have different optimal growth temperatures. Bacteria that affect the body tend to grow best at temperatures between 20°C and 40°C.

Key term

Spores are produced by bacteria and fungi. They are able to reproduce by themselves and are adapted to travel and withstand unfavourable conditions

Activity

Research legionnaire's disease and how it is spread.

1. Identify the temperature that is optimal for legionnaire's disease growth. How can legionnaire's disease be prevented?
2. Does the temperature have any implication for care practice?

Table 5.1 Examples of disease caused by bacteria

Bacteria and general information	How it is spread	Signs and symptoms	Treatment and prevention
Tuberculosis Caused by the bacteria Mycobacterium tuberculosis This condition mainly affects the lungs It usually develops slowly	Spread through inhaling droplets from an infected person	A cough that lasts for over 3 weeks and brings up phlegm. The cough may contain blood Pyrexia Weight loss and extreme tiredness Night sweats The lymph nodes in the body may have swellings which are not reducing in size	Antibiotics normally for 6 months A hospital admission is not always necessary Can be cured with treatment, but can be fatal if not treated A vaccination called the BCG (Bacillus Calmette-Guérin) is given to individuals in high-risk areas and some groups such as health and social care practitioners
Salmonella poisoning It affects the gastrointestinal system	Eating contaminated food	Diarrhoea Stomach cramps Vomiting Fever	Symptoms usually last from 4 to 7 days. Most people recover without treatment Some require treatment for dehydration Prevention is through effective hand hygiene and adequate storage, preparation and cooking of food
Staphylococcis Cause a wider range of infections which vary in severity and affect the skin and soft tissues or an **invasive infection** Examples include: impetigo, a skin infection; and septic arthritis, which is when the bacteria enter a joint causing infection and inflammation. It can occur in any joint, but knees and hips are the most commonly affected	Impetigo affects the skin and is easily spread through close contact with another individual who has the condition Septic arthritis: bacteria enter an open wound and travel in the blood stream to the joint. Certain groups are more at risk of developing septic arthritis such as those that have injured a joint or had recent surgery	*Impetigo* Red sores appear normally around the nose and mouth. The sores then burst *Septic arthritis* Pain, swelling and redness in the area	*Impetigo* Antibiotic cream or tablets can be used for treatment Prevention is through not sharing towels or flannels used by someone with impetigo and avoiding touching the area *Septic arthritis* Treatment is with antibiotics

Key terms

Pyrexia a raised body temperature

Invasive infection an infection affecting the internal parts of the body that are normally free from pathogens

Take it further

The incidence of TB and those affected by the condition has changed from being the whole population at risk to certain groups and areas. Investigate the incidence of TB across the country.

Viruses

Viruses are the smallest of all the microorganisms. 500 million of the virus that causes the common cold can fit on a pinhead.

Viruses are only able to multiply inside the cells of something else. Viruses replicate by latching on to another cell and getting inside them. Once inside the cell, the virus enters the cell and takes control of the cell. The cell is then instructed to make new viruses. The cell becomes so full that it bursts and releases the viruses. Each of these new viruses will invade another cell and reproduce. This process can occur in just a few hours.

Viruses are simple organisms. They have a strand of genetic material and a protein coat. Some have an additional protective coat layer.

Viruses are constantly changing. As the virus replicates itself, small changes are made. Initially these changes do not change the virus significantly, but over time the changes are significant enough for the human immune system to not recognise. Therefore an individual can become ill from the common cold or influenza more than once, as different viruses cause the infection.

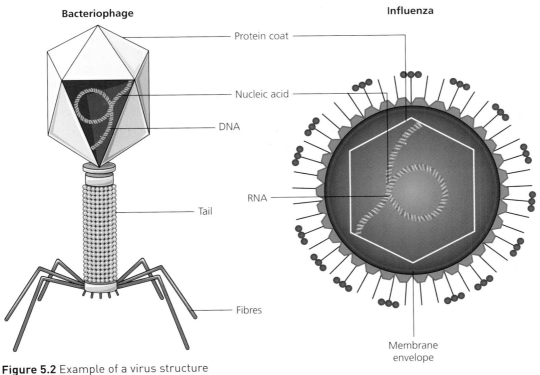

Figure 5.2 Example of a virus structure

Table 5.2 Examples of diseases caused by viruses

Type of virus and general information	Spread	Signs and symptoms	Treatment / prevention
Influenza (flu) A common condition that has similar symptoms to a cold, but is more severe and longer lasting	• Tiny droplets spread by coughing or sneezing. • The droplets can remain in the air and then settle on a surface	• High temperature • Tiredness and weakness (the individual will feel so exhausted it will be difficult to get out of bed) • General aches and pains	• Vaccinations are available, which must be given annually as the virus changes • Management of symptoms, e.g. paracetamol • Some limited evidence for the use of antiviral medication, but this is not routinely administered
Measles A highly infectious viral illness. It is uncommon in the UK due to vaccination programmes	• Carried on tiny droplets that are breathed, coughed or sneezed out. • It is also possible to catch measles through touching an object that has been contaminated	• Cold-like symptoms • High temperature • Sore and red eyes • Red brown blotchy rash	• Contact GP. Measles is a **notifiable disease**, but individuals should ensure they contact the GP surgery before arriving to avoid infecting other individuals • A combined vaccine to prevent measles, mumps and rubella is offered to all children as part of The Routine Schedule. Some symptoms can be treated with paracetamol for example

Type of virus and general information	Spread	Signs and symptoms	Treatment / prevention
Mumps A disease that causes painful swellings at the side of the face	Infected drops of saliva that can be inhaled or picked up from surfaces	• Swellings at the side of the face • Headaches • Joint pain • High temperature	• Contact the GP. Mumps is a notifiable disease but contact surgery before arriving • Rest • Paracetamol / Ibuprofen • A combined vaccine to prevent measles, mumps and rubella is offered to all children as part of The Routine Schedule
Human immunodeficiency virus (HIV) is a virus that attacks the immune system and weakens the body's ability to fight infection and disease. **Acquired immune deficiency syndrome** (AIDS) An individual is considered to have AIDS when the body is not able to fight infection and disease as the immune system has become very badly damaged. Not everyone who has HIV will develop AIDS.	HIV is found in the body fluids of an infected person such as semen, vaginal, anal fluids, blood and breast milk. Sexual contact is the most common way of acquiring HIV A health and social care practitioner in certain situations, such as when using sharps and having a sharps injury can increase the risk of transmission	• Individuals may have a short flu-like illness initially (e.g. fever, sore throat and a rash), then there may be no symptoms for several years • As HIV progresses and causes immune system damage (which may take up to10 years) there are several symptoms such as weight loss, diarrhoea or recurrent infections	• Early identification and diagnosis is critical as there is no cure, but treatment is available • Antiretroviral drugs can help stop the HIV virus replication, keeping the level of HIV low. This means the immune system has time to repair itself • Regular blood tests are required to monitor the progression of the condition • Prevention is the best form of treatment, by avoiding the transmission of body fluids • Using condoms to prevent transmission through sexual contact • Avoiding sharing needles • Blood transfusions in the UK are screened for a number of conditions including HIV, but this should not be used as a method of getting a HIV test • Pregnant woman with HIV should receive treatment to reduce the risk of passing the virus on to the baby • Post Exposure **Prophylaxis** is available and involves taking HIV medication to reduce the risk of developing HIV. It is, however, not guaranteed and should never be used as a substitute for any of the preventative methods

Key terms

Notifiable disease a disease which must be reported to the Government by law

Prophylaxis refers to treatment given or action taken to prevent disease

Routine Immunisation Schedule a schedule of vaccinations offered at different ages (predominantly children and older adults) offered free of charge by the NHS

Take it further

Research the **Routine Immunisation Schedule** and identify the diseases that the vaccinations aim to prevent.

Fungi

Structure and life cycle

Fungi can be single-celled or complex multicellular organisms. Only a small number cause disease in humans. They live on dead and living cells and cause irritation and damage to the cells. The body of a fungus is called a mycelium, which has fine threads called hyphae. These hyphae release digestive enzymes. The enzymes work to digest and absorb nutrients to help growth. Some of the hyphae branches grow into the air and spores form on these aerial branches. These spores enable the fungus to reproduce.

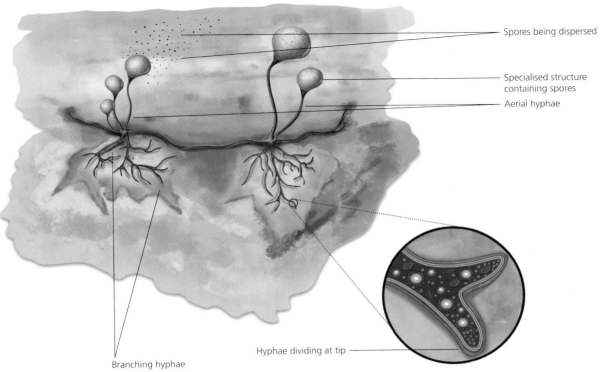

Spores being dispersed

Specialised structure containing spores

Aerial hyphae

Hyphae dividing at tip

Branching hyphae

Figure 5.3 Example of hyphae branches of fungi

Table 5.3 Examples of diseases caused by fungi

Condition/fungus and General information	Spread	Signs and symptoms	Treatment/prevention
Athlete's Foot A fungus that usually appears between the toes	Can be spread to other people by touching the infected skin or coming into contact with contaminated surfaces	The skin may appear itchy, red, dry and cracked or white soggy and cracked	*Treatment* <ul><li>Antifungal creams which can be bought at a pharmacist. Hands should be washed after application</li><li>*Prevention*</li><li>Good foot hygiene such as keeping feet clean and dry, not sharing towels, socks or shoes with others</li><li>Avoid walking around barefoot in places where the infection can spread easily, for example showers and swimming pools</li></ul>
Candida is a fungus that can sometimes cause thrush, which can affect the vagina, mouth, penis or skin (usually where folds of skin come together such as the armpit) Invasive yeast infections which affect the blood stream	Opportunistic infection from candida fungi, i.e. when the conditions are right, the fungus will reproduce. Growth of fungi requires moisture, nutrients such as sugars for food and low temperatures. High temperatures will lead the fungi to be inactive	*Penis* <ul><li>Irritation, discharge and redness of the head on the penis</li><li>Discharge</li></ul> *Vagina* <ul><li>Itching and soreness in vaginal area</li><li>Discharge</li><li>Stinging sensation when urinating</li></ul> *Oral* <ul><li>White patches in the mouth that can be wiped off, leaving a red area that may bleed</li><li>Painful burning sensation</li></ul> *Skin* <ul><li>Red and painful rash which may then scale over with curd-like substance</li></ul>	*Treatment* <ul><li>Antifungal medications (oral or topical, e.g. cream or ointment)</li><li>Blood sugar levels in diabetes should be kept under control</li></ul> *Prevention* <ul><li>Clean skin and genital areas with plain unperfumed soaps, as some soaps and shower gels contain irritants</li><li>Avoid tight fitting underwear</li><li>Rinse mouth after meals</li><li>Visit dentist for check-ups</li><li>Remove dentures at night</li></ul>

Protozoa

Structure and life cycle

Protozoa are single-cell organisms and live in a wide range of habitats. Many are harmless, but some cause disease. Protozoa are mobile and their structure supports movement. Many types of protozoa are able to reproduce using binary fusion. There are four types which are divided on the basis of their movement:

Amoebas have thread-like extensions on their cell membrane and use these to assist movement. Amoebas are able to engulf their food and are single-celled microbes.

Flagellates have a whip-like extension, which enables them to move through liquid environments.

Ciliates have cilia which move in a wave to help movement.

Sporozoans are specifically shaped to help pierce and enter host cells.

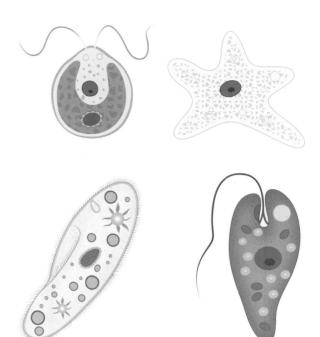

Figure 5.4 Example of a protozoa structure

 Key term

Parasites organisms that live in or on something, such as an animal, which is known as a host. The organism is then transmitted in various ways, for example as a bite from the infected animal

Table 5.4 Examples of diseases caused by protozoa

Type of protozoa and general information	Spread	Signs and symptoms	Treatment / prevention
Plasmodium Causes malaria, a serious tropical disease. There are four different species of the plasmodium. It is found in more than 100 countries including large areas of Africa, Asia and South America	• From the bite of an infected mosquito. One bite is all it takes to become infected • According to the WHO, 3.2 billion people – almost half of the global population – are at risk of malaria • In 2015, there were around 214 million malaria cases and roughly 438,000 deaths attributed to malaria	• High temperature, which may be intermittent • Sweats and chills • Vomiting and diarrhoea • Muscle pains • Symptoms appear between 7 and 18 days after becoming infected, but can take up to a year to appear • Some types of species can cause individuals to have relapses after they have recovered from an initial episode of symptoms	• Medical attention is advised Malaria can be treated • Antimalarial medication is used to both treat and prevent malaria • Prevention is paramount if travelling to an infected area Prophylactic medication, using insect repellent, wearing loose-fitting clothes with sleeves and trousers in the early evening and night
Schistosomiasis is also known as bilharzia It is an infection caused by schistosoma (parasitic worms) that live in fresh water in certain tropical and subtropical areas	• Swimming, paddling or showering and washing with infected water. The larval form of the worm penetrates the skin • The larve then grows into adult form in the body's blood vessels	• High temperature • Diarrhoea • Joint pain • An itchy, red, blotchy and raised rash • Many people are unaware they are infected for months or years	• Praziquantel medication, which destroys the worms

Type of protozoa and general information	Spread	Signs and symptoms	Treatment / prevention
Giardiasis An infection of the digestive system caused by parasites called Giardia intestinalis This is widespread in certain parts of Sub-Saharan Africa, Central and South America, Turkey, Romania and some others	• When an individual with the **parasite** goes to the toilet, some of the parasites enter the sanitation system • Another individual will contract the condition through drinking water that has been contaminated by the infected faeces	• Stomach cramps • Diarrhoea • Nausea • Loss of appetite • Flatulence	• Hand hygiene • Avoid drinking untreated water
Toxoplasmosis A common condition that often has no symptoms caused by Toxoplasma Gondii (T.Gondii)	T.Gondii is found in the faeces of infected cats. It is ingested by humans if there is opportunistic infection, for example getting hands contaminated from touching cat litter and then not washing them	• There are often no symptoms as the immune system can fight the infection. • May experience flu-like symptoms. It can be problematic in pregnancy and for individuals with weakened immune systems	• Most cases do not require treatment as symptoms often do not appear. • Individuals with weakened immune systems or pregnancy require treatment with medication

Command word activity

Identify (AC 1.1)

Design a poster to raise awareness of one condition such as influenza or mumps. Outline the condition, including the microbiological organism that causes it, and identify signs and symptoms. Identify treatments and preventative strategies.

Check your understanding

1. Define the word 'pathogenic'.
2. Identify one disease caused by bacteria and describe how it can be treated.
3. Outline the process of binary fusion.
4. Identify one disease caused by a virus and outline the signs and symptoms.
5. Identify one disease caused by fungi and outline how this may be an 'opportunistic infection'.

Take it further

Explore the incidences of disease on the World Health Organization website **http://www.who.int/campaigns/world-health-day/2014/vector-borne-diseases/en/**

L02: Understand the features of vector borne disease

2.1 Explain the features of vector borne disease

Vectors are living organisms. They act as a method of passing on infectious diseases between humans or from an animal to a human. Common vectors include mosquitoes and ticks. Other examples are flies, fleas and aquatic snails. The diseases they can transmit include malaria, dengue fever, schistosomiasis, and yellow fever.

Body lice

Body lice are different from lice found on the head or in pubic areas. Human body lice can spread one of the forms of typhus fever. Typhus fever is caused by a bacteria Rickettsia, and the most serious form, epidemic typhus fever is caused by the Rickettsia prowazekii microorganism. The louse becomes infected by feeding on the blood of an individual with acute typhus fever. The louse then excretes the microorganism on to another person who becomes infected if this is rubbed into a wound (such as a bite mark). Epidemic typhus fever is present in Central and Eastern Africa, Central and South America and Asia. The disease occurs suddenly and the individual will have headaches, chills, fever and pain. They also develop dark spots on the body.

Malaria

Malaria is a serious disease caused by mosquitoes. Although treatable, it can be fatal. The plasmodium which causes malaria is spread by female Anopheles Mosquitoes who bite more frequently after dusk. The mosquito bites a person infected with malaria and then acts as a carrier of the disease. It then bites another person transmitting the malaria through the bite. The individual then develops the malaria. Once in the blood stream the disease enters the liver and red blood cells to multiply. Once sufficient multiplication has occurred, the red blood cells burst, releasing more of the disease into the blood stream. This results in fever, chills and sweating. Malaria cannot be passed on directly from person to person, but can be passed on through blood transfusions. For details on signs, symptoms and treatment see Table 5.4.

Ticks

Ticks are small blood-sucking animals. A common condition spread by ticks is Lyme disease, which is a bacterial infection. The tick bites an animal that carries the bacterial infection, becoming infected and also a carrier of the disease. The tick then bites a human, causing infection. Ticks in the UK are common in woodland, but can also be found in gardens and parks. Lyme disease is an example of a bacterial infection. One of the first symptoms is a circular rash, like a bullseye, in the area that has been bitten (although not everyone gets this rash). The individual may also experience tiredness, pain and fever. If left untreated, Lyme disease can cause long-term, chronic symptoms.

Key term

Incubation period the time between exposure to an infectious microorganism and displaying signs and symptoms

Rabies

Rabies is a serious viral condition that attacks both the brain and the nervous system. According to the World Health Organization, it is now present in more than 150 countries. It is transmitted by the bite of an infected animal. The virus then enters the body and travels to the spinal cord and through nerves to the brain. It multiplies rapidly, spreading back through the nerves to other organs and causes death. Preventative vaccination is advised if travelling to an area with rabies as once symptoms develop, it is usually fatal. The **incubation period** is usually around 2–8 weeks.

Command word activity

Explain (AC 2.1)

Obtain a map of the world. Annotate the map with examples of vector borne disease, along with the vector that carries them. Identify which areas have the greatest concentration. Explain two features of vector borne disease, supporting your answer with examples of vectors and disease from your map.

Check your understanding

1. Define a vector borne disease.
2. Identify two vectors and a disease carried by each.
3. Outline the process of vectors transmitting a disease between humans.
4. Identify one way in which vector borne disease can be prevented.

LO3: Understand transmission of disease

3.1 Describe how pathogenic microorganisms are transmitted

Microorganisms are passed from one infectious source to another. Understanding the way in which this occurs helps when implementing measures to reduce the transference. Some microorganisms have more than one route of spreading to cause infection.

Transmission by direct and indirect contact

Direct contact is physical contact from an infected person to another person who is vulnerable to transmission of disease or infection. This includes touching, sexual contact or contact with blood or bodily fluids. In a health and social care setting, this can occur through normal caring activities, with hands being the most common cause of direct contact transmission in care settings. Examples of disease spread this way include HIV and hepatitis B.

Indirect spread of infection occurs when someone comes into contact with the microorganism via a contaminated object (such as if an item of equipment has not been cleaned properly), through the air, or via vectors as described in Section 2.1.

Inhalation

Transmission by inhalation occurs when individuals breathe in the microorganism. This is through the droplets and secretions that are expelled by a cough or a sneeze. Air-borne transmission occurs with very small particles and can remain in the air for long periods of time before being breathed in via the respiratory tract of another person. Droplet transmission occurs with larger particles. These do not remain suspended in the air for as long and travel short distances (less than 1 metre), so closer contact to the new individual would mean they are prone to infection.

Inoculation

During the process of inoculation an individual is given a small amount of the disease which has been inactivated so it cannot cause harm. It is designed to stimulate the immune response into producing antibodies and memory cells that will react to the disease if exposed at a later date.

Take it further

For more information on vaccination see Section 3.3. in this unit.

Ingestion

Transmission of microorganisms can be ingested from contaminated food or water. They commonly enter via the mouth into the gastrointestinal tract. This may be from food spoilage, such as if it has been stored or cooked incorrectly, which provides conditions for microorganisms to grow. Water that has been in contact with faeces and then not treated but used for drinking or preparing food can also be a source of infection.

Reservoirs

Reservoirs are a supply or source of infection. They can be human beings, animals such as mosquitoes, or environmental including water and vegetation. The disease can then be transmitted from the reservoir. For example, a reservoir of legionnaire's disease is water. The water stores the legionnaire's disease which is then passed on when the contaminated water is drunk. Tetanus is an example of a condition where the reservoir for the bacteria is soil and animal faeces. The soil contains the disease, which is then transmitted through contact with the soil.

Key term

Reservoir a store of the infection. It can live and multiply within the reservoir

Fomites

Fomites are non-living objects that can cause cross-infection if they are contaminated with microorganisms or pathogens. This might happen through the touch or droplet transmission of an infected person that lands on an object, which is then touched by another individual. One example of a fomite would be a doorknob. Common sources of fomites are household items and hospital equipment.

Activity (AC 3.1)

Make a list of five fomites that can carry disease. Think about the types of objects that you might come into contact with every day. For each, identify a method of preventing this from becoming a source of transmission.

Carriers

A carrier of disease is someone who transmits disease but does not realise they are infected. As a result of not having symptoms, they are unlikely to have taken any precautions to prevent transmission. Animals such as mosquitoes, ticks and fleas can also be carriers of disease.

Take it further

For more information on this, see Section 2.1 in this unit.

Key term

Asymptomatic when an individual has no symptoms

Case scenario: Mary Mallon 'Typhoid Mary' (AC 3.1)

Humans, like animals, can be carriers of disease. In the early 1900s, Mary Mallon who worked as a cook for wealthy families was a carrier of typhoid. She herself remained asymptomatic even though she transmitted the disease. Each time Mary moved to a new place of employment, she spread typhoid to many people, leaving them very ill and even causing death to some.

Outline how Mary Malone could be considered to be a carrier of the disease, even though she remained asymptomatic.

Explain one other way typhoid can be transmitted, linking to the methods listed above.

3.2 Explain why individuals may be more vulnerable to infection

A number of groups of individuals are more prone to infection. This means either the individual is more at risk of contracting the infection or that their immune system is not as effective as others in fighting the infection.

Infants and children

Young infants are susceptible to disease as their immune systems have not fully developed. Some immunity is received through the placenta and breast milk. Some children may have additional health needs such as requiring a feeding tube, which can present a source of infection if not maintained.

Pregnant women

Pregnant women, although not necessarily more prone to infection, are considered a high-risk group because of the possible effect of disease or illness on the foetus. One example is chickenpox. There is a risk that if contracted during pregnancy foetal varicella syndrome (FVS) can occur. This can result in brain damage, eye defects and shortened limbs.

Older people

People aged 65 years and older can be more prone to infection for a variety of reasons. As we get older, physiological changes such as a decline in effectiveness of the immune systems occur. A common sign of an infection is an elevated temperature; however, in older people this may not be present. The infection then may be missed, causing further deterioration of the individual. Changes in behaviour such as drowsiness or acute confusion can be a sign of infection.

Impaired immune system

People who are chronically ill such as individuals who are receiving cancer treatment have a weakened immune system. Not only does the cancer weaken the immune system, the medication used to treat it can also reduce the body's defences against illness, due to a drop in the number of white blood cells. HIV is another example, as this damages the cells of the immune system (see Section 1.1 for more detail), the body's immune system is prevented from fighting the infection.

Individuals may also have an impaired immune system due to accident or injury to the spleen or if has been removed, as the spleen contains white blood cells used to fight infections. Autoimmune diseases can make an individual more vulnerable to infection because they may take medication to suppress the functioning of the immune system, meaning it is less able to fight off pathogens, or

Take it further

Lupus is an example of an autoimmune disease. Carry out some research on signs, symptoms and treatments.

Command word activity

Explain (AC 3.2)

You are running a clinic for new patients at a busy GP surgery to provide information about the surgery as well as to take blood pressure, height and weight measurements and a urine sample. Identify three individuals that may be at an increased risk of infection.

Explain why each individual is at risk of infection, and any tasks that you may do in the new check that increase the risk of infection.

the way the autoimmune disease affects the body can reduce the body's ability to fight disease.

Diet and nutrition

People on inadequate diets and at risk of malnutrition are more prone to infection. This can be over nutrition, where you get more nutrients than needed, or under nutrition, when someone does not get enough nutrients. There is evidence that malnutrition impairs body resistance to infection, meaning that an individual is more likely to contract a disease and less able to fight the infection, making the condition last longer or increasing the severity of the symptoms. Some symptoms of infections can impact upon nutrition status, for example, if the individual has reduced appetite, is unable to eat or has vomiting and/or diarrhoea. In severe cases, an individual may require extra nutritional supplements prescribed by a dietician, a feeding tube or fluids administered intravenously.

Procedurally induced tissue damage

A variety of clinical scenarios, such as surgery or medical procedures, may increase the danger of infection. This includes undergoing a procedure where an instrument is used, such as

an endoscopy, or other surgical procedure. An infection can be transferred from the instrument to the tissues inside the body and infection results. Procedures such as these have a high risk of cross-contamination and therefore maintaining a sterile environment is crucial to prevent this from occurring. For more details on this see Section 4.1 of this unit.

3.3 Describe the body's defence mechanisms against infection

The immune system in the body has the role of responding to infection. There are methods in place to prevent an infection and a response, should these not be effective. The first line of defence aims to prevent microorganisms from entering the body.

Skin

To cause infection in the body, pathogens have to be able to enter the body. The skin provides a physical barrier and a key role in preventing infection. As well as preventing entry of microorganisms into the body, the skin has an acidic environment which prevents the growth of microbes. Any breaks in the skin such as from a

Key term

Intravenously given directly into the veins through a tube known as a cannula

Key term

Antigen the microorganism that enters the body triggering an immune response

wound are an opportunistic route of infection. It is because the skin can be punctured by vectors, such as mosquitoes, that they present such a risk of infection.

Cilia, acids and enzymes

If the microorganisms penetrate the body, then the immune system makes a response. So the body protects itself through cilia and naturally occurring acids and enzymes.

The mucous membranes which cover the cavities of the body, such as mouth or nose, provide a barrier, but a sticky layer which traps microorganisms. These are then expelled from the body by the cilia (tiny hairs) which have a rhythmic beat and sweep to the outside of the body to expel any pathogens. Nasal cavities, for example, contain nasal hair which creates a barrier between the lungs and any pathogens from the environment. Sneezing is a way of expelling pathogens that penetrate nasal hairs and enter the respiratory tract.

Body secretions such as sweat, tears, mucus or vaginal secretions contain lysosomes (an enzyme) which destroys pathogens. In addition, the stomach has a low pH (acidity) which kills most of the ingested microorganisms.

Immune response

The first line of defence includes physical and chemical barriers to infection. The second line of defence, once pathogenic microorganisms have entered the body, is to trap and break down the microorganisms before they can do any harm. Inflammation and white blood cells have a role in this. The third line of defence occurs when the first and second have not been successful, and is where the body recognises and targets the specific pathogen.

Inflammatory response

An inflammatory response is part of the body's response system to damage or trauma to an injury. The primary effect is to increase blood circulation to reach the infected area. The area will

Key term

Phagocytosis the process of a cell ingesting a pathogen or another cell

be red and warm as a result of the blood reaching the site. There may be swelling which is due to the increased presence of blood and cells used in **phagocytosis**. The area may also be painful due to the swelling, as this causes pressure on nerve cells. Phagocytes will destroy any harmful bacteria, and pus may be seen as a result.

White blood cells

White blood cells are the cells that are involved in the body's immune response. There are five main types which can be grouped into two main categories. These are granulocytes (neutrophils, eosinophils, and basophils) and agranulocytes (lymphocytes and monocytes).

Neutrophils

These are the most common type of white blood cells and are made in the bone marrow. They function by blocking microorganisms from gaining access to the blood from a wound or infectious area. They are the first cells to arrive at an area such as a wound. They engulf the microorganisms and damaged tissue, a process called phagocytosis.

Eosinophils

Eosinophils are made in the bone marrow. These are in small numbers and release toxins to kill pathogens. They have a role when the body has had an allergic reaction and therefore a high number of these in a white blood cell count may indicate an allergic response. They also have a major role in fighting parasite infestation such as when parasitic worms invade the human body.

Basophils

These contain histamine and other chemicals. These substances help increase blood flow to an area of damage which means that more can be at the site of the infection. They also have a role in allergic reactions.

Key terms

Antibodies are specific to an antigen; they attack the antigen and make it harmless to the body

Histamine a substance found in the human body that has a role in the immune system response

Key terms

Circadian rhythms sometimes known as the body clock. This is a process by which body functions are controlled or regulated, such as sleeping

Metabolism chemical processes needed to maintain living organisms; substances are broken down to provide energy

Lymphocytes

Lymphocytes have an important function in the immune system. The two main types are B and T-lymphocytes. The B cells produce antibodies and attack and destroy invading microorganisms. The T-cells destroy cells that have been taken over such as those taken over by viruses. Some lymphocytes produce cells that remember pathogens. If the individual becomes infected with the same pathogen, then the immune system is able to destroy it quickly. The individual is less likely to become ill.

Monocytes

These also have a role in phagocytosis and help T-lymphocytes produce immunity. There are different types of immunity.

Take it further

For more information on blood cells and immunity, see HSC DM3, Section 1.1.

Body temperature

A normal core body temperature is between 36°C and 37.2°C to maintain cell metabolism. This core temperature is regulated by the hypothalamus in the brain. Body temperature can fluctuate within the normal parameters, and factors such as circadian rhythms mean that it is often higher in the evening than the morning.

A raised temperature, known as pyrexia or hyper thermia, often indicates an infection. An infection from a microorganism triggers the immune response into releasing chemical substances known as pyrogens. These cause the hypothalamus to 'reset' at a higher degree. Following this, body temperature rises and causes the body to feel it is cold. As the core body temperature is lower than the temperature required by the hypothalamus, vasoconstriction (narrowing of the blood vessels) occurs and causes symptoms such as shivering and feeling cold. The shivering in a fever state is known as 'rigors'. A higher temperature helps prevent microorganisms from reproducing and releasing toxins. As the amount of toxins decreases in the body, fewer pyrogens are released and the temperature resets.

Although a high temperature is often the result of an infection, it can indicate other clinical issues, such as heat stroke. In infants with a high temperature there is a risk of febrile convulsions and these most often occur between 6 months and 3 years. They are quite common, affecting around one in every 20 children. The child will lose consciousness and limbs will twitch. They may vomit or lose control of bladder and bowels. Medical advice is required.

In clinical practice, a temperature is taken as part of regular observations on an individual.

When documenting this, or in handing over, it is poor practice to state the individual 'has a temperature' meaning a raised temperature or 'has no temperature' meaning that the temperature taken is within normal parameters. This is because everyone has a temperature! It is better to state the temperature numerically, for example 38.9°C.

Case scenario: Sepsis

Sepsis is a life-threatening condition triggered by infection or injury. Following infection, the body responds in an abnormal way causing injury to its own tissues and organs.

Signs and symptoms of sepsis include a high or a low body temperature, fast heartbeat and breathing, not producing as much urine as normal and cold clammy skin. Early identification and treatment is essential to prevent organ failure, an increase in morbidity or death.

1. Identify three methods that could be used to improve the awareness of health and social care practitioners of sepsis.

Take it further

Explore sepsis and the treatment using The UK Sepsis Trust website at **http://sepsistrust.org/**

3.4 Explain how to break the chain of infection

The chain of infection is a tool which demonstrates how infections are spread for example from person to person. It consists of six links. This is helpful in learning how to break the chain of infection at different stages. At each part of the chain, there is an opportunity to break the cycle and therefore stop the spread of infection.

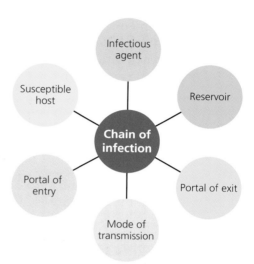

Figure 5.5 The chain of infection

Table 5.5 The chain of infection

Part of chain of infection	Definition and example	How to break the chain
Infectious agent	These are the microorganisms that cause the disease, such as meningitis bacteria or influenza viruses	The infectious agent is stopped, inactivated or unable to leave the reservoir of infection by: treating an individual with antimicrobial medication sterilising equipment to eradicate the organism from the surface identifying organisms to enable accurate and effective treatment preventative treatment
Reservoir	This is where microorganisms can be found, for example on people, equipment or surfaces. Animals can also be a reservoir of infection	Cleaning equipment and the environment Removing or changing stagnant water such as in flower vases

Part of chain of infection	Definition and example	How to break the chain
Portal of exit	The ways in which microorganisms leave the reservoir. For example: respiratory disease usually escapes through coughing or sneezing Nose or throat secretions enable microorganisms to leave the body Infections of the gastrointestinal tract leave the body through body secretions, such as stools or vomit Infections of the skin leave through skin lesions or drainage from the wound	Ensure that portals of exit are contained through safe infection control practice such as by: isolating an individual to minimise contact with others staff not going to work when unwell using face masks, for example by an individual who has active TB coughing into a disposable tissue, throwing it out and then washing hands afterwards keeping the environment clean and disposing of body secretions properly disposing of dressings and sharps in clinical waste or as instructed
Mode of transmission	How the microorganism comes into contact with the new host, such as air-borne or water-borne or via a vector	Stopping the transmission between objects or people by: having barriers and safe infection control practices such as cleaning surfaces, ensuring food hygiene airflow control such as in a negative pressure room which controls air flow into and out of the room
Portal of entry	How the microorganisms will enter the new host; for example, inhalation, ingestion, absorption, a skin break such as a cut or needle stick injury, through medical procedures	Protecting portals of entry so that microorganisms cannot enter by: good hand hygiene Personal protective equipment (PPE) such as eye wear or face shields wearing a mask or respirator for respiratory tract infections maintaining healthy skin
Susceptible host	This is the person who will acquire the infection due to entry of the infectious agent The mircoorganism may not develop into an infection if the immune system can effectively fight the infection If not, the susceptible host can become the future reservoir for transmission of disease	Individuals can keep themselves healthy as a healthy lifestyle boosts immunity and helps the body fight disease A good standard of hygiene and vaccinations can prevent infectious agents Environmental processes such as sanitation and disposal systems

Key term

Personal protective equipment (PPE) equipment that protects a worker from health and safety risks at work

Classroom discussion (AC 3.4)

Explain the strengths and weaknesses of methods to break each chain of the infection cycle.

Command word activity

Explain (AC 3.4)

Design a poster for your new patient health check clinic in Explain activity 3.2 that explains the cycle of infection. Identify and annotate the chain of infection with measures that could be implemented to minimise the spread of infection, explaining why these measures would break the chain. Consider the effectiveness of each intervention.

LO4: Understand methods of microorganism control

4.1 Explain methods of microorganism control

Items can be decontaminated to remove and destroy microorganisms that are going to be a threat to human health. This is a process consisting of cleaning, disinfecting and sterilising. Depending upon the use of the item, the part or parts of the process required will differ. Cleaning is always the first stage of any microorganism control technique. This reduces the number of microorganisms and debris and is used on low-risk items, such as floors.

Sterilisation

Sterilisation is a process that aims to make the object as completely free from microorganisms as possible. Items that have been sterilised must not be left out too long as continual exposure to air can cause recontamination from pathogens. Items that come into close contact with a mucous membrane or are invasive should be sterilised; examples include surgical instruments or babies' bottles.

Disinfection

Disinfection uses heat or chemicals to reduce the presence of microorganisms on items. Not all microorganisms will be destroyed, but they will be reduced to a level that will not be harmful to health. Items that come into contact with intact skin, such as bed rails or commodes, are disinfected.

Pasteurisation

Pasteurisation is a process which destroys pathogens through heat. It is frequently used in the dairy industry, i.e. on milk. This helps to protect individuals against food-borne illnesses that may occur through drinking or eating.

Sanitation

The process of sanitation is about implementing and maintaining good hygienic conditions in society. It covers a range of services including rubbish collection, wastewater disposal and safe disposal of human urine and faeces via sewage systems. Poor sanitation has a major role in causing death and spreading disease.

In the UK, before the public sanitation that we have today, water-borne diseases such as typhoid and cholera were common. Although these diseases have since been eradicated in the UK, they are more common in countries with poorer sanitation and limited access to clean drinking water. The risk of these diseases occurring increases following natural disasters such as hurricanes and earthquakes, which can cause disruptions to the water supply.

Asepsis

Asepsis is a process carried out to reduce the risk of contaminating an area with microorganisms. The aim of asepsis is to reduce the risk of infection; for example avoiding contaminating an open wound with microorganisms when cleaning and dressing it.

There are different actions taken and levels of asepsis depending upon the procedure undertaken. For example, surgery is carried out in a specialised room with staff who are wearing sterile clothing. In contrast, when inserting a cannula into an arm, the use of sterile clothing is not required but all contact with the needle used to insert the cannula and the cannula itself must be avoided.

Take it further

Carry out some research on the procedure for wearing sterile gloves and using a sterile wound dressing pack. Identify how the procedure supports the asepsis process.

Command word activity

Explain (AC 4.1)

Explain one advantage and one disadvantage of each of the methods of microorganism control.

 Check your understanding

1. Define the term 'decontamination'.
2. Identify which process would destroy more microorganisms: sterilisation, cleaning or disinfecting.
3. Explain the process of pasteurisation.
4. Outline why sanitation is important.
5. Outline the concept of asepsis and one reason when you would use this in clinical practice.

LO5: Understand precautions to be taken to reduce the spread of infection in a health or social care setting

LO6: Be able to minimise the spread of infection

5.1 Explain the importance of personal hygiene and attire in relation to infection control

Staff should ensure that they maintain a good level of personal hygiene to help minimise the spread of infection.

Cleanliness

All staff should ensure that they keep themselves clean. Personal hygiene is an essential part of infection control. Equipment should also be kept clean. Staff should ensure that they keep their own wounds clean and use a tissue to cough or sneeze into, which should then be binned, followed by hand washing to reduce the spread of infection. Hands should be washed using correct hand washing technique to ensure all areas of the hands are covered. In addition to the obvious hand washing occasions (such as after using the toilet

Take it further

For more information on methods of cleaning, refer back to Section 4.1 in this unit.

or before eating), in a clinical environment hands should be decontaminated in all of the following circumstances:

- before every episode of direct individual contact or care
- after an episode of direct contact with an individual
- immediately after an episode of direct care given to individuals
- immediately after exposure to bodily fluids
- immediately after contact with an individual in a surrounding hospital or other activity that could result in contamination
- after the removal of gloves.

Alcohol gel can be used instead of hand washing, but there are a number of exceptions to this use. If the hands of a worker are visibly soiled, after coming into contact with body fluids and bacterial infections that produce spores (for example, Methicillin-resistant Staphylococcus aureus (MRSA)) then hands must be washed.

Badges

Staff should wear a badge stating their name and, if possible, their status and clinical area. This helps with security and provides individuals with a visual reminder of the professional caring for them. Badges should be cleaned daily and should be made from material that enables this. Lanyards should be avoided as they can dangle into clinical work. If they are worn they should be clean, changed if visibly soiled, tucked away for clinical work, and fitted with an anti-tug device so it will break if pulled – this helps to avoid strangulation.

Hair

Hair should be clean, brushed and tied back off the shoulders to avoid touching the face or falling in a clinical area. The style should be neat and not need adjusting on a regular basis to minimise the contact with hands and hair. As well as maintaining a professional image, keeping the hair off the shoulder minimises the amount of microorganism growth on the collar of a uniform.

Jewellery

Jewellery should be removed to prevent the spread of infection. Bracelets and wrist watches can interfere with hand washing, as the area behind jewellery needs to be washed; this makes it is difficult to perform the hand washing technique effectively. Bracelets and wrist watches also provide a route for the transmission of infections. Microorganisms can remain beneath the jewellery after hands have been washed.

Rings, apart from a plain wedding band, should be removed. There is evidence that stones, raised elements or intricate designs on the ring, or wearing more than one ring, can increase the quantity of microorganisms. Although a plain wedding band can be worn, this should be manipulated throughout hand washing. Stones or raised rings can tear gloves and increase the risk of cross-contamination from both health care practitioners to the individual and vice versa. They also pose a risk of grazing the skin of the individual being cared for.

Earrings, if worn, should be plain studs, as these help to maintain a more professional image. Earrings can harbour infection. In some situations, such as in theatre, earrings should not be worn in case they fall into the sterile field, or even into the body of an individual undergoing surgery.

Dress and uniform

These are also a key element in infection control. Since 2007 in the UK, there has been a 'bare below the elbows policy'. Health and social care professionals should wear short sleeves and remove all jewellery. This is because there is a risk that clothes can become contaminated with microorganisms when caring for individuals, and cannot be quickly and easily cleaned during a shift. The only exception would be if a risk assessment has been carried out which states that there is a risk to the health care professional if they wear short sleeves (for example, being

scratched by an individual they are caring for).

Within many health and social care settings, such as hospitals, uniforms are worn. These promote infection control. Certain procedures should also be followed by health and social care professionals:

1. The design and material used for these is made for reducing the risk of infection spread. Uniform material is robust. It should be washed after every use, at a hot wash (at least 60°C).

2. Uniforms should be washed separately to general or family washing.

3. Hand washing of clothes should be avoided, as it is ineffective.

4. Uniforms should also be ironed.

5. A clean uniform should be worn for every shift to minimise the spread of infection.

6. Where available, staff should change in and out of their uniform in their place of work.

7. Dirty uniforms should not be carried in the same bag as clean uniforms.

In some situations such as theatres, intensive care units or delivery units, scrubs are worn. This is to minimise the spread of infection as there is a greater risk of exposure to infection. In these circumstances, scrubs should not be worn outside the clinical area, unless there is an emergency. A scrub suit should cover any other clothing such as underwear, and trouser legs should not touch the floor to avoid the risk of cross-contamination. Shoes should also be changed on leaving the clinic area.

Theatres take increased measures to minimise the spread of infection, because of the risk of pathogens entering the body due to surgery being an invasive procedure. Theatre staff must complete a process known as 'scrubbing'. It is essential that this is followed to promote infection control. **Scrubbing** is a method of washing hands, forearms and scrubbing finger nails using specialist techniques and antibacterial wash. Although total sterilisation is not possible, this process aims to make

Figure 5.6 Clean uniforms reduce the spread of infection

Key term

Scrubbing a process of hand and forearm decontamination

the hands and arms as free as possible from pathogens. Surgical gown and gloves are then added in a way to maintain the sterile nature of these items.

In general, closed shoes should always be worn, as this reduces the risk of infection and offers protection to the health and social care worker. For example, if a nurse drops a needle there is less chance of damage to the foot, and therefore cross-contamination, if closed shoes are worn.

However, dress is not restricted purely to uniforms. All members of the multi-disciplinary team and support staff should ensure that their dress promotes infection control. In a number of settings, such as for some community settings, might not be work uniforms are not worn, though it is still important to dress appropriately for work. Each organisation will have its own policy on dress or uniform.

As a general principle, items of work wear should be washable at high temperatures, robust and kept clean, as well as being able to promote good hand hygiene (i.e. no sleeves, or sleeves that are easy to roll up). Glasses, if worn, should be easy to clean. Neck ties should not be worn in the clinical environment, as evidence suggests that these can harbour pathogens and therefore act as a method of

Activity

Create a guide for a new student nurse to explain how they should present themselves on their first day in placement to meet good standards of personal hygiene and attire. Include examples to help your explanation.

cross-contamination. They tend to move around freely, which causes them to pick up and transmit pathogens more frequently.

Nails

Fingernails can be a source of infection and therefore should be kept short and clean. If a member of staff turns their hand over to the palm, their nails should not be visible from the tops of the fingers. As well as harbouring infection, long nails also increase the individual's risk of being accidently scratched during care or contact.

5.2 and 6.1 Explain and use the correct hand washing technique

Hand washing is an effective way to minimise the spread of infection. It is essential that whenever care is given, there are facilities for hand washing. In key clinical areas, the taps that are used should be turned off using elbow or non-touch. Soap should be near to the sink washing area to minimise soap or water dropping on to the floor. To minimise the risk of allergic reactions, soap should be non-perfumed. Towels should be disposable.

Prior to hand washing any rings, bracelets and wristwatches should be removed. Sleeves should be rolled up. Cuts and abrasions should be covered with a waterproof dressing, as these can become contaminated with bacteria.

This procedure is a step-by-step guide that intends to cover all areas of hands that are commonly missed during hand washing: thumbs, fingertips and between the fingers. Before starting hand washing, the water should be 'hand hot' as this can help to destroy

microorganisms. If the water it is too cold then it may also prevent effective hand washing, as it is not comfortable. Similarly, water that is too hot will increase the risk of scalding. Soap is also more effective with hand-hot water and this combination will remove the dirt and microorganisms on hands.

Hands should be dried using disposable paper towels. Damp hands can become sore and also encourage microorganism growth. A pat dry method is recommended as this causes less damage to hands than rubbing them dry. Care should be taken to ensure that hands are not re-contaminated when disposing of the paper towels in the bin. A foot-operated bin is recommended.

Suitable hand cream should be reapplied regularly as frequent hand washing can dry the hands, which in turn can cause cracks and abrasions. The hands and wrists should be wet before applying soap as using soap on dry skin can cause further dryness of the skin. This also helps soap to work effectively, which helps to speed up hand washing time.

Correct hand washing technique

The steps in the correct hand washing technique are as follows:

1. Wet hands with water.
2. Apply enough soap to cover all hand surfaces.
3. Rub palm to palm: this is to ensure that the back of the palms are covered. Lathering and scrubbing creates friction, which helps to remove microbes and dirt from the hands.
4. Rub the back of each hand with fingers interlaced.
5. Rub palm to palm with fingers interlaced. This should be done using both sides to fully cover all areas of the hand.
6. Rub the backs of fingers to opposing palms with fingers interlocked.
7. Rub each thumb clasped in opposite palm using a rotational movement.
8. Rub finger tips in a circular motion on palm.

9. Rub each wrist.
10. Rinse hands thoroughly from wrist down.
11. Dry with a single use, disposable towel. Wet hands can lead to further multiplication of microorganisms and damage the integrity of the skin.
12. Use towel or elbow to turn tap. The towels should be disposed of in a foot-operated waste bin to avoid recontaminating the hands.

5.3 and 6.2 Explain and use personal protective equipment

Personal protective equipment includes items that will protect the user against health and safety risks. In health care, these include gloves, aprons, eyewear and masks. The provision of these should be at no cost to the employee and their provision and use is required under legislation. Although PPE should always be worn when required, all effort should be in place to minimise the risk to health and social care practitioners.

PPE is covered under the Control of Substances Hazardous to Health (COSHH) (see Section 8.1 for further information) and The Personal Protective Equipment at Work Regulations 1992. These Regulations require PPE to be supplied, properly assessed before use to make sure it is fit for purpose, maintained and stored properly.

The employee should be provided with instructions on how to use it safely; and be able to use it safely. Training should be provided by the employer. PPE selection is on the basis of the hazards that it is aiming to reduce; for example, face masks should be used only if there is a risk of breathing in serious microorganisms. The equipment should be adjustable to fit the wearer, for example different sized gloves. It should be stored in a way to ensure that it remains fit for purpose, for example unused aprons should be stored away from possible sources of contamination; equipment such as safety goggles or specialist clothing worn when taking x-rays should be well maintained and be kept within the expiry date (if applicable). An organisation should identify who is responsible for maintaining the equipment. Training should be given to staff on correct usage and how and when to wear PPE.

Some examples of common PPE in healthcare are described in Table 5.6.

Table 5.6 Commonly used PPE

PPE	Usage	Disposal
Disposable apron: These are available either in a box or on a roll. They may be used when assisting an individual with personal care or serving food	Remove from packaging Place neck loop overhead and the ties behind the back to ensure that as much of the front of the body is protected as possible. This minimises the amount of body that is not protected	These should be disposed of after use and only used once If gloves are also used remove these first, as they have a higher risk of contamination Break the neck loop and ties Grasp the inside of the apron as this should be clean Dispose of the apron in a hazardous waste bag (or as otherwise instructed)

PPE	Usage	Disposal
Non-sterile disposable gloves Some practitioners and individuals are allergic to latex and this should be checked prior to donning the glove	These should only be worn in some circumstances, for example when assisting an individual with personal care or changing bed linen They are available in different sizes Hands should be cleaned before putting on gloves Remove gloves from the box one at a time to avoid cross-contamination with gloves in the box Hold the cuff and pull this into position, avoiding contact with skin that has not been washed If gloves are damaged during the procedure, then they must be replaced	Disposable gloves should only be worn once Gloves should be removed as soon as the procedure is completed, as this reduces the risk of cross-contamination Remove the first glove by holding the outside of the wrist and pulling the glove off inside out. The inside of the glove is non-contaminated and turning it inside out reduces the risk of cross-contamination Place the fingers of the non-gloved hand inside the wrist of the remaining glove and pull it off, turning it inside out Dispose of the gloves in a clinical waste bag (or as per policy) Wash hands after the procedure has been finished
Face goggles or eye protection are used where there is a risk of exposure to body fluid droplets or aerosol-generating properties	Hands should be clean Remove eye protection from packaging Some goggles require a demister solution to help promote visibility Place over eyes and secure, adjusting if necessary. This must be correctly done or they may fall during the procedure or be uncomfortable	Remove by handling the ear pieces or band and lift away from the face without touching the front of the goggles, as this part may be contaminated Dispose into clinical hazardous waste bag; or clean if it is a reusable item, according to the Trust or manufacturer policy Clean hands with soap and water
Face mask If organisms are spread by air or by droplet use a face mask or respirator Respirators are used in high-risk infectious situations and are a specialist type of face mask with a filter	Clean hands Remove one mask from the box at a time to prevent contamination with the remaining masks Remove glasses if worn as these will obstruct positioning Place mask over nose, mouth and chin and secure at the back, adjusting to fit Respirators should be fitted according to the manufacturer's guidelines, after training has been given and always tested prior to use Replace glasses if worn	Grasp the ties or straps and break or pull over top of the head without touching the front of the mask, as this may be contaminated Dispose of it in clinical or hazardous waste bag unless instructed Clean hands with soap and water

Activity

Research and produce a step-by-step guide to putting on a pair of gloves in an asepsis procedure.

Command word activity

Explain (AC 5.3)

Create a booklet explaining the types of PPE used in a health and social care setting. Include examples of when these PPE may be used.

5.4 and 6.3 Explain the process of safe waste disposal and dispose of waste safely

Health and social care workplaces will produce waste such as syringes, sharps, swabs and bandages. Some of these may be hazardous and harmful to health as they may be infectious, containing microorganisms that can cause harm, or be radioactive or toxic. It is therefore essential that this waste is disposed of in a safe way.

Table 5.7 Legislation relating to infection control

Legislation	How it applies to infection control
Health and Social Care Act 2008 Updated July 2015	Code of practice on the prevention and control of infections
The Personal Protective Equipment at Work Regulations	Requires employers and managers to supply their employees with PPE
Control of Substances Hazardous to Health (COSHH) 2002	Requires employers to control substances hazardous to heath (this include microorganisms)
Reporting of Injuries, Diseases and Dangerous Occurrences Regulations 2013	Certain workplace incidents must be reported
Environmental Protection Act 1990	Employers that produce waste have a duty of care to ensure waste is segregated, stored and disposed of safely and that this is documented

Legislation, policies and procedures.

All organisations will have policy and procedures that relate to safe waste disposal. These should always be followed. Examples of policies that relate to safe waste disposal include:

- collection, handling and storing of specimens
- disposal of waste
- disposal of PPE
- food hygiene procedures.

Some examples of legislation that relate to waste disposal are given in Table 5.7.

Clinical / non-clinical waste

Clinical waste is common in health care settings. It includes medical waste such as swabs, dressing, syringes, and any blood, human tissue or other bodily fluids and unwanted medicines. It will need to be disposed of in a safe way to ensure that it does not cause harm to others.

Non-clinical waste is everything else such as food, paper, packaging, and so on. Equipment should be decontaminated and then disposed of in accordance with the manufacturer's instructions.

Activity (AC 5.4)

Make a list of five items of waste in placement or a health and social care setting you know well. Are these clinical (relating to treatment of individuals) or non-clinical waste? Explain the methods to dispose of each safely.

Responsibilities

All employees have a responsibility to ensure that clinical waste is disposed of in a safe manner. Health and social care practitioners have a responsibility to follow all policies and procedures such as disposing of waste in the correct waste bag. Employers have a responsibility to train staff and ensure that the right facilities are in place. The cleaning team have a responsibility to clean areas safely especially when using chemicals, for example in decontaminating a cubicle.

Environmental Health Officers are part of the local council and have a responsibility to ensure that living and working surroundings are safe, to investigate health hazards, and take required actions.

Colour codes

Colour coding is part of a good practice system to ensure correct waste disposal. Bags, bins and boxes have colours that are universal, meaning they should be the same regardless of where you work. Some examples are given in Table 5.8.

Linen

Used linen

The health care professional should wear disposable gloves and apron to remove used linen from the bed. It should be placed in the correct linen bag (often white) and taken to the designated collection area. Beds should be changed regularly. In a clinical area this is normally on a daily basis or more often if required due to soiling or individual needs.

Soiled linen

Soiled linen must be managed to reduce the risk of any individual coming into contact with risk. The linen should be gathered so that the contaminated area (e.g. faeces) is contained within the linen to minimise the risk of contamination to any of the surrounding area. The linen should be placed in a water-soluble laundry bag which can then be placed directly into the washing machine and

Table 5.8 Colour coding of waste equipment

Colour	Type of waste
Purple	Waste that is **cytotoxic** and requires incineration
Yellow	Infectious or clinical waste which is disposed of by incineration
Blue	Medicinal waste such as out-of-date medicines
Orange	Infectious waste which may need to be treated to make it safe before it can be disposed of. May also be incinerated
Black	Landfill waste that cannot be recycled. It must not contain any hazardous material

 Key term

Cytotoxic refers to medication or treatments which are toxic to cells by preventing growth and are used to treat conditions such as cancer

therefore means that laundry workers do not have to handle the soiled linen.

Sharps and equipment

The Health and Safety (Sharp Instruments in Healthcare) Regulations 2013 covers the use of sharps. Health and social care practitioners will come into contact with sharps when using needles for injections, suturing and removing sutures. Practitioners should avoiding walking around with sharps and use a clean tray to place the items in. Sharps should be disposed of in a sharps box, which is a plastic container with a lid that cannot be opened. They should never be filled past the mark on the box. Needles should never be resheathed as this process greatly increases the risk of a sharps injury. A sharps injury in clinical practice should receive immediate medical attention and the individual must go to the Accident and Emergency Department.

There is a variety of equipment used within health and social care settings. Some is disposable, for example feeding tubes and cannulas. Care must be taken when inserting these devices to avoid contamination. They must be disposed of appropriately, such as in a clinical waste bag.

Some equipment is reusable, for example pumps to regulate IV medication or specialist mattresses to reduce the risk of pressure ulcers. This equipment must be decontaminated following the policies and procedures of the organisation and the manufacturers' instructions prior to storage and reuse.

Body fluids

Bodily fluids, particularly blood and faecal matter, can present a hazard as they carry pathogens. PPE and appropriate buckets and cleaning equipment should be used to avoid transmission of infection. The mop and bucket used should be different for clinical and non-clinical waste areas. Residues should be scraped off and placed in a container for disposal. Any contaminated material that needs laundry or disposal should be placed in the appropriate bag. If soft furnishings, such as pillows, are heavily soiled, they may need bagging and disposing as clinical waste.

Check your understanding

1. Outline with examples how appropriate dress can reduce the spread of infections in health and social care settings.
2. Describe the correct hand washing technique.
3. Identify two colours of waste bags that may be seen in a clinical setting and what waste is disposed of within them.
4. Describe two examples of PPE and how and when these would be used.
5. Explain how sharps can be used safely in clinical practice

LO7 Understand how infectious diseases can be controlled and treated by medication

7.1 Evaluate the use of drugs to control and treat infectious disease

There are many medications that can be used to treat infectious diseases. Some, such as cream to treat athlete's foot, can be brought in a pharmacy; others, such as antibiotics, require a prescription.

Examples are given in Table 5.9.

The use of medication can save lives. It enables people to spend less time in hospital and can provide a cure especially in the case of short-term illness.

However, although medications have strengths, there are important considerations. Individuals may be allergic or develop allergies to specific medications and therefore will not gain this benefit. There is a problem of increasing resistance from microorganisms to infections (see 7.2). Medications are expensive and are not always 100 per cent effective. Finally, medications can only do so much. It is far better to prevent an illness occurring in the first place (for example taking malaria prophylaxis or having good standards of hygiene) than to treat the disease.

Table 5.9 Medications for treating different types of infection

Microorganism	Medications	Examples
Bacteria	Antibiotics work by destroying the DNA to stop growth or damaging and bursting the cell wall of a bacteria These can be 'broad spectrum' so destroying both gram positive and gram negative bacteria, or 'narrow spectrum' which are targeted against a particular type of bacteria	Amoxicillin Tetracycline Cephalexin Doxycycline
Viruses	Antiviral medications work by stopping the growth and multiplication of viruses	Aciclovir, Valaciclovir Famciclovir Econazole Miconazole
Fungi	Antifungal medications work in two different ways: by destroying the fungus by damaging the cells walls, and by stopping the fungi from growing	Clotrimazole econazole miconazole Terbinafine
Parasitic	Anti-parasitic medications work by damaging the DNA of the parasite or by stopping it from reproducing	Mebendazole Lindane

Command word activity

Evaluate and evidence (AC 7.1)

Create a table with three strengths and three weaknesses of using medication to treat infectious diseases.

For each strength and weakness explained, use supporting evidence from wider reading such as health care journals or organisations such as the World Health Organization.

Consider factors such as efficiency and efficacy of medications, availability and costs and other methods that can be used to reduce the spread of infection. Ensure an accurate record is kept of each source for your supporting bibliography.

7.2 Explain how antimicrobial resistance occurs

Antimicrobial resistance is a term used to describe a microbe that stops responding to a medication that previously was effective. The microorganism initially survives exposure to the medication that would normally kill it, then mutates and changes shape to protect its structure against the medication. These microorganisms then multiply and spread, or transfer their resistance to other organisms.

This increased resistance is a major concern with the use of antibiotics, but is not limited to just bacterial infections. Individuals with infections that are resistant to medications are at increased risk of worse clinical outcomes and even death. It also adds extra pressure on health care resources both financially and staff in caring for unwell individuals.

Methicillin-resistant Staphylococcus aureus (MRSA) is one of the most well-known bacteria, that is resistant to nearly every type of antibiotic. It is carried on the skin and inside the nostrils and throat. If these bacteria get into a break in the skin, they can cause life-threatening infections. Screening normally occurs within hospitals and if MRSA is found, the individual will be treated with antibacterial wash. There are also strains of tuberculosis and malaria that are resistant to drug treatment.

As discussed in LO1, viruses constantly change and mutate. This can happen slowly over a period

Key term

Pandemic an outbreak of disease which affects a large number of people across different countries

of time or suddenly. Once the virus has mutated, the body's immune system is no longer able to recognise it and therefore treats the disease as a new invasion. Influenza is an example of a virus that mutates. Annual influenza vaccines are required each year, which offer protection against the predicated season's three or four most common virus strains. Occasionally, the virus can mutate quickly and create a new strain. Pandemics can result as individuals have little immunity to this new virus.

Misuse and overuse of antimicrobials are thought to have had a major contribution to this issue. Examples include: the prescription of antibiotics to treat conditions where antibiotics are not indicated, such as a common viral cold; or from antibiotics being prescribed 'just in case' when they are not needed. It can also be the result of having an inadequate dose or duration, due to individuals not taking antibotics as prescribed, stopping the course when they feel better, or not taking them at intervals as directed.

There is now more awareness of this as a major concern and guidance is available on using antimicrobial medications and the roles and responsibilities of all people involved in health care practice.

Take it further

Research the role the government and the World Health Organization have in promoting antimicrobial stewardship **https://www.gov.uk/government/collections/antimicrobial-resistance-amr-information-and-resources**

Command word activity

Explain and evaluate (AC 7.2)

Explain two ways in which antimicrobial resistance can be reduced. Evaluate the measures, giving one strength and one weakness.

Check your understanding

1. Outline how antibiotics work.
2. Outline how antifungal medications work.
3. Describe the concern over antimicrobial medications.
4. Identify one condition that is largely resistant to treatment.
5. Outline two reasons for antimicrobial resistance.

Key term

Phlebotomist a member of the multi-disciplinary team who takes blood samples from individuals

Command word activity

Explain (AC 8.1)

In your placement, find out who is responsible for health and safety. What is their role? Explain how two aspects of their role promote the health and safety of people within the organisation.

LO8: Understand the requirements of RIDDOR and COSHH in relation to infection prevention and control

8.1 Explain the requirements of RIDDOR in relation to infection prevention and control

RIDDOR is the Reporting of Injuries, Diseases and Dangerous Occurrences Regulations 2013 (RIDDOR 2013). All health and social care settings are legally obliged to follow its requirements.

RIDDOR requires and places a responsibility on employers and others to report deaths, certain types of injury, some occupational diseases and dangerous occurrences that arise out of or in connection with work (HSE 2013b). Each organisation will have a responsible person (this may not be the manager) who has the duty to notify and report. Under RIDDOR all employees should receive training on policies and procedures to minimise the risk of injuries, disease and dangerous occurrences. Furthermore, risk assessment must be carried out to reduce the risk of incidents occurring.

Records must be kept of anything under RIDDOR which include the date, time and place of the event, who was involved, the injury and a description.

Examples of incidents that relate to infection control are:

1. Occupational dermatitis, for example a care worker develops dermatitis after using detergents while cleaning surfaces in a care home
2. A phlebotomist acquires a needle stick injury from a patient who has hepatitis B
3. A cleaner develops tuberculosis after cleaning the room of an individual who has contracted the disease
4. Two children who attend the same nursery contract legionnaire's disease.

8.2 Control of Substances Hazardous to Health (2002) COSHH

This legislation covers chemicals, but also covers infectious microorganisms under the term biological agents. In a similar way to chemicals, infectious substances need to be identified, assessed and controlled, but there are also additional requirements for laboratories. Organisations have a duty to protect both employees and the public.

Hazards within Health and Social Care

COSHH defines biological agents into four hazard groups which assist with an indication of containment and control measures that should be in place. Risks should be assessed and if an organisation has more than five employees this must be documented. If an employee acquires an infection as a result of work, then it must be reported under Reporting of Injuries, Diseases and Dangerous Occurrences Regulations (1995).

The groups are as given in Table 5.10.

Table 5.10 Groups of biological agents

Group	Outline	Example
1	Unlikely to cause human disease	Only hazard groups 2–4 appear on the list, but this does not mean that an unnamed biological agent is in this group
2	Can cause human disease and may be a hazard. There is often prophylaxis or treatment available	Staphylococcus aureus Candida Bordetella pertussis (whooping cough)
3	Can cause severe human disease. May spread to the community, but there is usually prophylaxis or treatment	Escherichia coli (E Coli) Creutzfeldt-Jakob disease
4	Can cause severe human disease. It is likely to spread to the community. There is usually no effective treatment or prophylaxis	Ebola virus Smallpox

Source: HSE (2013a)

Risk assessments

A risk assessment uses a rated system to determine the severity of the risk, likelihood of the risk and associated action to take to minimise or mitigate the risk. Risk assessments are an integral procedure within health and social care settings. A risk assessment may change according to different activities, hazards or risks.

Identifying the risk should consider the microorganism that can cause illness and the source. Examples of the source include blood or body fluids, faeces, urine or vomit, respiratory diseases such as coughs and sneezes or contact with the skin. It should be noted that deceased individuals can still pose an infection risk. Activities such as personal care or disposing of waste, which may mean an individual comes into contact with the microorganism or source, should also be identified as a hazard. Individuals should not be limited to employees, but can also include visitors and contractors.

Assessing risk involves considering the severity and likelihood of the risk. For example, how often is the task carried out? How severe is the cross-contamination risk? In a health and social care setting it is important to consider that microorganisms as well as infections can also cause allergic reactions.

Controlling the risk should be considered first, for example, can the hazards be eliminated? If this is not possible, then methods of reducing the risk should be implemented. With microorganisms the risk of spores forming, their growth and multiplication should also be considered. Provision of PPE can help to reduce the risk; employers should ensure that staff are trained so they know how to use the equipment safely and effectively and the equipment should be maintained in good condition. Monitoring should occur to ensure that there are no new hazards and that measures to reduce the risk are being effectively used. Consultations with employees should take place either in a meeting or through a health and safety representative, in case there are hazards that employers are unaware of and to feedback on the effectiveness of measures. Employers cannot charge employees for PPE.

In addition, COSHH requires employers to have a system in place to ensure that staff are aware of what to do and provision is in place for emergency situations. For example, if a member of staff has a sharps injury (they pierce their own skin with a needle used on someone else), then that individual needs to attend Accident and Emergency promptly. Employers should also offer staff guidance on uniform washing and provide sufficient work clothes (if applicable) to ensure the risk of cross-infection from this source is reduced.

Check your understanding

1. Define RIDDOR and COSHH.
2. Identify three examples of incidents that should be reported under RIDDOR.
3. Identify two substances that are covered by COSHH.
4. Identify a responsibility of the employer under COSHH.
5. Identify a responsibility of the employee under COSHH.

LO9: Understand the role and responsibilities of the health and social care practitioner in relation to infection prevention and control

9.1 Analyse the role and responsibilities of the health and social care practitioner in relation to infection prevention and control

Policies and procedures

Infection control is the responsibility of every member of the multi-disciplinary team. All members of the team should follow policies and procedures of the setting and report incidents. Policies and procedures should be followed to ensure consistent implementation of infection control measures. This also provides a benchmark for practice to be judged and identifies areas of improvement. All staff should feel confident to reflect on their own practice and challenge the poor practice of others. Policies and procedures provide a framework to do this.

Maintaining own knowledge and skills

Health and social care practitioners that have direct individual contact must ensure that they keep up to date with knowledge and standards of clinical practice. This can be from attending clinical updates organised by the organisation they are working for or reading clinical journals. They must ensure that any incident where best practice has not been implemented is reported. The infection risks to others and signs of infection in themselves and others should be responded to with prompt action, for example if a nurse notices a surgical site has signs of infection. Health and social care workers should act as role models and promote messages and good practice in infection prevention. They also have a role in educating individuals and their carers and families about infection control procedures. However, although everyone has a role to play in infection control, completely minimising the spread of infection is not always possible; for example, individuals can make mistakes or may forget to complete one part of the infection control procedures.

Responsibilities of others

Individuals in hospital or care homes and their family or friends who visit have a role to play in infection control and hygiene. Specifically, family and friends should delay a visit if possible if they are unwell themselves, especially with diarrhoea or vomiting symptoms. Families, friends and individuals should ensure they wash their hands in clinical settings and not sit on hospital beds.

Codes of practice and infection control

Many health and social care practitioners have a responsibility in adhering to professional codes of practices. Paramedics for example in section 15.5 of their code of practice have a professional responsibility to be able to establish safe environments for practice ... particularly infection control (HCPC 2014). All health and social care workers have a responsibility to follow legislation. The Health and Social Care Act (2008) contains a code of practice that governs infection control. It applies to NHS bodies and providers of independent healthcare and adult social care in England, including primary dental care, independent sector ambulance providers and primary medical care providers (HMSO 2015). There are ten criteria against which health care providers will be judged on how they comply with infection control. The ten criteria are:

1. Have systems to manage and monitor the prevention and control of infection.
2. Provide and maintain a clean and appropriate environment.
3. Ensure appropriate antimicrobial use. This helps to reduce antimicrobial resistance.
4. Provide suitable accurate information on infections to individuals and their visitors on nursing/ medical care in a timely fashion.
5. Ensure prompt identification of people who have or are at risk of developing an infection. This is important to ensure that they receive timely and appropriate treatment and therefore reduce the risk of transmitting infection to other people.
6. Have systems to ensure that all care workers (including contractors and volunteers) are aware of their responsibilities in the process of preventing and controlling infection.
7. Provide or secure adequate isolation facilities.
8. Secure adequate access to laboratory support as appropriate.
9. Have and follow policies, designed for the individual's care and provider organisations that will help to prevent and control infections.
10. Have a system in place to manage the occupational health needs and obligations of staff in relation to infection.

The Care Quality Commission will judge how well organisations are doing against infection control standards and report on this under Regulation 12: Safe Treatment.

Policies on infection control should include details on key personnel involved and those that can be contacted in the case of an outbreak, along with their roles. They should include risk assessments and action to be taken. Policies and procedures will provide guidance about hand hygiene and reflect current evidence for management. They should state procedures for waste management and for reporting concerns.

Command word activity

Analyse (AC 9.1)

A student nurse is about to start a placement on a ward. As well as patients, there are nurses, doctors, cleaning staff, caterers, a physiotherapist, an occupational therapist and a pharmacist.

Create a booklet which will analyse the roles and responsibilities of each in relation to infection prevention and control. You should consider:

- the policies and procedures they must each follow, and their lines of reporting
- your own role and responsibilities (as a student nurse) in relation to the other staff
- any consequences of any staff member not maintaining their roles and responsibilities.

✓ Check your understanding

1. Identify who is responsible for infection control
2. Outline one reason why it is important to maintain your own knowledge and skills
3. Identify two ways in which visitors to hospitals can help reduce the spread of infection
4. Describe how one code of practice supports the practitioner's responsibility to promote infection control

Read about it

Brooker, C. and Nicol, M. (2011) *Alexander's Nursing Practice*, London: Churchilll Livingstone

Health and Safety Executive (2013) *Personal Protective Equipment at Work*, HSE

HCPC (2014) *Standard of Proficiency Paramedics*, London: HCPC

HSE (2013a) *The Approved List of Biological Agents*, HSE

HSE (2013b) *Reporting Injuries, Disease and Dangerous Occurrences Regulations*, HSE

HSE (2013c) *RIDDOR in Health and Social Care*, HSE

RCN (2013) *Wipe it Out*, London: Royal College of Nurses

Weston D. (2013) *Fundamentals of Infection Prevention and Control*, Wiley, Chichester

Websites

Cancer Research (2014) *The Immune System and Cancer*. Accessed from http://www.cancerresearchuk.org/about-cancer/what-is-cancer/body-systems-and-cancer/the-immune-system-and-cancer#cancer

Fenn (2009) *Disease Control in an Emergenc.* Accessed from http://www.who.int/diseasecontrol_emergencies/publications/idhe_2009_london_malnutrition_fenn.pdf

HIV treatment information based (2015) http://i-base.info/

http://www.nhs.uk/Conditions/Flu/Pages/Introduction.aspx

NHS Choices (2015) http://www.nhs.uk/pages/home.aspx

WHO (2012) *Hand Hygiene*. Accessed from http://www.who.int/gpsc/tools/Five_moments/en/

WHO (2015) *10 Facts on Malaria*. Accessed from http://www.who.int/features/factfiles/malaria/en/

WHO (2016a) *Typhus Fever*. Accessed from http://www.who.int/ith/diseases/typhusfever/en/

WHO (2016b) *Rabies*. Accessed from http://www.who.int/mediacentre/factsheets/fs099/en/

WHO (2016c) *Hand Hygiene*. Accessed from http://www.who.int/gpsc/tools/faqs/evidence_hand_hygiene/en/

Unit HSC CM5: How will I be graded?

The table below shows what the learner must do to achieve each grading criterion. Learners must achieve all the criteria for a grade to be awarded (i.e. criteria D1 to D3 must be achieved to pass this unit assessment at grade D). A higher grade may not be awarded before a lower grade has been achieved in full, although component criteria of a higher grade may have been achieved.

Grade	Assessment criteria number	Assessment criteria	Assessment of learning / What you need to show
D1	1.1	Describe types of microbiological organisms that cause disease	The description must: • demonstrate understanding of microbiological organisms • relate to the microbiological organisms that cause disease
D2	2.1	Explain the features of vector borne disease	The explanation of the features must: • demonstrate understanding of vector borne disease • show knowledge of modes of transmission by known vectors
D3	3.1	Describe how pathogenic microorganisms are transmitted.	The description must: • demonstrate an understanding of pathogenic micro-organisms • show knowledge of the modes of transmission appropriate to pathogenic micro-biological organisms

Grade	Assessment criteria number	Assessment criteria	Assessment of learning / What you need to show
D4	3.2	Explain why individuals may be more vulnerable to infection	The explanation must provide more than one reason why individuals may be more vulnerable to infection.
D5	3.3	Describe the body's defence mechanisms against infection	The description must show understanding of different defence mechanisms related to: ● physical barriers to infection ● the immune system
D6		D6 Show evidence of reading or use of sources.	There should be evidence of learners' reading or use of sources. Learners must use a minimum of 2 traceable references to support the discussion.
C1	3.4	Explain how to break the chain of infection	The explanation must demonstrate understanding of the chain of infection. Reference to commonly accepted methods or strategies should be used to explain how to break the chain of infection.
C2	4.1	Explain methods of microorganism control	More than one method of micro-organism control must be explained. The explanation of the methods selected must demonstrate understanding of micro-organism control.
C3	5.1	Explain the importance of personal hygiene and attire in relation to infection control	The explanation must show an understanding of the importance of personal hygiene and attire in relation to infection control. Relevant examples of personal hygiene and attire may be given to support the explanation.
C4	5.2. 5.3	Explain the correct hand washing technique. Explain the use of personal protective equipment and the key issues that relate to it	The explanation should include reasons for each element of the procedure. The explanation should include the key issues that relate to the use of personal protective equipment.
C5	5.4	Explain the process of safe waste disposal	An explanation of safe waste disposal must be undertaken in relation to: ● body fluids ● linen ● sharps and equipment
C6		Show evidence of reading or use of sources with referencing relevant to the explanations. Good use of vocabulary and grammar.	Use of referencing should show evidence of reading or use of sources. Vocabulary and grammar should be appropriate and accurate for purposes.
B1	8.1	Explain the requirements of RIDDOR in relation to infection prevention and control	Provide a detailed explanation of the requirements for RIDDOR in relation to infection prevention and control in accordance with current regulation.

Grade	Assessment criteria number	Assessment criteria	Assessment of learning / What you need to show
B2	8.2	Explain the requirements of COSHH in relation to infection prevention and control	Provide a detailed explanation of the requirements of COSHH in relation to infection prevention and control in accordance with current regulations. Relevant examples of substances hazardous to health in a health or social care setting may be given to support the explanation.
B3		Show evidence of reading or use of sources. Referencing supports discussion.	Use of reading or use of sources should be shown through a range of relevant referencing. Referencing should be used appropriately to support view or discussion.
A1	7.2	Explain how antimicrobial resistance occurs	Provide a detailed explanation which: ● Demonstrates understanding of antimicrobial resistance ● Gives reasons why antimicrobial resistance may occur
A2	7.1	Evaluate the use of drugs to control and treat infectious disease	Evaluation must consider the use of drugs to control and treat infectious disease taking account of different views and perspectives. Provide examples of types of drugs used to treat infectious diseases to support the evaluation.
A3		Show evidence of wider background reading or use of sources. Referencing supports discussion and evaluation.	Wider background reading should be evident or a wide range of source material should be used.
A*1	9.1	Analyse the role and responsibilities of the health and social care practitioner in relation to infection prevention and control.	A detailed analysis of the role and responsibilities of the health and social care practitioner in relation to infection prevention and control should consider a range of relevant issues such as: ● following policies, procedures and lines of reporting ● own role and responsibilities in relation to other involved practitioner groups. ● The analysis may include the consequences of non-maintenance of roles and responsibilities.
A*2		Show evidence of a range of background reading or use of sources used selectively.	Learners should show the ability to consider or explore relevant issues which contribute to the analysis. An extensive range of background reading or use of sources should be used selectively and cited appropriately.
Skills	6.1 6.2 6.3	Use of the correct hand washing technique Use of personal protective equipment Dispose of waste safely	

HSC CM6
Psychological Perspectives in Health and Social Care

Learning outcomes

LO1: Understand psychology within health and social care

1.1 Describe the role of psychology within health and social care
1.2 Describe types of psychologists and the roles of each within health and social care settings.

LO2: Understand the nature versus nurture debate

2.1 Describe the concepts of nature and nurture in relation to human development and behaviour
2.2 Explain the nature versus nurture debate

LO3: Understand psychological theories relating to health and social care

3.1 Describe psychological theories
3.2 Explain the impact of psychological theory on health and social care practice
3.3 Compare and contrast approaches to health and social care practice based on psychological theory

LO4: Understand psychological approaches in relation to a mental health condition

4.1 Discuss psychological approaches in the management of an identified mental health condition
4.2 Analyse a psychological approach in relation to an identified mental health condition

About this unit

Psychology is the science of the mind and individual human behaviour. People working in health and social care need to understand why others behave the way that they do so that they can support them to live longer, healthier and more fulfilled lives. In this unit we look at how the genes we inherit and the way we are raised can affect our development, behaviour and our health and care needs. We examine behaviourist, cognitive and social learning theories among others, and explore how they are used in health and social care. We will study how different psychological approaches can be used to help people with specific mental health conditions and analyse a psychological approach in relation to an identified mental health condition.

LO1: Understand psychology within health and social care

According to the British Psychological Society, 'Psychology is the **scientific study** of people, the mind and behaviour.' (www.bps.org.uk). Understanding some of the basic ideas in psychology can help us understand ourselves and others, and can help in interactions with other people.

1.1 Describe the role of psychology within health and social care

Understanding the mind and the behaviour of ourselves and others is especially useful in health and social care where we work with people. We have to be aware of relationships and how they influence health and well-being. Understanding psychology can help us with interactions and communication.

How psychology contributes to health and social care

According to the World Health Organization, health is 'a state of complete physical, mental and social well-being and not merely the absence of disease or infirmity' http://who.int/about/definition

Such a definition acknowledges that health is not merely a matter of physical health but that mental and social well-being are important too. This is why psychology has a role in health and social care.

Examples of when psychology is used in health and social care include:

- help with quitting smoking
- help with weight loss, exercise and diet
- counselling for stress, anxiety and depression
- help with relationships
- counselling to help cope with loss and grief
- help with anger management.

Take it further

You can read more about:
- the NHS Stop Smoking services at **www.nhs.uk/Livewell/smoking**
- weight loss at **www.nhs.uk/Livewell/loseweight**
- stress, anxiety and depression at **www.nhs.uk/Conditions/stress-anxiety-depression**

Figure 6.1 Group therapy

1.2 Describe types of psychologists and the roles of each within health and social care settings

All **psychologists** work with other health and care professionals as part of a team, for example:

- in mental health teams (in hospital and in the community)
- with people who have addiction or relationship problems that affect their lives
- with social work teams
- with the probation service.

Clinical psychologists work in the NHS with a variety of patients. They may work with children with emotional and behavioural difficulties, or with young offenders with anger management issues, or with mothers with post-natal depression. They may work with young people with eating disorders either in the hospital or in the community. They may also support those in hospices with life-limiting illnesses and their families.

Counselling psychologists work with individuals, couples or groups. They may work with people who want to stop smoking, or those who have been bereaved or with people with mental health issues. Often counselling psychologists work in the NHS in hospitals or in GP surgeries. They may also work in universities offering counselling to students and staff.

Forensic psychologists work with offenders to help them understand and change their criminal behaviour. They may be employed by the prison service. Forensic psychologists work with the police and probation services and may present evidence in court. They may have to assess offenders before release. At times they may be involved in child protection cases.

Health psychologists focus on people's attitudes to health and they often work in public health. They focus on how to change unhealthy behaviours such as addictions, and how to encourage healthy behaviours. Much of their

Key term

Psychology the scientific study of people, the mind and behaviour

Scientific study planned, rational, organised approach to investigating a topic

Psychologist works with individuals to help them understand their thoughts, feelings and behaviour so that they can overcome problems. A psychologist has a degree and higher degree in psychology and usually specialises in a particular aspect of psychology

Cognitive behavioural therapy a treatment that uses talking and listening to help individuals question negative thoughts, beliefs and attitudes that are causing them problems. It combines a cognitive approach, examining the individual's thoughts, with a behavioural approach, examining how they behave, so they can change their behaviour and their thinking

Case scenario (AC 1.1, 1.2)

Jenny is 16 and lives with her mum and dad, Mick and Sue. Jenny's great-grandmother, Mary, is 90 years old. She is Mick's gran and brought him up when his parents died in a car accident. Mary now has dementia and lives in a residential home nearby. Jenny goes with her dad to visit every week but he gets really upset because Mary thinks he is her husband and asks when they are going home. (Her husband, Mick's grandfather, died years ago.) When

Mick is upset he gets angry and starts shouting at Mary, telling her that her husband is dead. Mary starts crying. They are asked to leave because of his behaviour.

1. How could an understanding of psychology help carers to manage the situation?
2. How may psychologists help Mick?
3. How may psychologists help Jenny?

work is about preventing ill-health rather than trying to help people recover from ill-health.

The high intensity therapist uses **cognitive behavioural therapy** (see p. 124 for definition) for short interventions. The therapist may sometimes refer patients on to other psychological services.

Educational psychologists work with children and young people who may have social or emotional problems or learning difficulties. Often the educational psychologist works with a social worker and the child's parents and teachers to help the child or young person overcome difficulties.

Command word activity

Describe (AC 1.1, 1.2)

1. Describe how psychology contributes to health and social care in the following ways and give a brief example for each:
   a. understanding mind and behaviour of self and others
   b. promoting health and well-being
   c. relationships
   d. interaction
   e. communication.
2. Describe the role of each of the following:
   a. clinical psychologist
   b. counselling psychologist
   c. health psychologist.

Check your understanding

1. What is psychology?
2. Give five ways that psychology can help in health and social care.
3. Briefly explain the role of three different types of psychologists in health and social care.

LO2: Understand the nature versus nurture debate

What makes us the person we are? Is it due to our genetic inheritance or is it due to the experiences that change us as we mature? To what extent do our genes determine who we are?

Key term

Genetic inheritance refers to the characteristics we get from our parents through their genes, for example, eye colour or the likelihood of developing breast cancer

Can we change? This discussion is known as the nature/nurture debate.

2.1 Describe the concepts of nature and nurture in relation to human development and behaviour

Nature refers to our **genetic inheritance.** Inherited characteristics are decided by the **genes** we inherit from our parents. Such physical characteristics include eye colour, hair colour, the size and shape of our nose, and many other features. This is why identical twins, who share almost exactly the same genes, look identical.

Sometimes our genes are responsible for genetic disorders, for example, cystic fibrosis and sickle cell disease. Psychologists who suggest that most of our development, personality and behaviour is determined by our genes are called 'nativists'. They suggest that most of our development is a result of genetic evolution; for example, everyone goes through puberty at roughly the same period in their life and children learn to walk and talk at around the same age.

Nurture refers to what happens to us as we grow. **Environmentalists** (see p. 126 for definition) hold the view that every child is a blank slate and it is the environment that shapes individuals. Aimee born and brought up in France learns to speak French; Gareth born and brought up in Wales may learn Welsh as his first language. Each child is shaped by their environment.

The experiences individuals have will impact on their behaviour, opportunities and even their aspirations. For example, a child who is encouraged to engage in physical activity is likely to develop routines that involve physical activity, whereas a child that is not, may not.

Key terms

Nature refers to our genetic inheritance. Inherited characteristics are decided by the genes we inherit from our parents

Nurture refers to all the influences on us as we grow and develop

Nativist a person who thinks that certain skills, abilities and traits are inherited

Environmentalists those who consider that the environment has a greater influence than our genes do on how we develop

Gene a basic unit of DNA that carries instructions for traits and diseases from one generation to the next. Genes are contained in the chromosomes. Every child has two copies of each gene, one from each parent. In total humans have between 20,000 and 25,000 genes

Chromosomes thread-like structures in pairs in the nucleus of cells. Humans usually have twenty-six chromosomes. Each chromosome is made up of genes

Meta-analysis a systematic review that combines data from other studies to produce findings with a greater statistical significance

2.2 Explain the nature versus nurture debate

It is difficult to decide how far nature or nurture is responsible for an individual's development and behaviour. Someone may be intelligent because of their genes or it may be that their parents value education and brought them up to work hard at school. A person may be short because of their genetic inheritance or because they did not get sufficient nutrition in their early years, or they might be obese because of their genes or it might be because of the family's diet.

Why is the nature/nurture debate important?

An understanding of psychology is important for all throughout life; however, early childhood influences can affect how we develop not only physically and socially but psychologically too. For this reason, there has been a lot of interest in issues such as the nurture/nature debate.

The influence of nature and nurture is debated because of the ethical, economic and social implications for society. Environmentalists suggest that personality, intelligence and behaviour are shaped by the environment so it is important to provide a nurturing and supportive environment to help individuals achieve their potential in order to contribute positively to society.

Albert Bandura's theory of social learning suggests that children learn behaviour from others. If they see aggression they are likely to become aggressive; if they see kindness, they are more likely to be kind. This has implications for how we raise children. If they play violent video games or see domestic violence at home they may learn and adopt such behaviour.

It is possible to modify the environment. The implications of the environmentalist approach are that ethically we should provide the best possible environment for all children to develop. In turn, this has economic implications as facilities to enable this have to be paid for. There are social implications too. Should the state intervene to modify the environment in family life if parents want to expose their children to violence? Therefore, modifying the environment is possible but it has implications.

Biological theory suggests that personality, intelligence and behaviour are determined by genes and that some people are born with genes that predispose them to (or mean that they will have) low intelligence or criminal behaviour. Such ideas at the beginning of the twentieth century led to the biological movement and the forced sterilisation of patients in psychiatric hospitals. People with learning disabilities

Activity (AC 2.2)

You are a local councillor deciding how to spend the limited money your council has.

1. Thinking of the nature/nurture debate, what reasons could you put forward for spending money on a children's play area in a rundown estate where gang culture predominates?
2. What reasons could other councillors put forward for spending money on a park in a better area?

were institutionalised and not allowed to marry. Sterilisation or isolation of these people who were deemed 'undesirable' people was used to modify the gene pool so that only 'desirable' people were allowed to have children.

Today we view forced population control as unethical and aim to value each person as an individual; however, science has brought new ways of modifying genes which some find more acceptable. Gene therapy, developed in the 1990s, and the Human Genome Project offer the possibility of modifying genes to eradicate hereditary diseases such as cystic fibrosis. Gene therapy also offers the possibility of modifying genes to produce 'designer babies' with characteristics modified to parental preferences. This raises ethical issues about the rights of the unborn child and the rights of parents. It also raises issues of equality – whether designer babies are available for all or just for those who can afford them. Gene therapy also raises issues about the society – whether we evolve into a society where everyone has to be perfect or whether we can value difference.

The latest conclusions

The nature/nurture debate has concerned society for many years. Over the last 50 years, sets of identical and non-identical twins were studied to find out whether nature or nurture has most influence on development. More recently, researchers at the University of Queensland and VU University of Amsterdam carried out a meta-analysis of 2,748 studies already carried out on more than 14.5 million pairs of twins. They found that genes account for 49 per cent of variation in traits and disease and 51 per cent of variation in traits and disease are due to environmental factors and/or measurement errors in the studies. It is now accepted that both nature and nurture have equal impact on individuals.

Take it further

Read about this research:

Meta-analysis of the Heritability of Human Traits Based on Fifty Years of Twin Studies (2015), Polderman *et al.*, available at **www.nature.com/ng/journal/v47/n7/full/ng.3285.html**

Case scenario (AC 2.1, 2.2)

Is there a gene for violence?

Researchers in Finland studied the genes of 900 offenders and found two genes linked to violent criminal behaviour. Those with the gene were 13 times more likely to have repeated violent behaviour. Between 5 to 10 per cent of violent criminal behaviour in Finland could be caused by people with these genes; however, most people with these genes do not commit crimes because they understand the consequences of such behaviour and choose not to be violent. (For further reading, see Tiihonen *et al.*, 2015)

1. How may an environmentalist use this study to show that environment has more influence than genes on human development?
2. How may a **nativist** use this study to show that genetic inheritance has more influence on behaviour than does environment?
3. What ethical issues do these findings raise?

Classroom discussion (AC 2.1)

Debate the following topic: Should babies be screened before birth for genetic defects?

Produce three arguments for the suggestion and three arguments against the suggestion.

Command word activity

Explain (AC 2.2)

Give a detailed account of how 'nature and nurture' influence human development. Use examples from research to support your points.

Command word activity

Evidence

Use at least two different sources to find out more about the nature/nurture debate. Refer to these in your describe and explain activities. Use the Harvard reference system and include these sources in your reference list at the end of your work.

 Check your understanding

1. In the nature/nurture debate, what does 'nature' mean and what does 'nurture' mean?
2. Give three examples of how genetic inheritance can influence human development.
3. Give three examples of how the environment can influence human development.

LO3: Understand psychological theories relating to health and social care

3.1 Describe psychological theories

Theories are views, perspectives or ideas. Psychological theories, which attempt to explain human behaviour, are especially useful for those working in health and social care where an understanding of people and their behaviour is essential.

There are many different psychological theories. Those described here are just a few that are useful for practitioners in health and social care.

 Key terms

Behaviourist theory suggests that all behaviour, except **reflex behaviour**, is a response to a **stimulus** in the environment. The temperature falls so we put on a jumper or turn up the heating. Our behaviour is a response to the stimulus of falling temperature

Cognitive theory suggests that we understand the world through perception, language, thinking, and memory; for example, a baby learns to recognise faces then refines this perception until it recognises its mother's face

Social learning theory suggests that we learn from others in a social context. A baby learns behaviour by watching others

Behaviourist

Behaviourist theory was one of the earliest psychological theories. Behaviourists consider that all behaviour is a response to a stimulus in the environment with the exception of reflex behaviour; for example, a learned reaction, a typical or consistent response to any given situation.

Ivan Pavlov

Ivan Pavlov working in the late nineteenth century and early twentieth century, noticed that dogs salivate when there is food. This is a reflex. It does not need to be learned. He noticed that dogs also salivate when they expect food, for example if the person who usually feeds them enters the room. He developed an experiment where he rang a bell when a dog was fed. Sometimes he rang the bell but gave no food. The dogs expected food and salivated at

 Key terms

Stimulus a thing that elicits a reaction

Reflex behaviour an automatic response to a stimulus such as jumping when startled

Observable behaviour actions that can be seen by others

the sound of the bell. The bell had become the stimulus that elicited the response of salivation. The dogs were conditioned to respond to the bell. This is the theory of classical conditioning – classical because it was the first theory to be developed about learning and conditioning. Pavlov's theory is behaviourist because it focuses on the behaviour.

B.F. Skinner

B.F. Skinner worked in the early part of the twentieth century. He thought Pavlov's theory of classical conditioning was limited. Skinner developed the theory of operant conditioning, when behaviours are changed after the event. Operants can be neutral, reinforcers, or punishers. Skinner considered how responses became learned. For example, praise and encouragement are examples of positive reinforcement. The individual will be encouraged to repeat this behaviour. Negative reinforcement such as shouting typically discourages repetition of behaviour.

Operant conditioning

Behaviour modification, a technique developed by Skinner and based on operant conditioning, is used to change behaviour by reinforcing desired behaviour and ignoring or punishing unwanted behaviours. Behaviour modification is used in a variety of settings. Nursery teachers use tokens such as stars to reward good behaviour. After a certain number of stars, a child gets to choose a toy. Behaviour modification is used in prisons and in psychiatric hospitals to encourage acceptable behaviour. Prisoners can earn privileges as a reward for acceptable behaviour. Unwanted behaviour is largely ignored and because it does not attract attention, gradually it is extinguished.

Operant conditioning is a useful theory in understanding and managing behaviour, one that parents need to know. We have all seen parents giving in to persistent toddlers who

Key terms

Behaviour modification changing the way a person behaves

Operant conditioning using reward to encourage the repetition of a behaviour, or using punishment or ignoring to discourage a behaviour

ask for sweets at the supermarket checkout. Unfortunately, they are rewarding the toddler's unwanted behaviour and it is likely to be repeated next time they are at the checkout.

Psychodynamic

Psychodynamic theory focuses on the relation between the conscious (aware) and the unconscious (unaware) mind (the psyche). The relationship changes, hence it is dynamic.

Sigmund Freud

Sigmund Freud developed the psychodynamic theory in the late nineteenth century and continued working until the 1930s.

Some key ideas of psychodynamic theory:

1. Behaviour and feelings are affected by unconscious motives which are laid down in early childhood.

2. Personality is shaped by the changing dynamics between the conscious and the unconscious.

3. There is conflict between the unconscious mind (the **id** and **superego**) and the conscious mind (the **ego**). (see p. 130 for definitions)

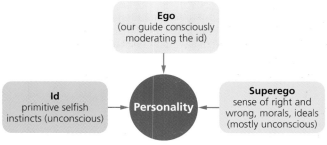

Figure 6.2 Influences on personality

Table 6.1 Psychosexual stages – each stage has tensions related to developing sexual instincts

Psychosexual stage	Example	Effect
Oral	A baby puts everything into its mouth	Ego developing
Anal	The focus on toilet training and gaining bladder and bowel control	Ego developing
Phallic	Awareness of sexual differences	Superego develops
Latent	Little interest in sexuality	Superego dominates
Genital	Sexual maturity	Superego dominates

Erik Erikson

Erik Erikson worked in the mid-twentieth century. He focused on the role of culture and society and conflicts in the ego, and developed a psychosocial theory within the psychodynamic framework. He suggested that personality can change through life and studied the effect of socialisation on personality. If a stage is successfully completed, the individual develops 'virtues'. A stage which is not successfully completed may be completed at a later date. Failure to complete a stage may delay an individual's psychological development, lead to a low sense of self-worth and in some cases mental ill-health.

Erikson described the stages given in Table 6.2.

Both Freud and Erikson are psychodynamic theorists because their theories suggest that personality can change under the influence of the psyche or mind.

Key terms

Generativity a period of creativity, guiding the next generation of children

Id unconscious primitive instincts influencing the behaviour of the very young

Superego the ideal moralistic aspect which sometimes consciously and sometimes unconsciously influences behaviour

Ego that part of us which has learned the rules of society and consciously moderates the primitive urges of the id

Schema patterns of how the world works, for example a hungry baby cries. This brings food. The baby learns the pattern of crying when it wants food

Table 6.2 Erikson's stages

Stage and psychosocial crisis	Virtue
Trust vs. Mistrust (0 – 1 ½) A baby cries and is comforted. If such care is consistent they learn to trust others and learn to be hopeful. If care is inconsistent or the baby is ignored, they learn mistrust and may become fearful	Hope
Autonomy vs. Shame and Doubt (age 1 ½ – 3) Children gain skills and become independent. If they are encouraged to gain skills and not criticised for failure, they develop self-confidence. If they are criticised for failure they learn to doubt their own abilities	Will
Initiative vs. Guilt (age 3– 5) Children learn through play how to use their initiative, be creative and interact with others. In this stage they can learn to develop ideas, lead and work with others, and develop a sense of purpose. Too much control at this stage can lead to feelings of guilt and the child will either rebel or become hesitant to try new things	Purpose
Industry (competence) vs. Inferiority (age 5–12) Peer groups are important at this stage. If a child learns skills which are valued by others, their competence will increase. If, however, they are not encouraged or they are not allowed to learn skills, they may develop a sense of inferiority	Competence

Stage and psychosocial crisis	Virtue
Identity vs. Role Confusion (age 12–18) Physical and psychological changes lead the adolescent to question who they are and what they want to be. Occupational and sexual roles are examined and the adolescent may form a clear sense of what they want to do with their life and of their sexuality. Success at this stage leads to acceptance of themselves and others – a sense of fidelity. Some people take longer than others to negotiate this stage and experience role confusion, not confident with who they are. Such crisis of identity may lead them to explore alternative lifestyles at this stage	Fidelity
Intimacy vs. Isolation (age 18–40) The young adult begins to explore relationships with others. Success at this stage leads to meaningful relationships but success is not always immediate. If a person has successfully negotiated previous stages they will have the confidence to accept rejection and try again until they meet someone with whom they can develop a relationship whether of friendship or something more. Someone who avoids intimacy and close relationships may become isolated and depressed	Love
Generativity vs. Stagnation (age 40–65) In the middle years, people may be in a close relationship, start a family, gain competence in work and start to give back to society caring for the next generation. Successful negotiation of this stage leads to a sense of creativity and feeling a valuable member of society. Those who do not may feel a sense of stagnation or a sense that their life is not moving in a forward direction	Care
Ego Integrity vs. Despair (age 65 plus) At this stage people look back on their lives and either feel a sense of achievement or feel regret. Those who have successfully negotiated life stages may have experienced sadness as well as happiness, but by engaging with the world and with life, they gain wisdom	Wisdom

Cognitive

Cognitive theorists focus on how we understand the world through perception, language, thinking, and memory. Piaget, Kelly and Gestalt are just three of many cognitive psychologists.

Jean Piaget

Jean Piaget, working in the twentieth century, studied cognitive development in children – how they develop an understanding of the world. He suggested that all children begin by forming schema, patterns of how the world works. At first these may be reflexes; for example, a baby will suck if the side of its mouth is touched.

Later, babies develop more complex schema; for example crying brings attention.

Developing these schema or patterns of behaviour helps the child understand the world. Babies use known schema to assimilate or adapt and deal with new situations – crying brings attention so it can be used when they are hungry/ uncomfortable/ need a nappy change/ or are bored.

 Key term

Repertory grid a tool to help individuals understand the way they see the world

When known schema fail to work, the baby experiences discomfort and disequilibrium or imbalance. They then have to change their schema by accommodation. Perhaps crying no longer brings an adult to entertain them, but burbling or producing a 'mamamama' sound will, so the baby changes or accommodates their schema to incorporate new ways of thinking.

Piaget described stages that he thought all children go through in developing an understanding of the world. See Table 6.3.

George Kelly

George Kelly developed the personal construct theory, sometimes called personal construct psychology (PCP), in the middle of the twentieth century. He suggested that everyone builds their own schema to help them understand the world

Table 6.3 Piaget's stage theory

Sensorimotor Stage (Birth–2 yrs)	Children explore the world through sight, sound, touch, taste and smell. They learn that an object still exists even when they cannot see it. A doll covered by a blanket is still there. This is 'object permanence'.
Preoperational Stage (2–7 years)	Symbolic thinking develops. A stick can represent a car or an aeroplane.
Concrete Operational Stage (7–11 years)	The beginning of logical or operational thought. Children learn the conservation of number, mass, and volume for example, that the number of counters remains the same whether they are spread out or pushed closely together. A cup of juice remains the same amount, whether it is in a tall narrow glass or a short wide one.
Formal Operational Stage (11 years and over)	Children learn to work problems out in their head. They can divide 144 sweets between 10 children without having objects to represent the sweets.

and that they change these schema through life. Sometimes they see a stereotype rather than a person, and anticipate how that individual will react. George Kelly thought that people should be helped to understand their own constructs rather than a psychotherapist put their interpretation on constructs. He designed a **repertory grid** to help people understand their own constructs or schemas (see example grid below). Here is how it works:

On a list of family members, (for example, mother, father, brother, sister, best friend), two of them are alike and one is different. For example, mother and brother are both tidy but sister is messy.

This gives the construct of tidy-messy.

> ### Activity
>
> Make your own list or grid based on individuals you know. You could include family members or think about a peer group.

This will give you a set of constructs. Results can be plotted on a grid: the preferred aspect of the construct is on the right side and that will score X. The aspects of each construct that are not preferred is in the left column and they score 0.

We can see from this example that the person completing the grid considers themselves to be happy, helpful, active, confident – the aspects they would like but they are messy and do not want to be.

Best friend and self are very much alike.

Self is quite different from mum, dad and sister.

Self is more like brother.

You can compare the number of matches between rows 1 and 2, 1 and 3, 1 and 4, 1 and so on until all rows have been compared. The highest number of matches shows what is most important.

Here is an example:

	Not preferred 0	Self	Mum	Dad	Brother	Sister	Best friend	Preferred construct X
1	Messy	0	0	0	X	0	X	Tidy
2	Unhappy	X	0	0	0	0	X	Happy
3	Selfish	X	X	0	X	0	X	Helpful
4	Lazy	X	0	0	X	X	X	Active
5	Shy	X	0	X	0	0	X	Confident

Row 1 and 2 = 4 matches

Row 1 and 3 = 4 matches

Row 1 and 4 = 4 matches

Row 1 and 5 = 3 matches

Row 2 and 3 = 4 matches

Row 2 and 4 = 4 matches

Row 2 and 5 = 5 matches

Row 3 and 4 = 4 matches

Row 3 and 5 = 3 matches

Row 4 and 5 = 3 matches

Rows 2 and 5 have the most matches which shows that the constructs of happiness and confidence are related as far as the person doing this grid is concerned.

This grid is a tool to help an individual understand themselves better. It is also used in market research to find out what qualities consumers value in a product.

Gestalt theory (Fritz Perls)

Gestalt theory, developed in the early twentieth century, focuses on the mind's ability to see whole aspects. We try to make sense of our surroundings by looking for patterns, so we see a colon and a parenthesis :) as a smiley face even when they are not meant to represent a face. We remember whole patterns rather than smaller units. We link events together even if they are not related; for example, we walk under a ladder, trip and fall down. Later when we see a ladder we avoid it, having linked walking under a ladder with tripping over. Gestalt theory suggests several principles; for example, the idea of closure – when we see an object partly drawn we automatically 'see' the whole object; two dots and a line can be seen as a face.

Social learning

Social learning builds on behaviourist ideas of classical and operant conditioning but goes even further in suggesting that learning is social; we learn how to behave by observing others.

Figure 6.3 A child copying aggressive behaviour in the Bobo Doll experiment

Albert Bandura

Albert Bandura worked in the 1960s and developed a theory of social learning which says that we learn from others, in a social context. In the Bobo Doll experiment, Bandura demonstrated that children copy behaviour such as aggression when they have seen others do it. The implications of this study are that exposure to violence, for example in online games or on television or in cartoons, increases violence in children.

Humanistic

Humanistic theories focus on the whole person, not just one aspect of them such as their unconscious mind or their behaviour.

Carl Rogers

Carl Rogers working in the mid-twentieth century developed the person-centred approach. He agreed with Maslow (see page 134) about focusing on the whole person but added that for an individual to fulfil their needs there are several core conditions to be met.

These are:

1. Genuineness where they are able to be open and where the counsellor working with them is also genuine and open
2. Unconditional positive regard where they are accepted for who they are and not judged

3. Empathy – they are heard and understood. This is not sympathy, where a person feels sorry for them, but empathy which has been likened to walking in their shoes.

4. Rogers also suggested that the person's ideal self must be congruent or fit with their actions. A doctor striving to become a top specialist will study their field of medicine, attend conferences, and conduct research in their field. They will publish papers and gain a reputation for being someone who really knows their subject. This is congruence.

According to Rogers, people who experience fulfilment have certain characteristics. These are very similar to the characteristics of self-actualisers that Maslow describes. Rogers' list includes:

1. Openness to new experiences
2. Living in the moment – accepting what happens and not prejudging
3. Self-reliance, trusting in their own judgement
4. Exercising choice and taking responsibility for their own actions and decisions
5. Being creative, exploring different ways of thinking rather than just accepting the usual way of doing things
6. Acting constructively with a concern for humanity
7. Experiencing all that life has to offer; whether happiness or sadness, not shutting themselves away from life.

The British Association for the Person-Centred Approach focuses on promoting the person-centred approach developed by Carl Rogers.

Abraham Maslow

Abraham Maslow working in the mid-twentieth century focused on the whole person and what motivates individuals. He suggested that people are motivated by needs. The levels of need are usually represented in a triangle with the most basic needs for survival at the bottom. Once these are fulfilled, an individual seeks to fulfil the next level of need and so on until they reach the highest level which is a need for self-actualisation and creative fulfilment. This is a hierarchy which builds on previous levels of fulfilment.

Events such as bereavement or war may force an individual back to considering how they can find shelter, food and warmth.

 Key term

Endorphins hormones produced in the body which influence mood

SELF-ACTUALIZATION
morality, creativity, spontaneity, acceptance, experience purpose, meaning and inner potential

SELF-ESTEEM
confidence, achievement, respect of others, the need to be a unique individual

LOVE AND BELONGING
friendship, family, intimacy, sense of connection

SAFETY AND SECURITY
health, employment, property, family and social abilty

PHYSIOLOGICAL NEEDS
breathing, food, water, shelter, clothing, sleep

Figure 6.4 Maslow's hierarchy of needs

Biological

Biological theories suggest that all behaviour and development is a result of biological causes; for example, depression or happiness are both the result of endorphins acting on the brain and nervous system. Aggression may be due to genetic inheritance or due to hormonal influences.

Arnold Gesell

Arnold Gesell working in the early part of the twentieth century studied child development and suggested that all children pass through the same stages but that each child takes their own time. This is a 'maturational' development theory that focuses on how children mature and develop. Internal factors such as genetics, and external factors such as family life all affect how quickly children pass through each stage. The six stages of a cycle are:

1. Smooth – when a child is in harmony with the environment and those around

2. Break-up – when disequilibrium occurs

3. Sorting out – the child sorts out what works and what does not

4. Inwardizing – the child internalises experiences, and may feel insecure while doing so

5. Expansion – a period of outgoing behaviour exploring wider

6. 'Neurotic' Fitting Together – the pendulum swings back, the individual is less outgoing, more cautious.

As the pattern is repeated it gets longer. Gesell described it as a spiral of repeating stages. Young children are learning a lot about the world around them which changes them.

Take it further

Find out more about Gesell's theory at **www.gesellinstitute.com/about-us/gesell-theory**

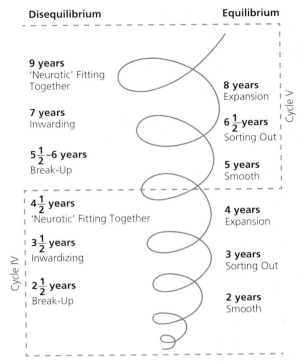

Figure 6.5 Gesell's spiral of repeating stages

Based on Gesell's work, four areas of growth and development are measured. They are:

1. Motor development (physical)
2. Cognitive development
3. Language development
4. Personal/social development

Hans Selye

Hans Selye working in the 1930s developed a General Adaptation Syndrome theory to describe how the body reacts to stress. He suggested that when a change in circumstances occurs, for example 'a stress', the body responds in the stages shown in Figure 6.6.

| Alarm – the sympathetic nervous system is activated and fight or flight hormones produced | Resistance – some basic functions return to normal but the body remains focused against the stressor | Exhaustion – continued stress exhausts the body's resistance and is potentially fatal |

Figure 6.6 General Adaptation Syndrome Selye

Stress or change may be positive, motivating a person to develop new skills, or it may be negative harmful stress. The body seeks to cope with stress by adapting, seeking a resolution of stress, or it may cope in a 'maladaptive' way (in a way that is not appropriate), causing more problems. An example of maladaptive coping is drinking too much as a way of dealing with social and emotional stress. People with emotional resilience may recover more quickly from stress.

John Tooby and Leda Cosmides

John Tooby and Leda Cosmides working in the 1990s developed the concept of evolutionary psychology. Using a biological approach they studied the structure and function of the brain and suggest that all humans have similar connections in the brain that influence how they see the world.

Evolutionary psychology applies five principles that come from biology. These are:

1. The brain is a physical system. Chemicals control how messages are passed from sensory neurons (nerve cells linking sense organs to the central nervous system) to the brain and then to motor neurons (nerve cells linking the central nervous system to muscles or glands to cause a reaction appropriate to the environment). Chemicals are responsible for the feeling of hunger or cold, which is transmitted to the brain. Chemicals again govern how we react, that is, whether we seek warmth and food or continue doing what we are doing.

2. Our neural circuits are the result of evolutionary selection. Circuits that lead to adaptive behaviour and enable the individual to survive will be passed on through genetic inheritance to the next generation. Circuits that lead to harmful behaviours will weaken the individual who may not then pass on their pattern of neural circuitry.

3. Most of what happens in the mind is hidden. Neural circuitry is complex. We do not understand how the unconscious works and influences behaviour.

4. Neural circuits are specialised, for example circuits for speech or understanding a language are different to neural circuits for movement.

5. Neural circuits evolve slowly. Our brains are wired to solve basic survival problems such as finding food, shelter, finding a mate, co-operating with others for defence.

Applying a biological and evolutionary approach to psychology offers another explanation of why people behave as they do.

Take it further

For more information on motor neurons, sensory neurons and the central nervous system, see Unit HSC CM3, Section 1.2.

Attachment theory

Attachment theory suggests that individuals are pre-programmed to attach to others as a means of survival. Some of the first studies in this area were conducted by Konrad Lorenz who worked with geese, which naturally imprint on the first moving thing they see after hatching.

John Bowlby

John Bowlby working in the period 1960–80 developed the theory of Attachment and of

Maternal Deprivation, which says that babies need a warm caring relationship with a significant carer early in life in order to form caring relationships later in life. At first Bowlby said that the bond must be with the mother, but later he adjusted this to suggest that the primary care giver did not have to be the mother. Key ideas of attachment theory include:

Children are born with an innate need to attach to one carer. Babies cry or smile, stimulating the care giver to respond.

The first two years are most important for the child, and up to the age of 5 the bond is extremely important. The attachment figure should give the child continuous care during this period. Disruption of this bond has serious consequences for later in life. The child may become depressed, aggressive, have lower levels of intelligence, develop anti-social behaviour and, at the most extreme, become an affectionless psychopath unable to empathise with others.

Short-term separation from the attachment figure leads to a pattern of behaviour known as the PDD model. Protest, then Despair is followed by Detachment. This behaviour can be seen in a short film, *A Two Year Old Goes to Hospital*, made by Bowlby and Robertson in 1953. This can be seen online at http://www.robertsonfilms.info/2_year_old.htm

Ainsworth and Bowlby developed the concept of different styles of attachment. The type of attachment a child experiences affects how they see themselves. Their working model of themselves is influenced by whether they see themselves as valued, whether they feel they can trust others, and whether they see themselves as effective in interacting with others. A child with a secure attachment feels positive and loved. They see their attachment figure as there for them. A child whose attachment figure is uncaring, not there when they are distressed and rejects them will be insecure and will not seek contact with the care giver. A third type of attachment is the insecure ambivalent or resistant type where the child experiences variable or differing responses from their caregiver. This leads to behaviour where the child may be clingy yet reject attempts

Key terms

Approaches methods of assessment and treatment based on a particular theory, e.g. psychodynamic approach

Theory a collection of ideas or concepts that attempt to explain a situation or behaviour, e.g. social learning theory

Command word activity

Describe (AC 3.1)

- Make a set of cards with a psychological theory on each.
- Summarise the work of each of the theorists on separate cards, omitting the name of the theorist.
- Exchange your set of cards with a friend.
- Turn all the cards over so they are face down.
- The aim is to pick out matching pairs, a theorist with what they said.
- When you have completed the activity, write out a description of each of the theories.

by the caregiver to comfort them. They are insecure, dependent on the caregiver yet reject them.

3.2 Explain the impact of psychological theory on health and social care practice

Understanding and interpretation of behaviour

Our understanding and interpretation of behaviour has changed as a result of psychological theories and we have changed how we care for people.

Behaviourist theory, developed as a result of research by Pavlov and later by Skinner, helped us understand why some people act as they do. Their understanding of reinforcement led to behaviour modification programmes for young offenders and methods for managing children's behaviour. Bandura's social learning theory, for example, helped us understand how people learn behaviour in a social context. Cognitive theory helped us understand disorders of information processing, such as in autism or dementia where resulting behaviour may seem inappropriate.

Person-centred practice

Person-centred practice developed as a result of humanistic theories suggested by Maslow and Rogers which put the individual at the centre of the process. Such holistic, 'overarching' theories revolutionised how we care for people in hospital and in the community. The recognition that a person's health can be influenced by whether they have a safe place to sleep and enough to eat brought approaches in health and social care closer together. A woman admitted to hospital with fractured ribs and a black eye may now be referred, while in hospital, to a social worker for referral to a refuge rather than being discharged back to an abusive home.

Research and evidence-based practice

Research and evidence-based practice in applying psychological theories has built a strong foundation for changing practice.

Bowlby and Robertson's study of a two year old in hospital exhibiting PDD behaviour led to shorter stays for children and more frequent visits by parents – just two of the changes brought about by Bowlby's theory of Maternal Deprivation (discussed earlier in AC 3.1).

Biological theories drive research into the causes, treatment and possible prevention of disorders where there is a known biological cause. Genetic research such as the Human Genome Project has identified the genes responsible for cystic fibrosis. Dementia, an increasing problem in ageing populations, is a biologically based disorder.

Gesell's maturational development theory (discussed in AC 3.1) is applied in childcare and in the care of adolescents; for example, it is now recognised that teenagers who are detained under the Mental Health Act should not be put with adults but should have special provision to meet their maturational requirements.

Therapeutic relationships

Therapeutic relationships developed from psychodynamic theory and the establishment of psychoanalysis, a therapy used to help those with anxiety or depression gain insight into their unconscious thoughts. Later humanistic theories encouraged the development of person-centred counselling based on work by Rogers and Maslow. These are all discussed in AC 3.1.

Appropriate interventions

Appropriate interventions followed. Instead of treating anxiety and depression with shock treatments such as electroconvulsive therapy (where an electrical impulse is passed through the brain), talking therapies were introduced. Both Kelly's personal construct theory and Gestalt therapy help individuals to gain insight into their thoughts and behaviour. Cognitive behavioural therapy is one method which has been found to be more effective than medication in helping people to manage their stress.

Awareness

Awareness has increased among health and social care professionals and among patients and service users. We now understand much more about the impact of the mind on the rest of the body. Selye's General Adaptation Syndrome theory is used to help understand autoimmune diseases where the body's own defence system starts to attack healthy cells, for example, in rheumatoid arthritis or in inflammatory bowel diseases such as ulcerative colitis, or gluten intolerance. There is more awareness of factors affecting health and many people no longer rely on care professionals as their only source of information. Instead they search online and arrive at the medical or social service with more knowledge about their own conditions and entitlements.

 Key term

Perception how something is seen or thought about

Perception

Perceptions change. The patient or service user is no longer seen as the passive recipient of care but an equal partner in the management of their health. Person-centred care empowers users and involves them at every stage. An individual's own perception of issues can also change. A person who has been in an abusive relationship may with the aid of person-centred counselling find the courage to break free and make a fresh start in life.

Take it further

To remind yourself about the importance of person-centred care, go to HSC CM3, Section 1.2.

Coping strategies

Coping strategies may be used by individuals to manage stress. They may focus on coping with emotions, for example reducing fear or anxiety, without tackling the underlying cause of stress. Such attempts to reduce emotional responses are useful when a situation cannot be controlled by the individual, but they do not remove the cause of stress. Talking to others, for example in cancer support groups where people share their experiences, can help people to cope with the emotions associated with their illness but the illness remains. Writing about emotions in a private journal is one way of coping with grief when an individual can do nothing about the situation.

Maladaptive ways (covered in AC 3.1) of coping with the emotions of stress may include eating too much or too little or relying on alcohol or drugs to get through. These strategies are harmful to health.

Problem-solving approaches

Problem-solving approaches developed as part of the holistic approach to care. These approaches are more effective when the situation is in the control of the individual and the underlying cause of stress can be tackled. The problem may be due to lifestyle – living a cash-rich but time-poor

Command word activity

Explain (AC 3.2)

How do each of the psychological theories you described for Activity 3.1 impact on health and care? Give an example of practical application for each theory. Aim to give examples from health and from care.

existence with multiple demands on time. Busy working parents may have to juggle a career, parenting, and caring for elderly relatives. A problem-focused approach might involve a person reassessing what is important to them and adjusting their workload to reduce stress. They may be aided by Kelly's personal construct theory and use a repertory grid to help them in this reassessment.

3.3 Compare and contrast approaches to health and social care practice based on psychological theory

There are some similarities and some differences in approaches to health and social care practice based on psychological theories. See Table 6.4.

Psychodynamic, cognitive and biological approaches focus on the relationship between the mind and behaviour, whereas behaviourists in contrast focus on only observed behaviour and are not concerned with emotional motivations. Roger's humanist approach is person-centred but Maslow's hierarchy of needs, a humanist

Table 6.4 Some contrasts between approaches to health and social care practice

Focus on the relationship between the mind and behaviour:	Focus on only observed behaviour:
Psychodynamic Cognitive Biological	Behaviourists
Person-centred theory: Rogers (Humanist)	**Stage theories:** Maslow (Humanist), Cognitive e.g. Piaget, Erikson, Bowlby
Focus on physical influences: Biological approach	**Focus on holistic influences:** Humanist

approach, and cognitive approaches such as that of Piaget and Erikson and Bowlby's Attachment theory look at stages common to all. Perhaps the greatest contrast is between holistic approaches such as that of Humanists which look at physical, social and emotional factors, or social learning which considers the impact of the social environment and a biological approach which looks only at physical influences on behaviour.

Behaviourist approaches

Behaviourist approaches are based on the idea that behaviour is a response to a stimulus in the environment. Behaviourists focus on observable behaviour not the ideas causing the behaviour. This approach uses techniques such as behaviour shaping and behaviour modification in order to change a person's harmful behaviour to healthier behaviour. Behaviour shaping helps to create healthier behaviour patterns such as taking more exercise and can be used to help eliminate unhealthy patterns such as snacking. It works by breaking changes down into small steps and rewarding the individual after increasing stages.

Behaviour modification techniques use reinforcement and punishment to change behaviour. (Behaviour shaping is one technique used in behaviour modification programmes.) See Table 6.5.

Table 6.5 Reinforcement vs punishment

	Reinforcement to increase a behaviour	Punishment to decrease a behaviour
Positive – something added to the environment	Praise or a hug when someone has done a good job	Making a child tidy their room as punishment for bad behaviour
Negative – something taken away from the environment	Removing discomfort, such as taking away an uncomfortable chair or removing from the room a younger sibling who knocks down a child's wooden brick construction	Taking away a child's favourite toy or removing their star from a star chart

Positive reinforcement, for example praise and encouragement, is more effective than negative reinforcement such as time-out or punishment, but positive reinforcement can be overused and lose its impact.

Using positive reinforcement effectively: at first reward the desired behaviour until it is consistently produced, then reward the behaviour every third time it is produced, then reward the behaviour every fifth time. Here is an example:

Zak has anger management problems. He is only four years old but can become aggressive and start hitting if he cannot have what he wants. If his mum says 'No', he has a tantrum and starts to hit her. She discusses his behaviour with the nursery teacher. They explain to Zak that when he is upset or angry, instead of shouting or screaming he can take some deep breaths and count to five. He can even walk a little way away to calm down.

Later that day, he wants a toy that another child is playing with. His nursery teacher reminds him to take some deep breaths. He does this and counts to five. His nursery teacher praises him immediately (positive reinforcement). Later at home he wants a toy his little brother is playing with. His mum told him to wait. He starts to get angry, but his mum reminds him how well he behaved at nursery, taking deep breaths. Zak remembers how he was praised, and starts to take some deep breaths. He even goes to the other side of the room. His mum gives him a hug and says what a good boy he is. Zak's mum and nursery teacher work together on the issue. They praise him every third time he manages to control his anger and then every fifth time. They behave as though they expect him to accept the situation that he cannot have everything he wants and eventually he does.

Other techniques used in behaviour modification include:

1. Extinction: this technique is used in combination with other methods. Behaviour occurs for a purpose. If the behaviour does not get the desired result, it will eventually

Take it further

To read more about Skinner's behaviour modification techniques and how they are used, read this article online: www.livestrong.com/article/105661-behavior-modification

become extinct. A child who screams at the checkout for sweets will discontinue the behaviour after some time if it does not get results.

2. Fading: uses the least intrusive prompts and gradually reduces them. It is used in combination with other methods. Zak's nursery teacher used prompts to remind Zak about taking a deep breath when angry. Gradually, she faded this prompt as Zak learned this technique and did not need reminding.

3. Chaining: breaking activities down into smaller steps is used with many learning activities, not just in managing behaviour. Getting fit is the ultimate goal but this can be broken down into smaller steps; for example, taking a lunch break in the park, then going for a lunch time walk, then walking twice a day, building up to going for a run.

Behaviour modification programmes are especially useful in helping people with depression and in managing challenging behaviour, for example when working with people with attention deficit disorder or with autism.

Psychodynamic approaches

Psychodynamic approaches look at the influence of the mind on behaviour. These are based on theories developed by Freud and Erikson. Psychodynamic therapy supports an individual to bring unconscious thoughts and feelings into conscious awareness in order that they understand why they behave as they do. Psychodynamic counselling has a more practical approach, focusing on immediate problems and supporting individuals in making their own changes. Psychodynamic approaches are not directive. They do not tell the person what to do but they are useful therapies for emotional/behavioural/relationship problems. Similarly

play, art and drama therapies help people to externalise their unconscious by expressing their thoughts and inner feelings.

Cognitive approaches

Cognitive approaches use techniques such as cognitive behavioural therapy (CBT), a talking therapy that helps individuals to recognise that how they perceive an action or event affects how they behave, which in turn affects how others behave towards them. They can become trapped in a cycle of negative thoughts, anxiety and depression. CBT helps people to see situations differently and by thinking about these things differently they behave differently. This breaks the negative cycle. CBT does not look back at the past but focuses on helping people to develop skills to manage current problems.

Cognitive training involves exercising the brain. An American study by Rebok *et al.* (2014) found that older people who completed training exercises for the brain were better at learning new things and better at thinking. Cognitive training is recommended for older people to help them remain independent in later life. In retirement, some people learn a new language; others learn to play a musical instrument.

www.nia.nih.gov/newsroom/2014/01/cognitive-training-shows-staying-power

Cognitive rehabilitation is a therapy used following brain injury to help a person regain skills they may have lost, or to learn how to adapt if they cannot regain those skills. Here is an example: Anjum had a stroke and this affected his ability to speak. He worked with a therapist to regain his speech for simple everyday words. Unfortunately, part of his brain was permanently affected and he could not associate the sound of the word with its meaning. He could say the word but could not remember its meaning. The therapist taught him to use different picture cards to show he wanted a drink of water or a cup of tea, thus adapting his mode of communication.

Social learning approaches

Social learning approaches focus on how we learn behaviour. In health and care, this approach is used with young offenders. Probation officers may model desired behaviour; the young person observes and copies their behaviour by observational learning. One technique combines this approach with behaviourist methods in pro-social modelling.

Attachment approaches

Attachment theory is used in managing transitions particularly for looked-after children in care. Children who are taken into care may protest, experience despair and eventually appear to be detached, not caring what happens to them. Informed practice using attachment theory recognises that children require stable emotional relationships to thrive and social workers aim to place looked-after children in a stable foster family placement where their emotional needs will be met (Furnivall 2011).

Humanistic approaches

Humanistic approaches look at individual needs and use co-operative/person-centred approaches to increase motivation. Person-centred approaches applied in health and social care promote the rights of the individual, involve them in decision making and collaborate for better improved outcomes. Assessment plans and care plans are based on a humanist approach and consider all the needs of the individual.

Biological approaches

Biological approaches offer biological explanations for challenging unwanted behaviour; for example, low levels of chemicals such as serotonin, norepinephrine and dopamine are associated with depression. Unlike the humanistic approach, it does not consider environmental influences on behaviour. Biological approaches to treating depression focus on balancing chemicals in the brain by using antidepressants. They do not deal with external causes of depression such as poverty or poor housing.

Take it further

You can read about this research on the NHS website at www.nhs.uk/news/2011/05May/Pages/genetic-link-to-depression-found.aspx

In 2011 Breen *et al.* published a paper presenting research showing a genetic link to depression. This discovery does not mean that those with the gene will automatically get depression but does indicate a biological basis for some types of depression.

Biological investigations such as neuroimaging and blood chemistry are used to diagnose some conditions. Neuroimaging produces images of the structure and functioning of the brain. Structural changes such as a brain tumour and functional changes as in types of dementia may cause changes in behaviour.

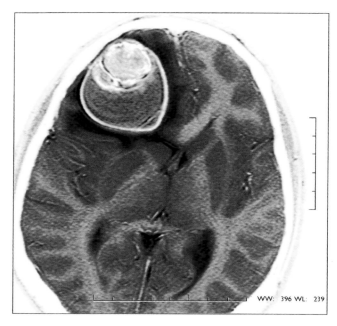

Figure 6.7 Image of a brain tumour

Medical treatments

Medical treatments include medication and brain stimulation. Both depression and Attention Deficit Hyperactivity Disorder (ADHD) are treated by a combination of therapy and drugs. The effects of drugs are to chemically alter the mood, although many drugs have unwanted side effects and can cause further behavioural problems. Ritalin, used to treat ADHD is a stimulant used to improve the ability to concentrate. The side effects of Ritalin include nervousness, anxiety, and inability to sleep. Paroxetine, an antidepressant manufactured as Seroxat, has been banned for under 18 year olds following a re-analysis of a study in 2001 that found a previous study under-reported side effects. Paroxetine was found to trigger suicidal thoughts in children.

Take it further

You can read more about this and find a link to the research on
www.nhs.uk/news/2015/09September/Pages/Antidepressant-paroxetine-study-under-reported-data-on-harms.aspx

Brain stimulation is being developed to treat some disorders. Deep brain stimulation which is invasive is used to control tremors in Parkinsonism. A probe is inserted into the part of the brain causing tremors. The charity Parkinson's UK has information about this.

Virtual reality is non-invasive brain stimulation. Burns patients use Snow World, an interactive virtual reality game, to control pain at the University of Washington Seattle and U.W. Harborview Burn Center. The game, developed by Hoffmann and Patterson, involves interactive virtual reality snowballing and brain scans show a reduced perception of pain in those using the game during treatment, such as changing wound dressings.

Activity (AC 3.3)

1. Review your understanding of these psychological theories:
   a. Behaviourist
   b. Psychodynamic
   c. Cognitive
   d. Social learning
   e. Humanistic
   f. Biological
   g. Attachment

The person-centred approach views each person as a unique individual, influenced both by their environment and their personal history, as well as their genetic inheritance, so that their needs may differ from the needs of another person.

1. Draw up a table to compare and contrast the person-centred and medical model approaches.
2. Which psychological theories might be relevant for the person-centred approach to health and social care?
3. Which psychological theories may be relevant for a medical model approach to health and social care that categorises people by physical factors or disorders?

Classroom discussion (AC 3.3)

Look at this list of psychological approaches:
- Behaviourist: Pavlov, Skinner
- Psychodynamic: Freud, Erikson
- Cognitive: Piaget, Kelly, Gestalt
- Social learning: Bandura
- Humanistic: Rogers, Maslow
- Biological: Gesell, Selye, Tooby and Cosmides
- Attachment: Bowlby

Choose one psychological theory from the list above.

1. Explain the theory and how it fits within the approach where it is listed; for example, what theory did Pavlov develop and why is it a behaviourist approach?
2. Research your chosen theory; pick out three key points from the theory.
3. Show how this theory can be applied in health and social care.
4. Present your findings to the rest of your group.
5. In your group, discuss the similarities and the differences you have found between approaches.

Case scenario (AC 3.1. 3.2, 3.3)

Scenario 1

Kamal is a fifty-year-old taxi driver, who has recently been diagnosed as diabetic. He does not follow the diet given to him by the dietician and seems to lack motivation. The diabetic nurse is concerned that his blood sugar levels remain high. She asks him about his diet and he explains that usually he eats rice, fish and vegetables. He has a large extended family and meals are social occasions, which always finish with sweet dishes. His wife does all the cooking at home. The nurse asks Kamal to bring his wife to the next appointment and together they devise a suitable diet for Kamal's health and preferences.

Scenario 2

Jo is overweight and has a family history of diabetes and heart disease. She has a stressful job, grabs coffee and a sandwich at her desk midday and when she gets home sits in front of the TV with a ready meal. The practice nurse helps Jo to devise a programme that includes more exercise in her day and eating healthily. Jo likes clothes so that is her reward. Each stage is cumulative or has a snowball effect so she continues with week 1 activities while doing week 2 activities. By week 4 she is also doing the activities for previous weeks:

Week 1 take a lunch break and go and sit in the nearby park. When she has taken five lunch breaks, she can buy a new top.

Week 2 during the lunch break walk to the nearby shop to buy some fruit and salad for lunch and some vegetables for home. When she has done this five times she can buy a new pair of shoes.

Week 3 before setting off for work put vegetables in a slow cooker to make soup for when she gets home. When she has done this five times she can buy a new pair of jeans. (She has to go down one size!)

Week 4 in the evening after supper, go for a walk round the local park. When she has done this five times she can buy a new pair of trainers.

1. Which psychological theory is the nurse using with Kamal?
2. Which psychological theory is the practice nurse using with Jo?
3. In which ways are these approaches similar?
4. In which ways do these approaches differ?

Check your understanding

1. Name three theories that describe stages of development.
2. Give an example of how psychological theory impacts on health and social care practice.
3. Compare two approaches to health and social care practice based on psychological theory.

LO4 Understand psychological approaches in relation to a mental health condition

Just as our physical condition can be healthy or unhealthy, our mental condition can be healthy or unhealthy. Of course, most of us have a few minor physical ailments so we may not be perfectly healthy. We may get flu or break a leg and are temporarily not in good physical shape. In just the same way, people can have mental health issues that temporarily means they are not in good mental shape. They may get depressed or feel stressed. Of course, some people have really serious and permanent health conditions, which may be physical or mental or both, but with support they can still enjoy some quality of life.

Psychological approaches have been especially useful in improving mental health. According to the mental health charity, MIND, one in four people in England will experience mental health issues each year. Mental ill-health can put a strain on relationships and cause people to lose friends and employment. Psychological approaches help people to understand their own mental health and they help care professionals provide more effective treatment.

4.1 Discuss psychological approaches in the management of an identified mental health condition

Mental health conditions which negatively impact on health may be temporary or permanent, severe or mild. These are just a few of the mental health conditions that can negatively impact on health: addiction, phobias, eating disorders, and mood disorders.

Addiction

Addiction has three aspects: intense craving, loss of control, and continued addiction, even though the behaviour may be harmful to self and others. People may be addicted to substances such as drugs, alcohol, nicotine and they may be addicted to behaviours such as gambling.

Neuroimaging has shown that addiction changes the structure and function of the brain. Biological approaches to addiction show that dopamine, a neurotransmitter, is released in response to the pleasurable activity whether it is taking drugs, smoking or gambling. This encourages the person to repeat the behaviour. It is reinforced by memory and learning, linked to survival mechanisms. You can read more about this in a help guide published in collaboration with Harvard Medical School

www.health.harvard.edu/newsletter_article/how-addiction-hijacks-the-brain

One of the first ways addiction is managed is through social learning. Self-help groups such as Alcoholics Anonymous, or a smoking cessation (or Stop Smoking) group may help individuals because they see others managing to break their addiction and they copy their behaviour. Sometimes a residential session of rehabilitation can help people to move away from harmful role models.

A person-centred humanist approach is used, because every person who is addicted is different, with different needs. Some people respond to certain approaches better than others do. Behaviourist approaches recognise addiction as a stimulus–response pattern. Cognitive approaches help the individual to understand their addiction and how to overcome it. Cognitive behavioural therapy combines these two approaches in a talking therapy. It is person-centred, giving the individual choice over the steps they take to overcome addiction.

Occasionally, for drug addicts a biological approach is used if, for example, there is no immediate access to therapy. Heroin users may be prescribed Methadone or Buprenorphine as substitutes, so that they can stop injecting heroin and do not need to commit crimes to fund their habit. The dose of the substitute drug is gradually reduced. This biological approach is not a cure for addiction but is sometimes used while waiting for cognitive behavioural counselling.

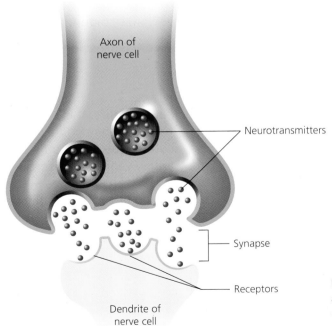

Figure 6.8 Neurotransmitters move across the synapse between nerve cells in the brain

Phobias

According to the NHS website, 'A phobia is an overwhelming and debilitating fear of an object, place, situation, feeling or animal'.

Phobias are treated firstly by self-help, for example by learning relaxation techniques, practising mindfulness, reading self-help books or following an online programme. If this does not work, talking therapies such as person-centred counselling, cognitive behavioural therapy, psychotherapy, and also gradual exposure may be used. Talking therapies are most effective. Anxiety, produced by the phobia, may be treated using a biological approach with drugs. Antidepressants such as escitalopram (Cipralex), sertraline (Lustral) or paroxetine (Seroxat) may be prescribed for panic attacks and social phobias; however, these can cause addiction and may have harmful side effects. Tranquillisers such as diazepam (Valium) are sometimes used for anxiety but may cause withdrawal symptoms when stopped. Beta-blockers slow the heart and may be used for palpitations, a symptom of anxiety.

Eating disorders

Eating disorders include over eating large amounts of food in a short time (binge eating disorder), or eating too little for the exercise done (anorexia nervosa), or eating and then deliberately vomiting or using laxatives (bulimia). The causes of eating disorders may be genetic or biological; for example, related to personality type, or a response to depression. Causes may be environmental, such as living with others who also have eating disorders. Often there are several causes and eating disorders may develop as a response to stress.

Management of the conditions is twofold – supporting the individual psychologically while monitoring their physical health. If a person becomes excessively under- or overweight, physical treatment may become a priority to prevent organ failure and save their life. Biological approaches focus on maintaining the body in a healthy balance. In emergency situations this may require intravenous therapy, a saline and sugar solution given through a vein, to stabilise the body and prevent organ shutdown. In cases of over eating, gastric banding where a band is placed to constrict the stomach, may offer a biological approach.

However, physical management does not treat the underlying cause of the disorders. For that, a person-centred approach is used:

1. Self-help and support groups, based on humanist and social learning approaches, then
2. Counselling, either cognitive behavioural therapy to help individuals think about what they are doing, and why and how to change their behaviour, or
3. Using a psychodynamic approach – psychotherapy or cognitive analytic therapy – may help them with interpersonal relationships that may be causing stress
4. Dietary counselling and family therapy may also be used
5. Occasionally a biological approach using antidepressants to alter the chemical balance in the brain may be used. Selective serotonin reuptake inhibitors (SSRIs) may be used to treat bulimia nervosa or binge eating.

Mood disorders

Mood disorders include prolonged depression, bipolar disorder (previously called manic depression) and generalised anxiety.

Prolonged depression with feelings of hopelessness that lasts for weeks or months can vary in severity. It can make people reluctant to do anything. At its most extreme it can lead to suicidal thoughts. It is often associated with a generalised sense of anxiety not related to one particular issue. A diagnosis of bipolar disorder may follow years of depression. Bipolar episodes swing between extremes – either total deep depression or excited manic behaviour – and each episode may last for days or weeks.

The causes and management of depression and anxiety have been mentioned earlier in the chapter. The causes of bipolar disorder are not fully understood but they are thought to be due to imbalance in neurotransmitters such

Classroom discussion (AC 4.1)

Choose one mental health condition.

1. Explain the signs and symptoms of the condition and how they impact on the individual concerned.
2. Discuss different approaches to managing the condition. Approaches should be considered from three different theoretical perspectives.
3. Explain how the approaches inform interventions for the identified mental health condition and likely outcomes from each intervention.

as noradrenaline, serotonin and dopamine in the brain. There is also thought to be a genetic link. Episodes may be triggered by stressful situations.

Managing bipolar episodes
Biological approaches use drugs such as lithium carbonate, anticonvulsant medicines and antipsychotic medicines – mood stabilisers which are taken long term. They are occasionally supplemented with antidepressants when required.

A humanistic approach focuses on person-centred care. Methods may include talking therapies such as cognitive behavioural therapy to help the person recognise the triggers for their episodes and reduce or avoid the triggers. This helps the individual to develop self-awareness and recognise when they may need help.

Psychodynamic approaches may include family therapy to help the family and the individual.

4.2 Analyse a psychological approach in relation to an identified mental health condition

Analyse means to break down, to consider different aspects. To demonstrate this, we will analyse one psychological approach to bipolar disorder. Bipolar disorder is managed by a combination of approaches: humanistic person-centred, psychodynamic, cognitive and biological approaches.

Important questions to ask when analysing include:

1. What are the advantages or benefits of this psychological approach?
2. What are the disadvantages or drawbacks of it?
3. Who are they advantages or disadvantages for?

The relevance of a person-centred approach for bipolar disorder

Advantages of the person-centred approach for the individual are that they:

- are treated as an individual with specific needs rather than one of a batch
- understand the management programme, and give informed consent
- are more likely to comply if they understand and give informed consent to management.

Advantages of the person-centred approach for care professionals are:

- care tailored to individual needs is more likely to succeed
- targeting resources such as time and skills avoids waste of resources.

Disadvantages of the person-centred approach for the individual are:

- this is not a quick fix – it takes time
- people must be comfortable talking about their problems.

Disadvantages of person-centred care for professionals are:

- it takes time to individualise management programmes
- it can be difficult for NHS staff to deliver with the resources they have.

Person-centred care may be offered in conjunction with medication such as lithium to stabilise moods, thus using a biological approach.

Relevant theoretical links which support the analysis

Person-centred care, developed by Rogers, puts the individual at the heart of the process, gives unconditional positive regard, empathy and remains congruent or consistent with the individual giving them space to explore and understand their condition. A cognitive approach helps them understand the disorder and a behaviourist approach helps them to recognise triggers for manic or depressive episodes. Psychodynamic approaches explore the relationship between mind and body and the impact of relationships on their health. Biological theories support the use of medication to restore the chemical balance in the brain and so control mood swings.

Evidence-based outcomes of the approach in relation to the identified mental health condition

The National Institute for Health and Care Excellence (NICE) Guideline on the Assessment and Management of Bipolar Disorder in Adults, Children and Young People in Primary and Secondary Care (Bipolar Update), was set up to 'evaluate the role of specific psychological, psychosocial and pharmacological interventions in the treatment of bipolar disorder and to evaluate the role of psychological and psychosocial interventions in combination with pharmacological interventions in the treatment of bipolar disorder' (Bipolar Update, 2014, p. 20). The guideline collated relevant research, evaluated the quality of the research and distilled this information into recommendations for the assessment and management of bipolar disorder.

According to this guide, research suggests that structured psychological interventions may have short- and long-term benefits improving symptoms and reducing the risk of relapse for those with bipolar depression. Research evidence shows that individual psychological interventions and collaborative care, group interventions, integrated cognitive and interpersonal therapy and psychoeducation for families were effective. There were no harmful effects and benefits continued after the interventions had ceased.

The guideline also states that 'evidence suggests that psychological interventions are cost effective in adults with bipolar disorder as they appear to improve clinical outcomes and result in potential cost-savings compared with standard care.' (Bipolar Update, 2014, p. 262)

Standard care with medication, based on a biological approach, had some limitations. Research shows that medication has side effects, requires close monitoring to adjust the level for the individual, and ceases to be effective when the person stops taking it.

Take it further

To investigate further, see the following web link: **www.nice.org.uk/guidance/cg185/evidence/full-guideline-193212829**

Command word activity

Analyse (AC 4.2)

Analyse one approach to an identified mental health condition.

1. Consider the benefits and drawbacks to the individual and to the health and care service.
2. Show how the psychological approach used is relevant to the signs and symptoms of the condition and how it links to psychological theory.
3. Include evidence-based outcomes of the approach applied to the identified mental health condition.

Classroom discussion (AC 4.2)

Take part in a group discussion to reflect work studied so far in relation to mental health.

1. Research information using at least three different sources and produce an outline of the symptoms of three different mental health conditions.
2. Choose one of the conditions you researched and describe different psychological approaches used in managing the condition.
3. How do psychologists' roles and responsibilities vary in each of the psychological approaches?
4. In your local area, what mental health support services are available?
5. Present your findings to the class.
6. Compile a guide to mental health services in your local area, based on the information you and your classmates have found.

Activity (AC 4.1, 4.2)

Z. is a lead singer in a boy band. He suffers from panic attacks and has had to cancel shows because of his extreme anxiety.

1. What psychological approaches might be most helpful so that he can manage the panic attacks? Explain your answer.
2. Which psychological approaches might be less helpful? Explain your answer.
3. Support your analysis with reference to at least three appropriate sources you have consulted and referenced in your work.

Check your understanding

1. Counselling is a talking therapy. Give three psychological theories that use counselling and say how each theory applies counselling differently.
2. What are three advantages of using a person-centred psychological approach?
3. When may talking therapies be combined with other therapy? Give at least two examples.

Read about it

Colman, A. (2015) *A Dictionary of Psychology.* 4th edition (Oxford Quick Reference), Oxford: OUP

Gross, R. (2015) *Psychology: The Science of Mind and Behaviour,* 7th edition, London: Hodder Education

National Collaborating Centre for Mental Health for National Institute for Health and Care Excellence, 'Bipolar disorder – The NICE guideline on the assessment and management of bipolar disorder in adults, children and young people in primary and secondary care, updated edition, National Clinical Guideline Number 185', (2014), The British Psychological Society and The Royal College of Psychiatrists. Available at www.nice.org.uk/guidance/cg185/evidence/full-guideline-193212829 (Accessed 10 September 2016)

Trotter, C. 'Pro-social modelling' in McIvor and G. Raynor, P. (2007), *Developments in Social Work with Offenders*, London, UK: Jessica Kingsley

Journal articles

Breen, G., Todd Webb, B., Butler, A.W., *et al.* (2011) 'A genome-wide significant linkage for severe depression on chromosome 3: The depression network study', *Am J Psychiatry*, vol.168, issue 8 pp. 840–7, (Online) http://dx.doi.org/10.1176/appi.ajp.2011.10091342 available at http://ajp.psychiatryonline.org/doi/abs/10.1176/appi.ajp.2011.10091342 (Accessed 10 September 2016)

Furnivall, J. (2011) 'Attachment-informed practice with looked-after children and young people', IRISS Insights, no.10. Available online at http://www.iriss.org.uk/resources/attachment-informed-practice-looked-after-children-and-young-people (Accessed 10 September 2016)

Polderman, T., Benyamin, B., De Leeuw, C., Sullivan, P., Van Bochoven, A., Visscher, P. and Posthuma, D. (2015) 'Meta-analysis of the heritability of human traits based on fifty years of twin studies', *Nature Genetics,* vol. 47, pp.702–9 (Online) doi:10.1038/ng.3285. Available at http://www.nature.com/ng/journal/v47/n7/abs/ng.3285.html (Accessed 10 September 2016)

Rebok, G., Ball, K., Guey, L., Jones, R., Kim, H.-Y., King, J., Marsiske, M., Morris, J., Tennstedt, S., Unverzagt, F., W. and Willis, S., (2014) 'Ten-year effects of the advanced cognitive training for independent and vital elderly cognitive training trial on cognition and everyday functioning in older adults', *Journal of the American Geriatrics Society*, vol. 62, 1, pp. 16–24 (Online) doi 10.1111/jgs.12607}. Available at http://onlinelibrary.wiley.com/doi/10.1111/jgs.12607/abstract (Accessed 10 September 2016)

Tiihonen, J., Rautiainen, M.-R., Ollila HM., Repo-Tiihonen, E., Virkkunen, M., Palotie, A., Pietiläinen, O., Kristiansson, K., Joukamaa, M., Lauerma, H., Saarela, J., Tyni, S., Vartiainen, H., Paananen, J., Goldman, D. and Paunio, T. (2015) 'Genetic background of extreme violent behavior', *Molecular Psychiatry,* vol. 20, pp.786–92(Online) doi:10.1038/mp.2014.130. Available at http://www.nature.com/mp/journal/v20/n6/abs/mp2014130a.html (Accessed 10 September 2016)

Websites

World Health Organization
who.int/about/definition

Autistic spectrum disorders fact sheets
www.autism-help.org/intervention-applied-behavioral-analysis.htm

Carl Rogers
www.bapca.org.uk/about/carl-rogers.html

BBS News – Health
www.bbc.co.uk/news/health-12297569

BBC News – Science & Environment
www.bbc.co.uk/news/science-environment-29760212

Shaping
www.behavioradvisor.com/Shaping.html

The British Psychological Society
www.bps.org.uk

Businessballs
www.businessballs.com

Counselling Directory
www.counselling-directory.org.uk/psychodynamic-therapy.html

www.helpguide.org/harvard/how-addiction-hijacks-the-brain

HIT Lab
www.hitl.washington.edu/projects/vrpain

Livestrong
www.livestrong.com/article/105661-behavior-modification

We need to talk
www.mind.org.uk/media/280583/We-Need-to-Talk-getting-the-right-therapy-at-the-right-time.pdf

NHS – Bipolar disorder
www.nhs.uk/Conditions/Bipolar-disorder

NHS – Cognitive behavioural therapy (CBT)
www.nhs.uk/Conditions/Cognitive-behavioural-therapy

NHS – Eating disorders
www.nhs.uk/conditions/Eating-disorders

NHS - Phobias
www.nhs.uk/conditions/Phobias

NHS – Overcoming addiction
www.nhs.uk/Livewell/addiction

NHS - Couch to 5K
www.nhs.uk/LiveWell/c25k

NHS – Stop smoking
www.nhs.uk/Livewell/smoking

NHS – Antidepressant paroxetine study
www.nhs.uk/news/2015/09September/Pages/Antidepressant-paroxetine-study-under-reported-data-on-harms.aspx

Parkinson's
www.parkinsons.org.uk/content/deep-brain-stimulation-surgery-parkinsons

Scientific film (1952) A two year old goes to hospital
www.robertsonfilms.info/2_year_old.htm

Unit HSC CM6: How will I be graded?

The table below shows what the learner must do to achieve each grading criterion. Learners must achieve all the criteria for a grade to be awarded (i.e. criteria D1 to D3 must be achieved to pass this unit assessment at grade D). A higher grade may not be awarded before a lower grade has been achieved in full, although component criteria of a higher grade may have been achieved.

Grade	Assessment criteria number	Assessment criteria	Assessment for learning / What you need to show
D1	1.1	Describe the role of psychology within health and social care.	Provide a description of the role of psychology within health and social care. The description must include how psychology contributes to health and social care.
D2	1.2	Describe types of psychologists and the roles of each within health and social care settings.	Describe more than one type of psychologist. Appropriate types of psychologists must be described. The roles of the psychologists described must be relevant to health and social care settings.
D3	2.1	Describe the concepts of nature and nurture in relation to human development and behaviour.	Provide a description of the concepts of nature and nurture. The description must show understanding of: <ul><li>the concepts of nature and nurture</li><li>the relationship to human development and behaviour.</li></ul>
D4		Show evidence of reading or use of sources.	There should be evidence of learners' reading or use of sources. Learners must use a minimum of two traceable references.
C1	2.2	Explain the nature versus nurture debate.	Explain: <ul><li>the principles of nature and nurture in relation to human development</li><li>reasons why nature and nurture is debated.</li></ul>
C2	3.1	Describe psychological theories.	Provide a description of more than one type of psychological theory, which may include: <ul><li>behaviourist theory</li><li>cognitive theory</li><li>social learning theory</li><li>other relevant theories.</li></ul>
C3		Show evidence of reading or use of sources with referencing relevant to the summary and description. Good use of vocabulary and grammar.	Use of referencing should show evidence of reading or use of sources. Vocabulary and grammar should be appropriate and accurate for purpose.
B1	3.2	Explain the impact of psychological theory on health and social care practice.	The explanation must demonstrate an accurate understanding of the impacts of psychological theory on health and social care practice. Relevant theoretical links to practice may be made to support the explanation.

Grade	Assessment criteria number	Assessment criteria	Assessment for learning / What you need to show
B2	3.3	Compare and contrast approaches to health and social care practice based on psychological theory.	Compare and contrast approaches to health and social care practice based on the psychological theories described in C2. The approaches should be examined in detail with similarities and differences shown. Links to C2.
B3		Show evidence of reading or use of sources. Referencing supports explanation.	Use of reading or use of sources should be shown through a range of relevant referencing. Referencing should be used appropriately to support explanations or compare and contrast.
A1	4.1	Discuss psychological approaches in the management of an identified mental health condition.	More than one psychological approach to management must be discussed. Discussion must identify the mental health condition and include: <ul><li>different approaches considered from more than one theoretical perspective</li><li>an account of how the approaches inform interventions for an identified mental health condition.</li></ul>
A2		Show evidence of wider background reading or use of sources. Referencing supports the discussion.	Wider background reading should be evident or a wide range of sources material should be used. Referencing should support discussion.
A*1	4.2	Analyse a psychological approach in relation to an identified mental health condition.	Analyse one approach to an identified mental health condition. The analysis must: <ul><li>demonstrate the relevance of the psychological approach</li><li>include relevant theoretical links which support the analysis</li><li>provide evidence-based outcomes of the approach in relation to the identified mental health condition.</li></ul> Links to B2 and A1.
A*2		Show evidence of a range of background reading or use of sources used selectively.	Learners should show the ability to consider or explore relevant issues which contribute to the analysis. An extensive range of background reading or use of sources should be used selectively and cited appropriately.

HSC CM7
Sociological Perspectives in Health and Social Care

Learning outcomes

LO1: Understand sociological perspectives in relation to health and social care

1.1 Summarise the sociological approach to the study of human behaviour

1.2 Describe sociological perspectives

1.3 Describe in relation to health and social care:
- social realism
- social constructionism
- labelling theory

1.4 Describe the biomedical, social and ecological models of health and well-being

LO2: Understand the social patterns and trends of health and illness in the population

2.1 Explain the social classes recognised in own home nation

2.2 Explain patterns of health across social classes

2.3 Explain how demographic data is used in planning health and social care services

2.4 Explain sociological explanations for the patterning of mortality and morbidity rates in the demographic groups:
- gender
- age
- ethnicity
- area of residence

About this unit

In this unit we explore what is meant by a sociological approach and how such an approach aids our understanding of human behaviour. We examine sociological perspectives, their role in health and social care and we examine different models of health and well-being. This unit also focuses on patterns and trends in health and illness and the link between these patterns and social class. We explore the use of population data in planning for health and care services and consider reasons for trends and inequalities in health care.

LO1: Understand sociological perspectives in relation to health and social care

The term 'Society' refers to a group of people. Sociology is the study of society. A sociological approach to health would look at the causes of ill-health in a population and pick out trends and patterns of disease in that population.

Ecological Systems Theory (developed by Uri Bronfenbrenner) describes five layers of influences on an individual, from the immediate to wider environment. The theory identifies five levels as follows:

1. Microsystems are the immediate environment, for example the home and family circumstances.

2. Mesosystems are the interaction between microsystems.

3. Exosystems are connections between two or more settings, which may not contain the individual but affect him or her. For example, a parent who works long hours resulting in a child being left for extended periods with a childminder – the child bonds with the childminder but has a weaker bond with their mother.

4. Macrosystems include cultural patterns and values, political and economic systems. For

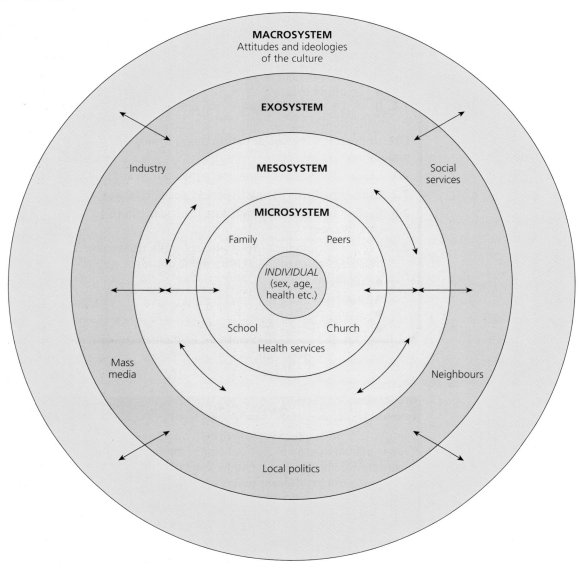

Figure 7.1 The Ecological Systems Theory

example, a political system that does not allow free speech may cause individuals to be wary in expressing their views.

5. The chronosystem includes changes in the systems over time. It might be a change in family structure due to death or divorce, change in home or school, or even a change in country. Changes in political and economic systems might include the outbreak of war or famine.

1.1 Summarise the sociological approach to the study of human behaviour

Sociological approaches consider issues such as social cohesion, norms and values. Social cohesion is the willingness of groups to co-operate and form a united group. The 'glue' that holds groups together is shared norms and values. Norms are ways of behaving; for example, we always shake hands when we meet someone. Values are what the group believes to be important, for example, loyalty to group members.

Culture and subcultures

In sociological terms, 'culture' refers to the ideas and behaviour shared by a society, for example 'British culture'. For some people, British culture includes supporting a football team, for others it includes eating fish and chips and for others it includes knowing Shakespeare's plays or the rules of cricket.

Subcultures are smaller cultures within a larger culture; for example, gang culture is characterised by violence, teenage membership and group loyalty. It is geographically based, and being in the wrong area can mean death for gang members. The Mayor of London's Office for Policing and Crime published figures for gang-related crime. Tower Hamlets and Hackney had the largest number of gang-flagged offences for the year ending August 2016. Hackney had 171 and Tower Hamlets had 191 (Mayor of London's Office 2016).

Just as gangs are a subculture of British culture, so too are 'Baby Boomers': the generation born between 1946 and 1964. They are characterised by an ageing group who grew up in an era of protests and demonstrations for equality. They value family and often are caring for elderly parents while still supporting their grown-up children. They share values of hard work, promoting positive social changes and they have a social conscience towards others. Baby Boomers and gangs have different values and norms but both are subcultures within British culture.

Social institutions, such as family, education, religion and the justice system, share a common set of norms or behaviours and values that are intended to shape a person into becoming a member of society.

The family is the first social institution that children experience. In the family they learn how to speak, how to eat and how to dress themselves. Toilet training is usually completed before children start school. In addition to gaining basic physical independence they learn the social norms of British society, saying 'please' and 'thank you', taking turns and being unselfish.

Education is a social institution which teaches children how to be a good citizen. It teaches acceptable social behaviour and a common body of knowledge that every member of that society is expected to know, for example how to read and write the language of that society.

Religion is another social institution where norms and values are transmitted with the aim of influencing how a person interacts as part of the wider society. Values such as generosity, and behaviours such as sharing, giving to charity, and helping others are transmitted through rituals, ceremonies and preaching. These values aid social cohesion. Norms or ways of behaving are ritualised; for example, passing a collection plate round for donations during a Christian church service, or Muslims giving Zakat, a 2.5 per cent wealth tax, to charity each year instils the value of caring for those less fortunate than oneself.

The justice system with police, probation officers, lawyers and judges forms another social institution to uphold the values of law and order and instil the norms of abiding by the law.

Social roles and status are embedded in institutions; for example, a teacher has a specific social role – to educate their pupils.

Teachers have responsibilities associated with that role; for example, they must be a good role model, plan learning to help students develop, keep order in the classroom and motivate students. Their status is linked to this role and they are usually regarded with respect in society. A teacher who turned up to class drunk and who swore in front of students would lose status and would probably lose their job for behaving in a way that was not consistent with their role. Social roles are usually based on a hierarchy, so the head teacher has a higher status than a newly qualified teacher. The head teacher's role carries more responsibility, has higher status and pay because they set the rules for the whole school, monitor teachers and pupils and ensure that the school meets the requirements of society.

Take it further

Gangs are subcultures. Follow this link to find out more about gang areas in London.

https://www.london.gov.uk/what-we-do/mayors-office-policing-and-crime-mopac/data-and-research/crime%20/gangs-dashboard

For an academic view of social institutions from a famous American university follow this link. Prepare for academic jargon!

http://plato.stanford.edu/entries/social-institutions/

Command word activity

Summarise (AC 1.1)

1. Give the key points of the sociological approach to studying human behaviour by briefly summarising each of these:
   a. Social cohesion
   b. Norms and values
   c. Culture and subcultures
   d. Social institutions
   e. Social roles and status.
2. Make this into a matching game. Write the title on one card and the meaning on another, then jumble them up and try to match the title with the summary.

1.2 Describe sociological perspectives

Sociological perspectives are ways that sociologists look at aspects of society. Some key sociological perspectives include Functionalism, Symbolic Interactionism, Marxism, Feminism and Conflict Theory.

Functionalism

Functionalism looks at the big picture, macro systems and, in particular, how social norms and institutions work together in order to make a society function. The family teaches a child values such as what is right and what is not; for example, we do not take other people's things. The education system continues to instil these values and the justice system enforces major norms such as not stealing.

Critics of this theory say that it does not explain how societies change. Other critics say that it does not account for inconsistencies in society; for example, the values of equality of opportunity are accepted as values we wish to promote in our society, yet some people are not given equal opportunities in education, health or social care. Women still earn less than men and have poorer career prospects. Functionalism presents a view of society that is harmonious and ignores conflict, for example class conflict.

Symbolic Interactionism

Symbolic Interactionism theory says that we act based on our understanding of the world around us. Max Weber, the sociologist, suggested that symbolic meanings bind people together in groups. Think of a Manchester United football shirt. Fans instantly recognise it and form a favourable opinion of someone wearing it. They attribute a positive meaning to the symbol and may chat to the wearer of the shirt. They attribute a meaning to the symbol and act accordingly. A Manchester City fan might interpret the symbol unfavourably, might feel uncomfortable if they were at the 'wrong' end of the stands and move to be with people wearing their symbols, Manchester City scarves. Symbols and gestures are given meaning and the meaning leads to action.

Here is another example: A woman wears a burqa covering her body and head but leaving her face uncovered. In some countries this symbol is interpreted favourably as showing modesty. In other countries this symbol is interpreted as a link to terrorism, seen as a threat, and banned. In France in 2016, policemen stood over a woman wearing a headscarf, trousers and tunic on a beach. They issued a fine for not wearing 'an outfit respecting good morals and secularism' and forced her to remove some of her clothing. The fact that she covered up her body in a place where everyone else had minimal clothing was interpreted as a threat and instigated action by the police.

National flags and religious symbols such as the Cross or Crescent are given such powerful meanings that sometimes they are used to rally people to war.

Marxism

Marxism is a theory originally developed by Karl Marx in the nineteenth century and focuses on economics and power. He suggested that a capitalist society is made up of the proletariat or workers who give their labour in exchange for wages, and the bourgeoisie who own the means of production such as land, factories and mines.

Marx suggested there is conflict between the proletariat and the bourgeoisie. In the Communist Manifesto, written by Marx and Friedrich Engels, Marx urged the proletariat to rebel. Later developments in Marxism have adopted the terms 'base' and 'superstructure' instead of proletariat and bourgeoisie. The base consists of the means of production, for example, factories, tools, raw materials, and also consists of the relations of production such as the workers, the owners, capital, and assets such as property. The superstructure is anything that is not directly related to production such as education, law, art, culture, religion and family. (You may recognise these as 'social institutions'.) Marxism suggests that the base shapes and maintains the superstructure and that the superstructure in turn maintains and shapes the base. An example of this might be demand from workers in unions for a minimum wage shaping the superstructure, and a law is passed enforcing payment of the minimum wage thus maintaining the workforce.

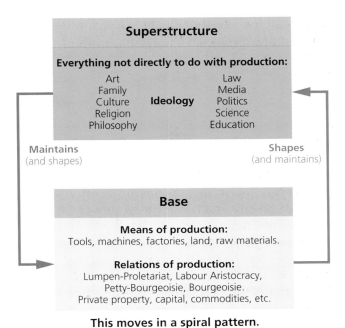

Figure 7.2 The relationship between base and superstructure

Feminism

Feminism examines society in terms of gender and power. Feminist theory suggests that there is a power imbalance between men and women. The United Nations Human Development Report (2015) shows the greatest gender inequality in Yemen, Niger and Chad, where women are more likely to be unemployed and live in poverty. Feminists look at inequality of opportunity between men and women, for example why there are fewer female members of Parliament than there are male members, or why in some societies it is assumed that a woman will stay at home to look after the children and the man will spend time developing his career. The 2011 Census shows economic inactivity (unemployment) rates for women were 28 per cent whereas for men the rate was 18 per cent. This was the case across all ethnic groups. Feminists examine gender oppression, where power is used to control women, for example in honour killings and in domestic violence.

Feminists also look at inequalities within gender, for example why some women have fewer opportunities than other women because of their race, class, ethnicity and age. According to the 2011 Census, economic inactivity, not in paid employment, rates were highest for women who were Arab (64%) Bangladeshi (61%), Pakistani (60%) and Gypsy or Irish Traveller (60%).

Conflict Theory

Conflict Theory looks at the problems in society. This is in contrast with Functionalism which assumes harmonious systems in society. Conflict Theory examines unequal power distribution in society and explains how such unequal power distribution can lead to change. Power bases may be economic, political or physical. A political power base is where a political system keeps one section of the population in power over another section. Apartheid in South Africa was based on racial segregation. Political power created laws governing where people could live, who they could marry and what jobs they could do. This in turn limited their access to economic power. The system was enforced by physical power in the form of police brutality. Eventually, the system was challenged and peacefully changed.

In 1956, C. Wright Mills, a sociologist, published *The Power Elite*, a classic text of sociology. In the study he outlined how a small power elite in politics, business and the military shaped the conditions of life in America to serve their own interests. They used their power to influence the 'superstructure' which in turn influenced the 'base' (Marxian terms) creating a consumer society heavily influenced by the media. People spend time watching television or on social media which influences their choice of what to wear, what to eat, how to raise their children, whether to own a gun. Meanwhile the powerful elite become wealthy by investing in producing material to meet the needs of the masses.

Conflict theorists would point to continuing inequalities in America as evidence supporting Mills' study. According to a report by Stanford University, the top 10 per cent of households controlled 68.2 per cent of the total wealth in 1983 and 73.1 per cent of the total wealth in 2007. By 2015 the top 1 per cent in America owned 40 per cent of the country's wealth. Conflict theorists highlight the increasing wealth of the elite while basic health and education services are run down, creating a disadvantaged underclass in society.

Command word activity

Describe (AC 1.2)

1. Describe these sociological perspectives:
   a. Functionalism
   b. Symbolic Interactionism
   c. Marxism
   d. Feminism.
2. How do they relate to health and social care?

1.3 Describe sociological concepts in relation to health and social care

Social realism

Social realism suggests that there are underlying structures in society that exist separately to individuals. Social realism explores social structures often through art or literature. The graffiti artist Banksy expresses his political and social view of society by creating murals in public spaces to draw attention to social issues.

Figure 7.3 Social realism

In 'Let them eat crack' he depicts a rat with a case full of money. The umbrella and tie refer to city investors. The words hark back to the time of the French Revolution, when ordinary people were starving. On being told about the lack of basic food such as bread, Queen Marie-Antoinette is reputed to have said 'Let them eat cake', showing her lack of understanding of the plight of the poor. Banksy is making the point that inequality in society leaves the poor with no hope except to take drugs. It is interesting to note that after Marie-Antoinette's remark, the French workers rose up and guillotined the aristocracy including Marie-Antoinette. We do not know whether Banksy intends to suggest revolution, but the link between inequality now and inequality then is made clear by this mural.

Social constructionism

Social constructionism combines sociology and communication theory. It suggests that we construct or build shared ideas of how the world works. These constructs seem obvious or 'common sense' to those who share them. (Constructs are like the schema Piaget suggests that babies form.) One social construct was that 'women should stay home, care for the children and keep house'. Women were seen as dependent on men. This construct persisted for much of the nineteenth and first half of the twentieth century. The Baby Boomer generation of women growing up in the 1960s overturned this social construct and now women and men share parenting and work responsibilities. The new social construct is that men and women are equal partners in a marriage.

Labelling theory

Emile Durkheim first suggested that labelling satisfied a need for some sections of society with power and influence to control the behaviour of others. Stereotyping involves not seeing an individual as a person but prejudging them based on fixed ideas. Stereotyping leads to labelling in an attempt to control; for example, in recent years, labelling someone as a 'migrant' has come to infer in some subcultures that they are unwanted in this country.

The number of attacks on Polish people has risen following the vote to leave the European Union. One example of this was Arek Jozwik a Polish worker in Harlow. In August 2016, he was punched and later died, allegedly because he was a migrant. Migrants have been stereotyped and labelled by those wishing to control the number of foreigners coming to Britain.

Stereotyping, labelling and stigma are linked. Stigma defined by the sociologist Erving Goffman, refers to a behaviour or quality or reputation that is seen as socially undesirable and causes an individual to be rejected by that society. If we consider mental health, social realists would say that there is a range of mental health which gives rise to behaviour that some might consider unusual but that many people with mental health issues function effectively in society. Social constructivists might suggest that what we consider mental ill-health is a construct of society and can vary in different societies. A person who hears voices may be respected as a saint in one society and labelled as 'mad' in another. Labelling theory would look at the effect of labelling someone mentally ill and how that label excluded them from fully participating in society, for example by excluding them from employment.

Attention Deficit Hyperactivity Disorder (ADHD) is a collection of symptoms which include inattentiveness, hyperactivity and impulsiveness. Children may be diagnosed with ADHD when they start school. Social realists might say that being impulsive, very energetic and having short attention spans is characteristic of many children. They would point to child developmental theories that suggest children are impulsive until they mature and learn to understand consequences. They may point to communities that give children no outlet for excess energy because there is no safe place to play outdoors. Social realists would argue that exposure to television, video and other media encourages short attention spans, typical of ADHD and we are socialising children not to concentrate too long.

Social constructivists would suggest that our concept of childhood has changed and that what was once considered 'normal' child behaviour is now consider 'abnormal'. A few generations ago, children would spend more time out of doors, engaged in physical activity. Now they stay indoors and we have different expectations of children. Social constructivists would argue that we are 'constructing' the disorder of ADHD in many cases to account for what might be considered 'normal' in other societies. They would point to the fact that 10 per cent of American children aged 4 to17 have been diagnosed with ADHD. In the UK, for children between the ages of 5 and 15 years the rate is 3.62 per cent of boys and 0.85 per cent of girls with ADHD.

Social constructivists would suggest the difference in rates between the UK and USA is evidence that childhood is socially constructed differently in these two societies. People with little understanding of ADHD may stereotype hyperactive restless children and label them as 'naughty'. This label then may become self-fulfilling as the child behaves in the way others expect. (Those who are familiar with the psychologist B.F. Skinner's work on reward and punishment may also recognise that a 'naughty' child gets attention, which rewards that behaviour and encourages them to repeat it.)

Take it further

Check back to Unit HSC CM6 and read about B.F. Skinner's theory of operant conditioning.

Key terms

Stigma a behaviour or quality or reputation that is seen as socially undesirable and causes an individual to be rejected by that society

Stereotyping not seeing an individual as a person but prejudging them based on fixed ideas

Command word activity

Describe (AC 1.3)

1. Describe these terms and give an example for each from health and social care:
   a. Social realism
   b. Social constructionism
   c. Labelling theory.

1.4 Describe the biomedical, social and ecological models of health and well-being

The biomedical model of health

The biomedical model of health dominates our health service, attracting funding and providing an established career structure for many. The biomedical model is characterised by a focus on physical health. The aim is to cure so that the individual is free of disease. The slogan 'A pill for every ill' is associated with this model. The focus is on specific body systems such as the circulatory system, or the digestive system. This model uses a pharmacological approach with medicines and if those fail, uses surgery to cure the patient. This model has its uses; for example, if someone has a burst appendix, antibiotic cover followed by surgery is the most effective method of treatment. A breast lump may be cancer and is best removed. The biomedical model is, however, not the most effective way of treating all conditions.

One of the criticisms of this model is that there has been an over-reliance on antibiotics. Microorganisms develop resistance to antibiotics. We now have drug-resistant Tuberculosis (TB) and gonorrhoea as well as Methicillin-resistant Staphylococcus aureus (MRSA). Another criticism of the biomedical model is that some disorders cannot be cured. The biomedical model is not helpful for conditions such as autism, inoperable cancer or dementia. A further criticism is that the biomedical model focuses on one system. Doctors specialise in systems such as the cardiovascular system or the nervous system and do not always consider the interplay of different aspects of the body on each other. SPRINT, a study in America to reduce blood pressure more quickly by giving more drugs, was halted because the researchers had not considered the side effects on other body systems. Lowering the blood pressure so quickly caused fainting in some, and risked kidney damage in others.

The social model of health

A social model of health developed in the 1970s and 1980s when it was realised that the medical model of health did not address all health issues. The social model focuses on health promotion and maintaining good health. It implies that for health to improve, change must happen in the wider influences on health such as social, economic, cultural and environmental factors. People cannot be healthy if they are socially isolated or lack sufficient income to feed and clothe their children. Cultural factors may cause them to be the target of discrimination. Environmental factors such as damp housing cause respiratory disease. The social model of health aims to reduce inequalities, and empower communities and individuals by increasing access to health care and increasing collaboration between different health and care sectors. CCGs in England plan health and social care in the community based on this model.

The social model of disability stated that society disables people, by making everyday living difficult for them. A train platform that can only be accessed by steps disables those in wheelchairs and parents with pushchairs. Failure to make adjustments for disabilities in the workplace denies people a chance to earn their own living and keeps them dependent on benefits. Adjustments in society enable all. This model has been used effectively to empower people with disabilities, increase their access to health care and help them to live independently. In the field of mental health a study in 2010 by Peter Beresford, Mary Nettle and Rebecca Perring found that the dominant medical model of mental illness was influential in shaping negative attitudes, terminology led to labelling and stigma thus creating barriers for mental health service users. Some people with mental health issues did not feel they had a disability but considered the social model of health a more empowering approach than the medical model.

One of the benefits of the social model for planners is that keeping people healthy is cheaper than trying to cure them. Increasing access to information and empowering individuals to manage their own health ensures that services are targeted where needed and there is less waste. For the individual, the social model approach ensures that people experience a better quality of life. There are, however, some problems with this model. Not everyone wants to take responsibility for their own health; changing lifestyles, taking more exercise and losing weight are not easy. A further problem is that not all health conditions respond to this approach. A person with multiple sclerosis may have a better quality of life by being able to work and live independently but they will still have the disorder.

The ecological model of health

Ecological models of health, such as the model described at the start of this unit, are based on four principles. These are:

- many levels of factors influence health behaviours
- influences interact across levels
- interventions across different levels are more effective than interventions at one level
- ecological models work best when focused on one specific behaviour.

Here is an example: Sue is a middle-aged working mother of teenagers. She has to lose weight for health reasons. She may be supported by her daughter who wants to learn how to cook healthy food. A local gym may have a special discount for her workplace. Diet and exercise are more likely to succeed if changes at work enable Sue to take a lunch break. If she joins a group preparing for a charity run, this additional influence increases the chance of successfully losing weight. Interventions at all levels should focus on increasing activity and eating a healthy diet. In this way each behaviour reinforces the other.

Just as multiple levels can influence an individual's health positively, they can also negatively affect health, as shown in Figure 7.4 on p. 162, where each of the factors could lead to low self-esteem, eating disorders and/or poor mental health.

One advantage of the ecological model is that it combines approaches on several levels to reinforce behaviour change. One disadvantage of this approach is the difficulty in co-ordinating interventions at different levels and the difficulty in personalising such an approach. It can only be a mass approach to health improvement.

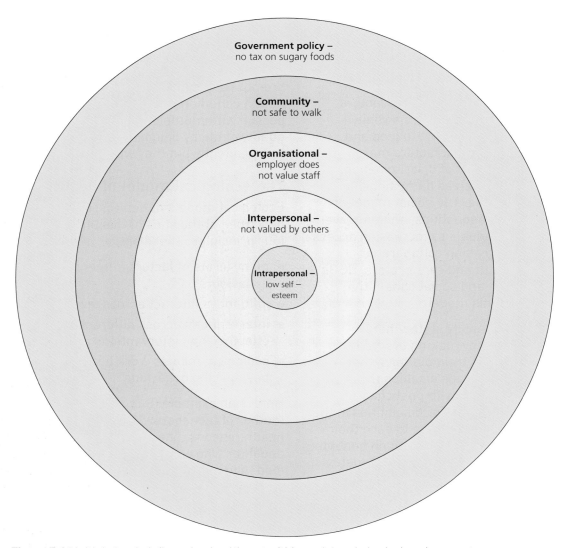

Figure 7.4 Multiple levels influencing health, set within social and physical environments

Command word activity

Describe (AC 1.4)

1. Work in pairs to prepare a presentation to describe these models of health and well-being:
   a. Biomedical
   b. Social
   c. Ecological.
2. Describe how they relate to health and social care.

Key terms

Sociological approach the way that sociologists tackle an issue. A sociological approach looks at groups of people. This contrasts with a psychological approach which looks at individuals

Social realism is about seeing things as they are, highlighting structures that often disadvantage the weakest such as how addiction keeps people poor, while others profit from drug sales

Social constructionism suggests that we build ideas of how the world works which seem 'common sense' to those who share them

Labelling theory a way for some sections of society with power and influence to control the behaviour of others

Case scenario (AC 1.1, 1.2)

M. is fifteen. He respects his older brother who is second in command of a street gang. All gang members have a tattoo to show their rank. The leader J has a gun and has just come out of prison. Any rival gang member straying into their territory is attacked. M wants to join the gang but has to prove his loyalty by stabbing someone.

1. How may a sociologist explain this gang? Consider social cohesion, norms and values; culture and subcultures; the gang's relationship to social institutions; their social roles and status.
2. Which sociological perspectives may be relevant in understanding gang culture and why?

Classroom discussion (AC 1.4)

1. What do you understand by 'health' and 'ill-health'?
2. How may the biomedical, social and ecological models of health each explain and treat ill-health?
3. What similarities and differences are there between the different models?

Work in threes, each person focusing on one model to answer the questions.

Share your findings.

Check your understanding

1. What encourages cohesion in societies?
2. Explain briefly: Functionalism, Symbolic Interactionism, Marxism, Feminism and Conflict Theory.
3. Describe how these relate to health and social care; social realism, social constructionism, labelling theory.
4. What are religion, education, and the judicial system examples of?
5. Which model of health focuses on the biological causes of ill-health and aims to cure people using medicines or surgery?
6. Which model of health and well-being considers that a person's health and well-being is influenced by government policy decisions, by local communities and by personal relationships?

Command word activity

Evidence

You are preparing an information pack for care assistants who are interested in becoming social workers.

Use at least two different sources to find out more about:

- Social realism
- Social constructionism
- Labelling theory.

Refer to these sources in your descriptions. Use the Harvard reference system and include these sources in your reference list at the end of your work.

LO2: Understand the social patterns and trends of health and illness in the population

Patterns and trends emerge when we examine populations rather than individuals. Trends are measured over time. For instance, according to Public Health England more people are becoming obese; there is an increasing trend of obesity. In 1993 13.2 per cent of men were obese but by 2014 it was 24.3 per cent. Based on this trend, it is predicted that by 2050, 60 per cent of men will be obese.

Some diseases follow patterns. For example, rates of meningitis fluctuate from year to year and vary with the type of meningitis. Meningitis C is in decline, but a new strain, Meningitis W, is increasing and is deadly. Meningitis also occurs in patterns related to place, time and people:

1. The UK has more cases of meningitis than other EU countries.
2. It is seasonal, with most cases in the winter months.
3. It attacks all age groups but is more serious in children and adolescents.

Health inequalities persist. The Marmot Review (2010) reported that in England people living in the poorest neighbourhoods will, on average, die seven years earlier than people living in the richest neighbourhoods. Different theories attempt to explain why there are inequalities in health.

The **artefact theory** says that any link between ill-health and class is an artefact, produced by the methods we use to measure society. This theory suggests that there may be health inequalities and there may be class inequalities, but health inequalities are not caused by a person's class. The fact that health inequalities persist even though fewer people today are in manual jobs supports this theory.

Natural and social selection theory suggests that healthy individuals 'rise to the top'. They are fitter, more able to take up opportunities and more likely to get better jobs. Those with poor health, unable to work, and on the margins of society will migrate to the lower classes, as they do not have the income to maintain a healthier lifestyle.

Cultural explanations for health inequalities focus on shared norms and attitudes to health. According to Thomas Abel (2008), cultural capital and economic resources are the deciding factors in determining people's health chances and their choices. Cultural capital includes social assets such as education, intelligence, style of speech and appearance. Those who are better informed and have a network of contacts have more health choices.

Deprivation, the lack of necessities, is one explanation for health inequalities and there appears to be some data to support this theory. According to a report by the Office of National Statistics based on the 2011 Census, 'Men and women (aged 40 to 44) living in the most deprived areas are around four times more likely to have "Not Good" health compared to their equivalent in the least deprived areas'.

Material or structural explanations of health inequalities suggest that overcrowded housing, poor diet, poor education, insecure employment and low pay have a direct impact on health. The structural explanation is that wide social inequality leaves those at the bottom with fewer choices about their health.

The sick role, first described by Talcott Parsons in 1951, describes social expectations about the rights and responsibilities of those who are ill. The sick have the right not to be blamed for being sick and can have time off work, but they also have responsibilities. They must see the doctor and try to get better. If they do not conform, they are censured; for example, smokers are blamed for bringing lung cancer on themselves. In some cultures people reject the sick role, because they fear being labelled 'weak'; for example, Hillary Clinton continued working with pneumonia during the run up to US presidential elections in 2016.

Key term

Artefact theory any link between ill-health and class is artificially produced by the methods we use to measure

2.1 Explain the social classes recognised in own home nation

Social class is a way of dividing society according to social and economic status. Other societies may divide according to caste or religion, but in the UK we divide society primarily by wealth and social standing.

The common three stratum or layer model of upper, middle, and lower classes, is frequently used.

The upper class are rich, connected by birth, form an elite and have power based on inherited wealth and connections.

The middle class are educated, but earn their wealth rather than inherit it. They may be socially mobile and form the professional class. They have power based on knowledge.

The lower class are those working for low pay and an underclass of unemployed people. They may receive benefits from the state. They have little power and few choices.

There are problems with this three stratum model. It does not account for social mobility; for example, someone from the lower class who becomes a doctor in the middle class.

Key term

Social class divisions in society based on economic, social and cultural factors

The Great British Class Survey (2011) conducted by the BBC was analysed by academics and the results were published in the journal *Sociology*. This model is based on work by Pierre Bourdieu in 1984 and recognises the wide differences in society and the fragmentation of the middle classes. Based on a combination of economic capital (a person's income, the value of their home and savings), cultural capital (their cultural interests and activities), and their social capital (the number and status of people they know), data indicated seven classes. These are:

1. The wealthy 'elite' with high levels of all three capitals, especially economic capital

2. Established middle class with high levels of all three capitals but less economic capital than the elite

3. Technical experts with high economic capital but less social and cultural capital

4. 'New affluent' – a young group with medium levels of economic capital and higher levels of cultural and social capital

5. Emergent service workers with low economic capital but high levels of 'emerging' cultural capital and social capital, a young group

6. Traditional working class with low social, economic and cultural capital, an ageing group

7. A 'precariat' with very low levels of all three types of capital and insecure lives

Social class is important however we measure it because, according to the World Health Organization and the Marmot Review, there is a social gradient in health – the lower a person's social position, the worse their health.

Command word activity

Explain (AC 2.1)

1. What is meant by the term social class?
2. Explain the factors considered and the structure of at least two systems of social classification.

2.2 Explain patterns of health across social classes

One way of measuring health is by looking at how long people live, and how long they live with good health. The evidence we have so far relates to the older method of social classification. As yet we have little data relating to health and the seven category social classification system.

Inequality starts before birth, with pregnant women in lower social classes having poorer health. Social class continues to affect health and life chances. The Black Report (1988) highlighted the link between social class and health. In 2010, *Fair Society Healthy Lives* (The Marmot Review) highlighted continuing inequality in health,

'in the wealthiest part of London, one ward in Kensington and Chelsea, a man can expect to live to 88 years, while a few kilometres away in Tottenham Green, one of the capital's poorer wards, male life expectancy is 71'. (Marmot, Executive Summary, 2010, p. 29)

Social class is linked to patterns of health and disease. Not only do poor people die earlier, but in their shorter lives they experience more disabilities than people in the higher social classes. The poor suffer from diseases of poverty. Infections such as tuberculosis (TB) occur more in the most deprived populations and spread rapidly where there is overcrowding and low resistance. In 2013, 70 per cent of cases were resident in the 40 per cent most deprived areas (Public Health England 2014). Diseases of affluence such as obesity, Type 2 diabetes, and cardiovascular disease are chronic, non-communicable and caused by lifestyle factors such as a high sugar and fat diet and lack of exercise. These occur in societies where calorific intake is greater than required, and where there is less manual labour.

Culture and health

Cultural factors can create health inequalities; for example, girls subjected to female genital mutilation are more likely to have problems in childbirth and to have problems of incontinence than girls who have not had this procedure done. Changing cultural norms in the UK have resulted in an increase in alcohol consumption by women of all ages, and as a result they are experiencing alcohol related diseases previously seen more often in men.

Gender

Women live longer than men. In the UK from 2010 to 2012, newborn males could expect to live 78.8 years and females 82.6 years. The number of people aged 100 and over in the UK has risen by 65 per cent over the last ten years. Seven out of ten of these are women. Although women live longer, they have poorer health in their later years than do men.

Age

In 2015, for those aged between 5 and 49, accidents such as road traffic accidents and suicides were the most common cause of deaths, with men three times more likely to die this way than women.

In 2015, for men and women aged 50 and over, cancer was the commonest cause of death, closely followed by heart disease and strokes. Respiratory diseases were the next biggest killer.

Of those aged 80 and over in 2015, twice as many women than men died of disorders such as dementia and Alzheimer's disease.

Ethnicity influences health

According to Diabetes UK, young people of African–Caribbean, Black African, Chinese or South Asian origin have a higher risk of developing Type 2 diabetes.

Sickle cell trait, which confers some resistance to malaria, is present in people who may have their family origins in the Middle East, India and the Eastern Mediterranean or who may be Black African, Black Caribbean or Black British. If managed well, sickle cell trait does not cause health problems but if ignored it can at times cause severe anaemia.

Area of residence

Health is related to where a person lives. There is a North/South divide in health, with people in the North having poorer health than those in the South of England. According to the Office for National Statistics, in 2012–14, at birth, females in Richmond upon Thames in the South could expect to live to 72.2 years in good health, while females in Manchester could expect only 54.4 years of good health. Men experience the same North/South inequality in health, with men in Wokingham in the South experiencing 70.5 years of good health compared with men in Blackpool who could expect only 55 years of good health.

The North East had the highest mortality rate in England in 2015.

Command word activity

Explain (AC 2.2)

1. Using examples, explain in detail how patterns of health vary between social classes. Include an explanation of health inequalities in relation to social class and give examples to support what you say.
2. Explain how cultural influences may affect health and give examples to support what you say.
3. Explain how factors such as gender, age, ethnicity and area of residence may be linked to patterns of health. Give examples.

2.3 Explain how demographic data is used in planning health and social care services

Demographic data is information that tells us about a population such as, for example, the number of people in each age group, their gender, their occupations and their income. We get this data from different surveys such as the Census, or surveys by not-for-profit organisations such as Joseph Rowntree Foundation. GPs too have to notify Public Health about certain diseases such as tuberculosis.

One of the main surveys providing data is the Census, an official survey of a population. In the UK the Census is conducted every ten years. Data is used as a basis for planning health and care services. Census data from 2011 shows that people in the South of England have higher disability-free life expectancy than those in the North and report being healthier. For those planning health and care services, this is useful information. It means they may have to put more resources into the North to support those with greater health needs.

Analysing population size and structure in relation to fertility, mortality, and migration helps planners. Demographic data gives us information about rates of fertility, mortality and migration. The Office for National Statistics publishes data as bulletins. According to the statistical bulletin *Births in England and Wales: 2015* there is a slight increase in the number of babies being born, the average age of mothers is getting older, and the total fertility rate is decreasing. Families are getting smaller. Also, 27.5 per cent of live births were to mothers born outside the UK, the highest level recorded which links with patterns of migration.

Take it further

Visit the Office for National Statistics for details of the Census at **www.ons.gov.uk**

Visit Public Health England for data on health inequalities at **www.gov.uk/government/organisations/public-health-england**

The statistical bulletin *Deaths Registered in England and Wales: 2015* tells us about death rates, causes of death by sex and age, by where people lived. In 2015 death rates increased, with most deaths occurring between January and March, when there was a rise in flu cases. This links with reports of hospitals being inundated with flu cases at the time. The trend in previous years has been for people to live longer as a result of better diet and lifestyles and medical advances. Over half the deaths are caused by cancer and circulatory diseases.

Demographic data tells us about migration, the movement of people within the UK and between the UK and other countries. The ONS statistical bulletin *Migration Statistics Quarterly Report: August 2016* shows that the number of people coming into the country minus the number leaving was 327,000 (down slightly from the previous year). The number of people coming in (immigrants) was down slightly to 633,000 and the number emigrating was down slightly to 306,000. The trend is broadly flat.

Such information helps planners. People coming into the country for work pay tax and help to fill the gap in working age population in the 30–40 age group. If older people leave the country, for example to retire to Spain, planners can reduce the resources allocated to their care. If younger people with growing families come into the country, more services for families and children are needed.

Key term

Demographic data information that tells us about a population

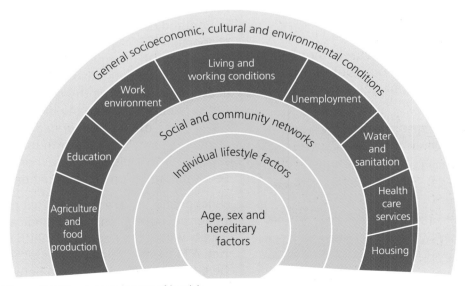

Figure 7.5 The determinants of health

Command word activity

Explain (AC 2.3)

1. Explain, using examples, how demographic data is used in planning health and social care services. Include data on mortality, morbidity and fertility from the Census, from Public Health England and one other source.
2. Explain how this information could be used to plan health and social care services.

2.4 Explain sociological explanations for the patterning of mortality and morbidity rates in demographic groups

According to the World Health Organization:

'The social determinants of health are the conditions in which people are born, grow, live, work and age'

Source: www.who.int/social_determinants/sdh_definition/en/

Dahlgren and Whitehead (1992) described the factors that influence our health – the social determinants of health. This idea fed into the Acheson Report and influenced government thinking. The Marmot Review (2010) focused on how to tackle inequalities in health caused by these social determinants. According to this, age, sex and hereditary factors have an immediate impact on the individual's health.

Individual lifestyle factors, such as whether to smoke, or exercise are within our control and can be influenced by health campaigns and health education.

 Key terms

Mortality rate the number of deaths per 1,000 people

Morbidity rate the frequency with which a disease appears in a population

Take it further

Read the executive summary of the Marmot Review at **www.instituteofhealthequity.org/projects/fair-society-healthy-lives-the-marmot-review** for a concise overview of social inequalities today.

Social and community networks affect our health. Someone living in a community where they feel safe and have lots of support is likely to have better health than someone who is isolated. Living and working conditions affect health. Someone growing up in an inner city with high levels of air pollution is likely to have worse health than someone growing up in an area with clean air. Socio-economic, environmental and cultural conditions affect health for better or for worse.

Poor housing, lack of adequate healthcare, lack of support for education and high levels of unemployment increase the chances of poor physical and mental health.

Mortality (death) and morbidity (sickness) rates vary with social determinants such as gender, age and genetic heredity.

Gender

There are gender differences in life expectancy and in causes of death. National Life Tables, United Kingdom: 2012–2014 show that newborn boys could expect to live 79.1 years and newborn girls 82.8 years if mortality rates remain the same. Although the life expectancy of men is increasing, it is still not as great as that of women. Despite the fact that women live longer, it seems that men are healthier. Morbidity rates show that 'in 2012 to 2014, males at birth in England could expect to spend a higher proportion (79.7%) of their remaining lives in "Good" health, compared with females (76.9%)'. The fact that women live longer but that men are healthier is known as the gender paradox. There are gender differences too in the cause of death. In 2013, the main cause of death among men was ischaemic heart disease with lung cancer as the second most frequent cause. For women it was dementia and then ischaemic heart disease.

Functionalists might suggest that people are living longer because of improved medical care in a society where the needs for health care are being met. A Marxist-feminist analysis might focus on the difference in 'good' health between men and women and might suggest that women's health is poorer because they had to work harder in meeting gender expectations. Women work outside the home in lower paid jobs then go home to childcare, housework and other domestic responsibilities, whereas men return home to relax, guard the remote control and wait for dinner to be ready.

Age

Age-specific mortality rates measure how many people die at certain ages. More infants and under 5s are surviving. Maternal deaths, which occur up to 42 days after giving birth or the end of pregnancy, are decreasing. At the same time, deaths are increasing in the over 80s. A functionalist explanation would say that this shows a society in which people are cared for from birth right to the end of life and die when they should. A Marxist analysis might point to inequalities in funding health care, with insufficient funding for care of the elderly who have relatively little power or influence in society.

Ethnicity

Ethnicity is a social determinant of health. An ethnic group shares a common culture, customs and language. The Joseph Rowntree Foundation and Manchester University in 2013 used data from the 2011 Census to show that rates of illness for Pakistani and Bangladeshi women have been 10 per cent higher than White women in 1991, 2001 and 2011. The White Gypsy, or Irish Traveller group, has twice the White British rates of limiting long-term illness.

Migration affects physical and mental health with higher rates of depression and anxiety among asylum seekers and refugees compared to the national population, according to the Migration Observatory unit at Oxford University. Racist attitudes cause stress and can impact negatively on a person's mental health when they experience discrimination. This has a cumulative effect. Data from the Millennium Cohort study shows that children who live in an area where they are racially abused are more likely to have social and emotional difficulties and lag behind with cognitive development.

A functionalist explanation for this would suggest that these groups fail to engage with health services such as GPs. A Marxist explanation would suggest that these groups are marginalised and powerless to get services that meet their needs,

for example lack of provision of interpreters or health care workers who understand their culture. Symbolic interactionists might point to the different way people from the group dress or live (for example, wearing hijab or living in a caravan) as sources of difference and discrimination which deny them access to health care.

Area of residence

The area of residence affects health. The North East of England had the highest mortality rate in England (2015) and the South East has the lowest. The North East is an area of poverty, high unemployment and has more people in lower social classes than the South East. It is an area of deprivation with a higher risk of premature death. Marxists would explain lower mortality rates in the South East are a result of the concentration of wealth and political power in the South East, giving this area better access to health care and more health choices. Functionalists would suggest that inequality provides an incentive to motivate people to work. People have poorer health in the North because they are unemployed or low waged. If they gained more skills and move to where they can get a job, they can improve their health.

Family structure and family breakdown influence health. A secure family network provides a basis for a child to develop self-esteem. Where there is a total breakdown of the norms and values that hold a family or society together (anomie), there is inevitably an impact on mental health. When measures of success such as owning a house are unattainable despite working long hours, it causes strain and results in anomie where individuals reject the rules of society. Deviant behaviour occurs. In individuals this may lead to self-harm or suicide attempts. In society this leads to a breakdown of accepted values, to the dominance of violent gang cultures. Marxists would suggest that anomie is to be expected when there are extremes of inequality. Functionalists would explain family breakdown as failure of one of the main social institutions holding society together and would expect the police, another social institution, to deal with gangs. Symbolic Interactionists might focus on the symbols binding gangs together and excluding others.

Demographic studies and statistical data can tell us a lot about the health needs of a population but data may be incomplete. The Census records data for a specific household at a specific date. Homeless people are excluded from the Census. GPs collect health statistics but homeless people cannot get a GP so their health needs are not included in surveys. Demographic statistics also can be skewed by over-representation. According to the Mental Health Foundation UK, people from black and minority ethnic groups are more likely to be diagnosed and admitted with mental health problems than people from other groups. Despite these limitations, demographic data is a useful tool for health and care planners.

Case scenario (AC 2.2, 2.3, 2.4)

The London Borough of Hackney's estimated population is 263,150 and growing.

- 25% of its population is under 20
- 21% are between 20 and 29 years
- 18% are over 55.

The population is culturally diverse with significant 'Other White', Black and Turkish communities. People get on well together.

In 2011, 14.5 per cent of Hackney residents said they were disabled or had a long-term limiting illness.

Life expectancy is increasing for men and women, and is now 78.5 years for men and 83.3 years for women. Life expectancy in Hackney is below the London average, especially for men.

Hackney was the eleventh most deprived local authority overall in England in the 2015 Census survey, which is an improvement on its second place in 2010.

Hackney is the third most densely populated borough in London, but it is also one of the greenest, with falling levels of car ownership. Nitrogen dioxide levels can be high, especially around main roads.

Crime rates are falling.

Source: *A Profile of Hackney, its People and Place*, LB Hackney Policy Team, January 2016, www.hackney.gov.uk/statistics-evidence-plans-and-strategies

1. What evidence is there in this information about health inequalities?
2. What services would you expect will receive more funding in view of this data?

Command word activity

Explain (AC 2.4)

Write a paragraph for each demographic group listed below, considering how sociologists may describe differing patterns of mortality and morbidity:

- gender
- age
- ethnicity
- area of residence.

Sociological perspectives may include:

- Functionalism
- Symbolic Interactionism
- Marxism
- Feminism.

You will need to give examples of differing patterns of morbidity and mortality for each of the demographic groups and then explain in detail for each example how more than one sociological perspective might account for the difference.

You may like to start by considering how a feminist could explain gender differences in health between men and women. How may a Marxist explain the North/South health divide? How may a Functionalist explain differences in morbidity and mortality in different age groups? How may Symbolic Interactionists explain ethnic traditions which impact on health such as female genital mutilation?

Classroom discussion (AC 2.3, 2.4)

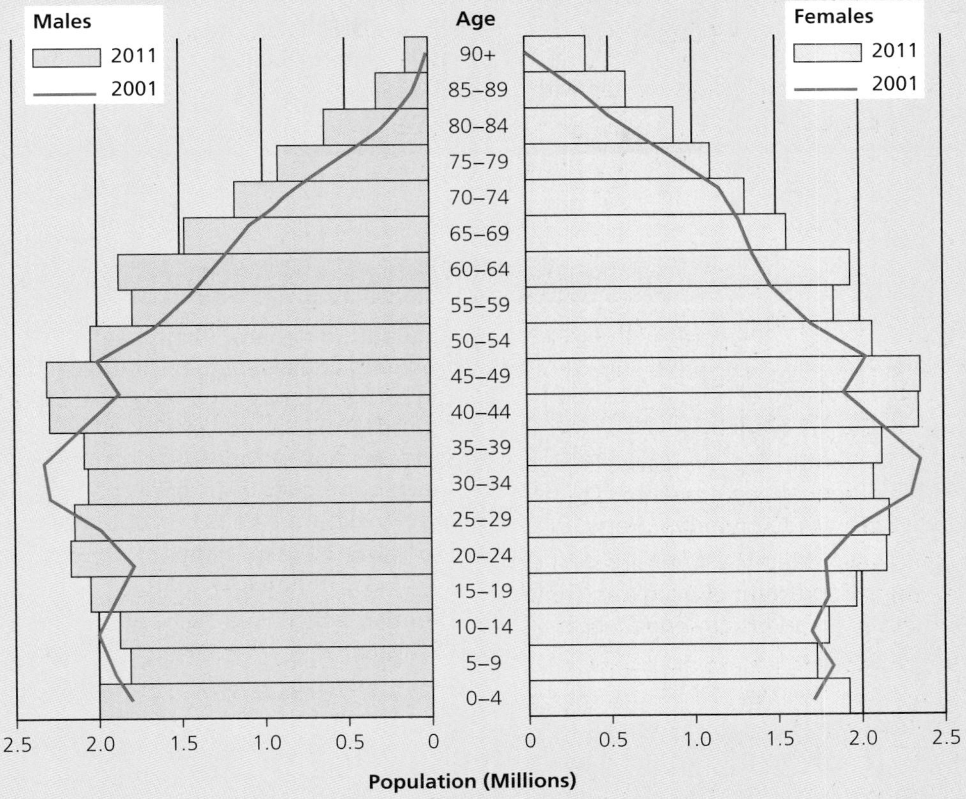

Figure 7.6 UK population by sex and five-year age group

Source: www.ons.gov.uk

Figure 7.6 shows the difference between the UK population in 2001 and 2011.

1. What happens to the population of men and of women over the age of 40 in 2011? Does it increase or decrease?
2. In 2011 are there more men or more women over the age of 90? How could health care planners use this information?
3. What happens to the age group 30–40 in 2011? These are of working age and tax payers. What are the implications of this population change?
4. What changes are there in the 15–29 age group in 2011? Why may health planners find this useful to know?
5. What is happening in the 0–4 age group? Why may planners need to know this?

Activity (AC 2.3, 2.4)

You are going to compare the population profile, level of deprivation and health of people in your local area with the national picture.

1. Find the population information for your local council. On the Government website neighbourhood statistics, input your postcode. http://www.neighbourhood.statistics.gov.uk/.
2. How does your local area compare with your local authority and with England as a whole for general health?
3. Click on the deprivation, population and health tabs to see how where you live compares with other areas.
4. What is the population profile of your area? Are there older people or younger ones?
5. Is your area more deprived or less deprived than other areas? The indicator dial gives this information.
6. What is the life expectancy for your area? What is the infant mortality rate?
7. Are there any surprises?

Check your understanding

1. Give two different examples of social classification and give at least one advantage and one disadvantage for each system.
2. Give three examples of how disease varies with social class.
3. How is demographic data used in planning health and social care services? Give three examples.
4. How does gender, age, ethnicity and area of residence affect health?

Read about it

Bessa, Y. 'Modernity theories and mental illness: A comparative study of selected sociological theorists', *International Journal of Humanities and Social Science*, vol. 2, no. 17, September 2012

Black, D., Morris, J.N., Smith, C., Townsend, P. and Whitehead, M. (1988) 'Inequalities in health: The black report: The health divide', London: Penguin

Pai, Madhukar and Ziad A. Memish 'Antimicrobial resistance and the growing threat of drug-resistant tuberculosis,' *Journal of Epidemiology and Global Health*, vol 6.2 (2016), pp. 45–7

Websites

About education – *The Protestant Ethic and The Spirit of Capitalism*. Available at http://sociology.about.com/od/Works/a/The-Protestant-Ethic-And-The-Spirit-Of-Capitalism.htm

About education – *What Mills' 'Power Elite' Can Teach Us About Society Today*. Available at http://sociology.about.com/od/Profiles/fl/Happy-Birthday-C-Wright-Mills.htm

Abel, T. 'Cultural capital and social inequality in health', *Journal of Epidemiology and Community Health,* 2008, 62:7 e13 doi:10.1136/jech.2007.066159. Available at http://jech.bmj.com/content/62/7/e13.abstract

Acheson, D. (1998) 'Independent inquiry into inequalities in health report'. Available at webarchive.nationalarchives.gov.uk/20130814142233/http://www.archive.official-documents.co.uk/document/doh/ih/ih.htm

'A detailed analysis of health deprivation divide using the 2011 Census: Part of 2011 Census analysis, inequality in general health and activity limiting health problems and disabilities', IMD 2010 Area Deprivation, England 2011, released 2014. Available at webarchive.nationalarchives.gov.uk/20160105160709/http://www.ons.gov.uk/ons/rel/census/2011-census-analysis/inequality-in-general-health-and-activity-limiting-health-problems-and-disabilities-by-imd-2010-area-deprivation--england-2011/rpt-health-inequality.html

Attention Deficit Hyperactivity Disorder (ADHD) *Data for US*. Available at www.cdc.gov/nchs/fastats/adhd.htm

Bécares, L. (2013) 'Which ethnic groups have the poorest health? Ethnic health inequalities 1991 to 2011', JRF and University of Manchester. Available at www.ethnicity.ac.uk/medialibrary/briefingsupdated/which-ethnic-groups-have-the-poorest-health.pdf

Beresford, P., Nettle, M. and Perring, R. (2010) 'Towards a social model of madness and distress? Exploring what service users say'. Available at www.jrf.org.uk/sites/default/files/jrf/migrated/files/mental-health-service-models-full.pdf

Bogg, D.(2012) 'Social workers need to fight the threat to social models of mental health care'. Available at www.communitycare.co.uk/2012/12/12/social-workers-need-to-fight-the-threat-to-social-models-of-mental-health-care/

Bronfenbrenner's *Bioecological Theory*. Available at bronfenbrenner3040.weebly.com/summary-of-bronfenbrenners-work.html

Burkini Ban Ruling. Available at www.independent.co.uk/news/world/europe/burkini-ban-ruling-france-sarkozy-nice-beach-pictures-muslim-islam-a7208476.html

Business Insider UK '80% of Americans own an unbelievably small portion of the country's wealth'. Available at http://uk.businessinsider.com/inequality-in-the-us-is-much-more-extreme-than-you-think-2015-6?r=US&IR=T

Change 4 Life. Available at www.nhs.uk/change4life/Pages/change-for-life.aspx

CNN 'Why are the burqa and burkini being banned?'. Available at http://edition.cnn.com/2016/08/19/europe/burqa-burkini-bans/

Confidential Enquiry into Maternal Death 2015. Available at www.npeu.ox.ac.uk/mbrrace-uk/reports

Currie, C. *et al.*, eds, 'Social determinants of health and well-being among young people. Health Behaviour in School-aged Children (HBSC) study: International report from the 2009/2010 survey', Copenhagen, WHO Regional Office for Europe, 2012 (Health Policy for Children and Adolescents, No. 6). Available at https://www.researchgate.net/profile/Oddrun_Samdal/publication/265034558_Social_determinants_of_health_and_well-being_among_young_people/links/548ae0310cf225bf669e135e.pdf

Doré, L., 'London gangs map'. Available at www.indy100.com/article/these-are-londons-gang-territories-in-a-single-map--Z1oinQab_g

Human Development Report (2015) *Work for Human Development, United Nations Development Programme, Interactive Web Version.* Available at report.hdr.undp.org/

Gangs dashboard. Available at www.london.gov.uk/what-we-do/mayors-office-policing-and-crime-mopac/data-and-research/crime%20gangs-dashboard

Independent '7 facts about France's burkini ban that make outsiders very uncomfortable'. Available at http://www.independent.co.uk/news/world/europe/burkini-ban-ruling-france-sarkozy-nice-beach-pictures-muslim-islam-a7208476.html

Interview with Polish woman on racist abuse in UK interrupted by racist abuse. Available at www.independent.co.uk/news/uk/home-news/interview-racist-abuse-channel-4-polish-interrupted-brexit-hate-crime-xenophobia-a7289996.html

Jayaweera, H. (2014) 'Health of migrants in the UK: What do we know?'. Available at www.migrationobservatory.ox.ac.uk/resources/briefings/health-of-migrants-in-the-uk-what-do-we-know/

'Health inequalities', Public Health England. Available at www.noo.org.uk/NOO_about_obesity/inequalities

Marmot, M. (2010) 'Strategic review of health inequalities in England post-2010 Fair Society, Healthy Lives: The Marmot Review. Available at www.instituteofhealthequity.org/projects/fair-society-healthy-lives-the-marmot-review

Meningitis Research Foundation. Available at www.meningitis.org/disease-info/types-causes/meningoccal-disease

Millennium Cohort Study, London: Institute of Education. Available at www.cls.ioe.ac.uk

Murder investigation launched in Harlow August 2016. Available at www.essex.police.uk/news/news-and-features/2016/08aug/murder-investigation-launched-in-harlow

Office for National Statistics '2011 Census analysis: Ethnicity and the labour market, England and Wales'. Available at http://www.ons.gov.uk/peoplepopulationandcommunity/culturalidentity/ethnicity/articles/ethnicityandthelabourmarket2011censusenglandandwales/2014-11-13

Priest, N., Paradies, Y., Trenerry, B., Truong, M., Karlsen, S. Kelly. and Y. 'A systematic review of studies examining the relationship between reported racism and health and wellbeing for children and young people', *Social Science & Medicine*, vol. 95, October 2013, pp.115–27. Abstract available at www.sciencedirect.com/science/article/pii/S0277953612007927

Public Health England (2014) 'Tuberculosis in the UK: 2014 report', London: Public Health England. Available at www.gov.uk/government/uploads/system/uploads/attachment_data/file/360335/TB_Annual_report__4_0_300914.pdf

Savage, M., Devine, F., Cunningham, N., Taylor, M., Li, Y., Hjellbrekke, J., Le Roux, B., Friedman, S. and Miles, A. 'A new model of social class: Findings from the BBC's Great British Class Survey Experiment', *Sociology* 0038038513481128, first published online 2 April 2013 doi:10.1177/0038038513481128

Shots health news from NPR 'Aggressive lowering of blood pressure carries risks as well as benefits', Available at http://www.npr.org/sections/health-shots/2015/11/09/455344298/aggressive-lowering-of-blood-pressure-carries-risks-as-well-as-benefits

Stanford Center on Poverty & Inequality '20 facts about US inequality that everyone should know. Available at http://inequality.stanford.edu/publications/20-facts-about-us-inequality-everyone-should-know

https://www.essex.police.uk/news/news-and-features/2016/08aug/murder-investigation-launched-in-harlow/

Stanley, D. (2003) 'What do we know about social cohesion: The research perspective of the Federal Government's Social Cohesion Research Network', *The Canadian Journal of Sociology / Cahiers Canadiens De Sociologie*, 28(1), 5–17, doi:1. Retrieved from http://www.jstor.org/stable/3341872 doi:1

Statistical bulletin: '2011 Census: Population estimates for the United Kingdom, March 2011'. Available at www.ons.gov.uk/peoplepopulationandcommunity/populationandmigration/populationestimates/bulletins/2011censuspopulationestimatesfortheunitedkingdom/2012-12-17

Statistical bulletin: 'Births in England and Wales: 2015'. Available at www.ons.gov.uk/peoplepopulationandcommunity/birthsdeathsandmarriages/livebirths/bulletins/birthsummarytablesenglandandwales/2015

Statistical bulletin: 'Childhood mortality in England and Wales: 2014'. Available at www.ons.gov.uk/peoplepopulationandcommunity/birthsdeathsandmarriages/deaths/bulletins/childhoodinfantandperinatalmortalityinenglandandwales/2014

Statistical bulletin: 'Deaths registered in England and Wales: 2015'. Available at www.ons.gov.uk/peoplepopulationandcommunity/birthsdeathsandmarriages/deaths/bulletins/deathsregistrationsummarytables/2015#main-points

Statistical bulletin: 'Healthy life expectancy at birth and age 65 by upper tier local authority and area deprivation: England, 2012 to 2014'. Available at http://www.ons.gov.uk/peoplepopulationandcommunity/healthandsocialcare/healthandlifeexpectancies/bulletins/healthylifeexpectancyatbirthandage65byuppertierlocalauthorityandareadeprivation/england2012to2014#main-points

Statistical bulletin: 'Migration statistics quarterly report': published August 2016. Available at www.ons.gov.uk/peoplepopulationandcommunity/populationandmigration/internationalmigration/bulletins/migrationstatisticsquarterlyreport/august2016

Statistical bulletin: 'National life tables, UK: 2013–2015'. Available at www.ons.gov.uk/peoplepopulationandcommunity/birthsdeathsandmarriages/lifeexpectancies/bulletins/nationallifetablesunitedkingdom/20132015

'The Great British Class Survey'. Available at www.bbc.co.uk/science/0/21970879

United Nations Human Development Reports. Available at http://hdr.undp.org/en/2015-report

'What are the top causes of death by age and gender?'. Available at visual.ons.gov.uk/what-are-the-top-causes-of-death-by-age-and-gender/

Williams, G. 'Understanding health inequalities: theories, concepts and evidence'. Available at www.wales.nhs.uk/sitesplus/documents/888/Gareth%20Williams.pdf

Unit HSC CM7: How will I be graded?

The table below shows what the learner must do to achieve each grading criterion. Learners must achieve all the criteria for a grade to be awarded (i.e. criteria D1 to D3 must be achieved to pass this unit assessment at grade D). A higher grade may not be awarded before a lower grade has been achieved in full, although component criteria of a higher grade may have been achieved.

Grade	Assessment criteria number	Assessment grading criteria	Assessment of learning / What you need to show
D1	1.2	Describe sociological perspectives.	Provide a description that shows understanding of sociological perspectives in relation to health and social care.
D2	1.1	Summarise the sociological approach to the study of human behaviour.	The summary should give the main concepts related to sociological approaches in a concise way.
D3		Show evidence of reading or use of sources.	There should be evidence of learners' reading or use of sources. Learners must use a minimum of two traceable references to support the discussion.
C1	1.4	Describe the biomedical, social and ecological models of health and well-being.	The description must demonstrate an understanding of each of the biomedical, social and ecological models of health and well-being in relation to health and social care.
C2	2.1	Explain the social classes recognised in own Home Nation.	The explanation must: ● show understanding of the notion of social classes. ● relate to the social classes recognised in own Home Nation.
C3		Show evidence of reading or use of sources with referencing relevant to the description or explanation. Good use of vocabulary and grammar.	Use of referencing should show evidence of reading or use of sources. Vocabulary and grammar should be appropriate and accurate for purposes.
B1	1.3	Describe sociological perspectives in relation to health and social care.	More than one sociological perspective must be described in detail. The description of each sociological perspective must demonstrate understanding in relation to health and social care. Relevant examples from health and social care practice should be used to support the description.
B2	2.2	Explain patterns of health across social classes.	Provide a detailed explanation of patterns of health across social classes to include consideration of patterns and trends such as: ● health inequalities. ● cultural influences. ● other relevant factors.

Grade	Assessment criteria number	Assessment grading criteria	Assessment of learning / What you need to show
B3		Show evidence of reading or use of sources. Referencing supports the description or explanation.	Use of reading or use of sources should be shown through a range of relevant referencing. Referencing should be used appropriately to support the description or explanation.
A1	2.3	Explain how demographic data is used in planning health and social care services.	The explanation must: ● include knowledge of different types of demographic data. ● demonstrate understanding of the use of more than one type of demographic data. ● take an analytical approach to the use of the demographic data in planning health and social care services.
A2		Show evidence of wider background reading or use of sources. Referencing supports the explanation.	Wider background reading should be evident or a wide range of source material should be used.
A*1	2.4	Explain sociological explanations for the patterning of mortality and morbidity rates in the demographic groups: ● gender. ● age. ● ethnicity. ● area of residence.	A detailed explanation which must: ● demonstrate understanding of mortality and morbidity rates. ● provide more than one relevant sociological explanation for the patterning of mortality and morbidity rates in relation to more than one demographic group. ● include a conclusion to support the perspectives used in the explanation.
A*2		Show evidence of a range of background reading or use of sources used selectively.	Learners should show the ability to consider or explore relevant issues which contribute to the explanations. An extensive range of background reading or use of sources should be used selectively and cited appropriately.

HSC CM8
Working in Health and Social Care

Learning outcomes

LO1: Understand legislation, policies and procedures in relation to health and social care

1.1 Describe the relationship between legislation, policies and procedures

1.2 Summarise legislation in relation to health and social care

1.3 Analyse how legislation informs policies and procedures in health and social care provision

LO2: Understand the requirements of professional standards and codes of practice

2.1 Explain reasons for professional standards and codes of practice within the health and social care sector

2.2 Summarise requirements of professional standards and codes of practice

LO3: Understand the functions of health and social care provision and factors which influence service delivery

3.1 Explain the functions of national and local health and social care provision

3.2 Describe factors that influence national and local service delivery

LO4: Understand the roles and responsibilities of practitioners within health and social care

4.1 Explain the roles and responsibilities of health and social care practitioners

4.2 Describe different working relationships in health and social care settings

4.3 Explain the need for health and social care practitioners to adhere to the boundaries of their own job role

About this unit

Working in health and social care can be both rewarding and challenging. The delivery of high-quality health and social care provision depends on having in place skilled, knowledgeable and experienced care practitioners. Promoting a culture where the experiences and needs of individuals are at the centre of all health and social care provision is integral to developing effective care, support and treatment.

In this unit you will find out about how policies and procedures in health and social care provision are underpinned by legislation. You will also learn more about the professional standards and codes of practice that are relevant to the health and social care sector and why these are important to the roles and responsibilities of care practitioners. Understanding the factors that influence both national and local service delivery as well as their specific roles will provide you with a useful insight into the health and social care sector.

LO1: Understand legislation, policies and procedures in relation to health and social care

1.1 Describe the relationship between legislation, policies and procedures

International and national legislation is the basis of all organisational policies and procedures in health and social care settings. Governments create laws to establish a set of rules and regulations that must be complied with by the people and work settings they govern. Legislation is also a way of giving permission to organisations such as health and social care providers to provide services in a controlled and structured manner, as well as make clear what activities are not allowed and are unlawful. Legislation can also enable the sector to access resources such as funding so that it can fulfil its legal requirements. You will learn more about relevant health and social care legislation in the section that follows.

Policies and procedures inform the services and activities of health and social care organisations. They also set out how every organisation is committed to and plans to put into practice all relevant legislative requirements that govern the sector. They **regulate** and provide a structure for guiding organisations' activities and working practices. An organisational policy will set out the organisation's purpose and the services it aims to provide. An organisational procedure will usually demonstrate how a policy is to be implemented by including a series of actions or steps that must be followed and any relevant documentation that must be used by health and social care practitioners in work settings.

Policies and procedures vary between health and social care organisations because they reflect different organisations' activities, purposes and **values**. Developing policies and procedures in the health and social care sector is essential for ensuring that all relevant legislation is being applied and complied with by everyone who accesses services, or works in the sector, to ensure their safety and the promotion of their rights.

 Key terms

Regulate to maintain control

Values principles or beliefs that are important to an individual

---

Taking it further

For more information on the relationship between legislation, policies and procedures you will find it useful to read Unit HSC CM3: Safeguarding (LO2).

Command word activity

Describe (AC 1.1)

1. Write down one sentence for each of the following terms: legislation, policy and procedure. In small groups of three share and discuss these with your peers.
2. Agree on a whole group definition for each of these terms and then give an account that includes all the relevant characteristics of two ways they are different, two ways they are similar and two ways they are interlinked. Work in small groups to define the terms:
   - Legislation
   - Policy
   - Procedure.
3. Identify the links between legislation, policy and procedure.

1.2 Summarise legislation in relation to health and social care

A range of specific legislation that is relevant to the health and social care sector; it is important for care practitioners to be aware of these as they underpin all current working practices and how care and support services are provided. Table 8.1 below provides a summary of the key points that are relevant to current legislation:

Table 8.1 A summary of current health and social care legislation

Legislation	Key information points
Care Act 2014	Relevant to individuals who are 18 and over and require care and support Requires all those involved in the health and social care sector to work together to keep individuals safe from abuse or neglect, i.e. the Act established adult safeguarding boards Local councils must provide individuals with services that meet their specific needs and improve their lives Local councils must provide services that are preventative, i.e. prevent the need for care and support or provide care and support as early as possible to prevent additional difficulties from developing Local councils must provide clear and accurate information and advice to all individuals who require this, i.e. this may be in relation to the different types of services available in the local area or the costs of care and support Local councils must work together with individuals, their families, organisations and other professionals involved in the health and social care sector to plan and deliver services that provide good-quality care and support and take account of individuals' well-being as well as what's important to them, i.e. this includes planning for both current and future needs Individuals as well as their carers have the right to have their individual needs assessed and understood, i.e. this includes being involved in their assessments and design of their care and support, as well as the right to have their views and preferences represented by, for example, an advocate
Health and Social Care Act 2012	Created a new framework for the planning, delivery and monitoring of healthcare services in England, i.e. it replaced primary care trusts with CCGs and established a new NHS Commissioning Board responsible for overseeing the activities of the CCGs, as well as the overall planning, delivery and monitoring of healthcare CCGs are required to involve individuals who use services as well as healthcare professionals and other relevant services and organisations such as those in the private and Third sectors (see p. 181 for definition) It established Health and Wellbeing Boards (HWBs) to enable different organisations to work together in planning and delivering local services, e.g. the NHS, adult social care services, children's services and youth services It established Public Health England that will be responsible for local public health services that will be planned, delivered and monitored by local authorities, i.e. no longer the NHS It established Healthwatch England (HWE) to provide information and advice to those who plan, deliver and monitor services It established Monitor, the financial regulator for healthcare services in England It established a voluntary register for all health care support workers, i.e. that includes the minimum training, knowledge and skills required for their job roles
Equality Act 2010	It ensures people are treated fairly It provides people with protection from discrimination It established nine characteristics that are protected from discrimination: age, disability, gender reassignment, marriage and civil partnership, pregnancy and maternity, race, religion and belief, sex, sexual orientation It requires public bodies such as local councils, hospitals and schools to ensure their services provide people who have diverse needs with equal and fair opportunities and for different groups of people to be treated fairly and equally, i.e. younger and older people, men and women, carers
Health and Social Care Act 2008 (Regulated Activities) Regulations 2014	Requires health and social care providers to appoint people in senior management roles who have passed the fit and proper persons test, i.e. the person must be of good character, have the necessary experience, qualifications, ability to carry out their duties in line with their job role The Regulations also place a duty on health and social care providers to not recruit people into senior management positions if they fall under specific categories, i.e. has been subject to a bankruptcy order or is on a children's or adult's barred list The regulators, the Care Quality Commission (CQC) and Monitor are responsible for assessing whether NHS providers have carried out the fit and proper persons tests to the correct standards; monitoring and, if necessary, ensuring the person is removed from their post if they do not meet the requirements

Legislation	Key information points
Care Quality Commission (Registration) Regulations 2009	Requires that all health and social care providers of children and adults services are registered with the CQC Requires that all providers of healthcare and social care conform to a set of fundamental standards, i.e. the provision of person-centred care, ensuring all individuals are treated with dignity and respect; that individuals' consent has been obtained in relation to their care and treatment; that all care and treatment provided is safe, promotes individuals' good health and is free from danger, harm, abuse and neglect; complaints systems are maintained; systems for monitoring the quality and safety of services are provided; services are staffed with fit and proper persons; the **duty of candour** in relation to individuals' care and treatment; and the display by services of CQC inspection ratings
Human Rights Act 1998	Requires all service providers and public organisations to respect and protect the rights and freedoms that everyone in the UK is entitled to, i.e. the right to life, freedom from torture and inhuman or degrading treatment, freedom from slavery and forced labour, the right to liberty and security, the right to education, freedom of thought, belief and religion, freedom of expression, the right to protection from discrimination in relation to these rights and freedoms
Data Protection Act 1998	Places a duty on service providers and public organisations to handle all personal information about an individual fairly and lawfully Established the data protection principles which must be followed when handling information, i.e. used fairly and lawfully, only when required, be time limited, used accurately and when relevant, be accurate, only kept for as long as necessary, kept safe and secure
Children's Act 1989 and 2004	The Children's Act 1989 established the 'welfare' principle, i.e. to ensure all decisions in relation to children take into account their best interests This Act also promoted the welfare of children, i.e. to be protected from harm, to have their beliefs and culture respected, to take into account a child's wishes and feelings in any decisions that affect them The Children's Act 2004 reinforced the duty of all organisations to safeguard and promote the welfare of children The Act introduced the 'paramountcy principle' that reinforces the importance of a child's welfare when making decisions, the rights of **children in need** to be able to access the services they require, placed a duty on local authorities to investigate when a child is being harmed or at risk of harm, created new Local Safeguarding Children Boards and systems to improve how services work together to promote and safeguard the welfare of children
Health and Safety at Work Act 1974	The main piece of legislation in relation to workplace health and safety in Great Britain It sets out the responsibilities of everyone for maintaining their own and others' health and safety at work, i.e. places duties on employers to undertake risk assessments, provide health and safety training, have reporting procedures for illnesses, injuries and incidents and on employees to attend health and safety training provided, comply with employers' health and safety procedures, take reasonable care of their own and others' health and safety
Inspectorate Regulations	Require regulators to inspect and monitor services to ensure they are providing safe, effective and high-quality care, e.g. CQC assess health and social care service providers against the five key questions: are they safe? are they effective? are they caring? are they responsive to people's needs? are they well-led?, Monitor have established Regulations to assess health services in England to ensure the rights and interests of individuals are safeguarded and promoted and that health services provided are efficient and of a high quality

Take it further

For more information on current legislation you will find it useful to access the Government's website: gov.uk. You will also find it useful to read the following units: HSC CM1; HSC CM3; HSC CM4; HSC CM9; HSC DM1; and HSC DM2.

 ## Key terms

Third sector also referred to as the voluntary sector, includes not-for-profit and non-governmental organisations

Duty of candour a duty that requires health and social care providers to be honest and transparent about the provision of all care and treatment

Children in need refers to children who are unable to attain the required level of health or development, or whose health or development may be affected without the provision of services

Command word activity

Summarise (AC 1.2)

In pairs, write down on a card the names of two pieces of health and social care legislation that you know about. Give your card to your partner and ask them to sum up in 60 seconds the main points about each.

1.3 Analyse how legislation informs policies and procedures in health and social care provision

Now that you understand the relationship between legislation, policies and procedures and have developed your knowledge of the legislation that is relevant to the health and social care sector, let us consider how legislation informs how health and social care services develop their agreed ways of working across the ten areas described below:

Duty of care – health and social care practitioners have a duty of care towards not only the individuals they provide care and support to, but also to those they work with such as their colleagues and professionals from other organisations. This means that health and social care providers must have in place policies and procedures for ensuring that they always act in individuals' best interests when providing care and support and not place them or others in danger, be harmed or abused (i.e. Safeguarding and Health and safety policies and procedures). Duty of care also means that health and social care provision must be of a high quality, safe and effective, i.e. health and social care practitioners must only carry out procedures they are competent to carry out and after training (Moving and handling policy and procedure) and

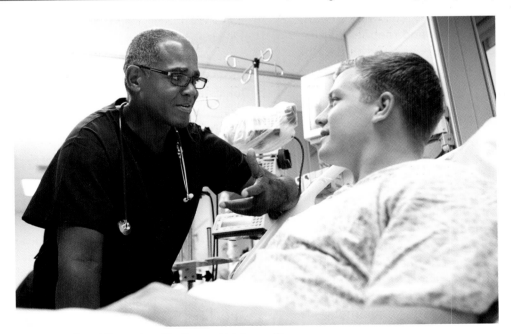
Figure 8.1 Providing safe, effective and high-quality care

must maintain care records that are accurate and up to date (Record keeping policy)

Protocols – health and social care provision must not only be safe, effective and of a high quality, but it must also meet the legal regulations that establish the required standards that everyone who accesses services can expect. For example, providers must have in place systems for handling and investigating complaints (Complaints policy and procedure), agreed ways of working for establishing consent for individuals' care and treatment (Consent policy and procedure), the agreed behaviours and conduct of all practitioners who work in a service (Code of conduct)

Guidance – legislation can also act as a guide of the agreed standard for health and social care provision, i.e. the induction process that care practitioners must follow in different care settings (Staff Induction policy) or how to provide support to adults or children who have specific needs (Special Requirements policy)

Key aspects of service delivery – all aspects of a health and social care provider's services are underpinned by legislative requirements from the recruit of workers (Disclosure and Barring Service policy), to the delivery of services (Equality and Diversity policy and procedures) to their monitoring and improvement (Review and Evaluation policy)

Current practice – changes in legislation mean that the rights, duties, roles and responsibilities of health and social care services and those who work for them and access them also require amending and updating; for example in relation to discrimination (Equal Opportunities policy and procedures) and safeguarding (Adult and Children Safeguarding policies and procedures)

Safety – promoting the safety of all health and social care provision is an underlying requirement of all aspects of services from the safe ordering, handling, storing and disposing of medication (Medication policy and procedures) to the safety of individuals (Missing Persons policy) and the safety of care practitioners (Lone Working policy and procedure), to the security of the premises where care and treatment is provided by care practitioners including the use of equipment (Health and Safety policy and procedure)

Consistency – ensuring that the quality of care and support provided is consistent across care practitioners in services is essential for meeting individuals' needs; Multi-agency policies and procedures are in place to enable different organisations who provide health and social care services to individuals to work together

Continuity – the continuity of health and social care provision is also of paramount importance; the Continuity of Care policy and procedures can enable services to ensure that they have sufficient care practitioners and that they are experienced, knowledgeable, skilled and competent so that individuals needs are met on a continuous basis

Public confidence – ensuring that services are inspected and regulated instils public confidence in the safety and quality of health and social care provision (Inspection and Monitoring policy and procedures). Policies and procedures in place for ensuring care practitioners undergo checks before being recruited, are qualified, trained and professional can also instil trust and confidence in the public (Disclosure and Barring Service policy)

Accountability – ensuring that services have systems in place for ensuring the accountability and monitoring of all work activities and services provided is crucial to the provision of high-quality care (Monitoring and Accountability policy and procedures)

Key terms

Protocols procedures and systems that are in place

Consistency the reliability of a service or working practice

Continuity the uninterrupted provision of a service over time

Accountability being held responsible for one's own actions

Activity

Research three examples of policies and procedures that are relevant to one health and social care setting. Useful sources could include managers from health and social care settings with whom arrangements could be made to interview them, as well as the internet.

Check your understanding

1. Name two differences between a policy and a procedure.
2. Name two pieces of legislation relevant to children and two pieces of legislation relevant to adults.
3. Give three examples of ways that the Care Act 2014 can inform health and social care provision.

LO2 Understand the requirements of professional standards and codes of practice

2.1 Explain reasons for professional standards and codes of practice within the health and social care sector

As you will have learned, a professional within the health and social care sector has a legal duty of care that involves providing high-quality care and support, treating individuals and others with whom they work fairly, respectfully and with dignity as well as instilling trust and promoting confidence in their skills, level of experience and knowledge.

Professional standards in the health and social care sector reflect the national minimum levels of performance that care practitioners are expected to achieve to be able to carry out their roles and responsibilities effectively.

Professional standards are important because they:

- influence the quality of health and social care provision through the regulation and monitoring of services
- are underpinned by the values that are important in the health and social care sector, e.g. privacy, dignity, respect, compassion
- make clear how the performance and accountability of health and social care practitioners will be measured
- provide information and guidance on the support that will be made available by services to ensure practitioners carry out their roles effectively, i.e. supervision, training
- provide information about the roles, responsibilities and the standards to expect when accessing health and social care services, i.e. so as to instil trust and confidence

Key terms

Regulation governing the way a service operates
Monitoring reviewing the quality and performance of a service on a regular basis

Take it further

For more information on the standards relating to professional development in health and social care you will find it useful to read Unit HSC CM9: LO1.

Codes of practice in the health and social care sector reflect how each health and social care organisation plans to implement national professional standards in their organisation and for their practitioners; they operate at a local organisational level. These will vary between different health and social care organisations because each organisation will interpret the standards differently, depending on what values they hold as important for their services.

Codes of practice are important because they:

- influence the nature and quality of working practices within organisations and specifically within the sector

- are underpinned by the values that are important in the health and social care sector, e.g. privacy, dignity, respect, compassion as well as specifically to the organisation, i.e. enabling individuals to lead fulfilling lives, providing high-quality support when needed and at times of crisis in individuals' lives, undertaking risk assessment and safeguarding individuals

- make clear what is expected of health and social care practitioners, including the public's expectations, i.e. their day-to-day duties and responsibilities and how these link to the work setting's policies and procedures

- provide a framework for care practitioners' continuous professional development, i.e. their strengths, areas for development and training required to develop their abilities and competence

- provide opportunities to model best practice, i.e. in relation to working approaches, problem solving.

Classroom discussion (AC 2.1)

Discuss the meaning of the terms professional standards and codes of practice in the health and social care sector.

Command word activity

Explain (AC 2.1)

Write an account of the reasons why both professional standards *and* codes of practice are important, and explain how standards and codes are different.

Ensure you also detail the consequences of not complying with them for care practitioners, service providers and individuals.

2.2 Summarise requirements of professional standards and codes of practice

Professional standards and codes of practice establish the required standards and behaviours that are expected from health and social care providers and the range of care practitioners that work within the health and social care sector.

Requirements of professional standards

Regulations – health and social care practitioners who practise in the UK are required to be registered with a regulator and must show that they meet the required professional standards for their profession, e.g. doctors with the General Medical Council (GMC), nurses and midwives with the Nursing and Midwifery Council (NMC), dentists with the General Dental Council (GDC) and social workers with the Health and Care Professions Council (HCPC). Health and social care providers are also legally required to ensure the services they provide are safe, of a high quality and can be held accountable.

Public expectations – the public, including individuals who access services and their carers also expect to be able to trust and be confident that the health and social care sector have the level of expertise necessary to meet their needs.

Other requirements – professional standards require health and social care providers to ensure their services respect and promote the rights of individuals to, for example, be treated with dignity, be independent while being kept safe from danger, harm, abuse or neglect.

Requirements of codes of practice

Regulations – health and social care practitioners must comply with their work setting's policies and procedures and agreed ways of working to ensure they are meeting their legal duty of care. For example, by supporting individuals to make informed choices about their care, by assessing the risks of them doing so with them, or by explaining to individuals how confidentiality is maintained in relation to their care records.

Public expectations – the skills, behaviours and qualities that are essential to meet the code of conduct, i.e. being able to communicate effectively with individuals, understanding the behaviours expected from them in different situations such as when a complaint is made by a carer or when an individual disagrees with their

plan of care or support, being honest, caring and compassionate.

Other requirements – codes of conduct require health and social care practitioners to respect and uphold individualsK' and their carers' rights at all times and through all their work activities and be supported in doing so by the organisations which employ them.

Command word activity

Summarise (AC 2.2)

Look at Figure 8.2 below. Research two examples of professional standards and two examples of codes of practice including: regulations, public expectations and other requirements that are relevant to the health and social care sector.

Produce a poster that includes brief details of the requirements for these.

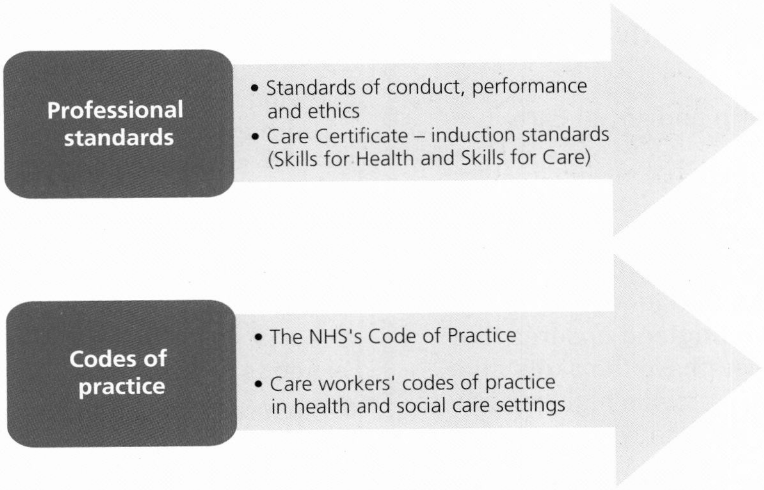

Professional standards
- Standards of conduct, performance and ethics
- Care Certificate – induction standards (Skills for Health and Skills for Care)

Codes of practice
- The NHS's Code of Practice
- Care workers' codes of practice in health and social care settings

Figure 8.2 Examples of professional standards and codes of practice

---

Command word activity

Evidence (AC 2.2)

Imagine you have been asked to discuss with a newly recruited care assistant, as part of their induction to the work setting, the requirements of professional standards and codes of practice. Ensure you support your discussion with evidence of the sources you have read; these should be relevant to your discussion. Each source should be recorded accurately.

Check your understanding

1. What are professional standards?
2. State two differences between professional standards and codes of practice.
3. Identify two examples of professional standards.
4. For one chosen code of practice give two examples of its requirements.

LO3: Understand the functions of health and social care provision and factors which influence service delivery

3.1 Explain the functions of national and local health and social care provision

Health and social care services are accessed by people throughout their lives and have a range of important functions both nationally across the whole of England and locally in specific areas. Governmental polices and guidelines influence the provision of health and social care in England.

Functions of national health and social care provision

The role of national health and social care provision is to:

1. Improve individuals' quality of life – through improving the care, support and treatment they require – NHS England protects the values of the NHS across national provision and **Health Education England** ensures that healthcare practitioners have the skills and training they require to provide high-quality care both nationally and locally

2. Prevent ill-health, i.e. to encourage and improve individuals' long-term health and well-being – the **National Institute for Health and Care Excellence (NICE)** provides guidance to health and social care professionals on delivery approaches based on current research

3. Promote healthy living among the population – **Public Health England** works in partnership with national and local organisations and its role is to promote public health

4. Enable individuals to live fulfilled lives, i.e. through increasing the range of **voluntary and private** health and social care providers

5. Ensure individuals who access services are treated fairly, with compassion, respect and dignity – by consulting with the public about their experiences of services, the **CQC** and **Healthwatch England** ensure national agreed standards for services are adhered to by health and social care providers

6. Fund health and social care services nationally and measure their effectiveness – NHS England provides funding for local commissioning groups to commission services for their local communities and **Monitor** ensures healthcare services are cost effective

Functions of local health and social care provision

The role of local health and social care provision is to:

1. Provide high-quality services to local communities – through clinical commissioning groups there will be a range of expertise and knowledge about local service provision

2. Promote and improve public health and well-being – the roles and responsibilities of local authorities by working in partnership with other local services to overcome health inequalities that exist in populations such as obesity

3. Provide cost – effective services to local communities – the roles and responsibilities of clinical commissioning groups for buying services for their local areas in response to the needs of their local communities

4. Ensure local health and social organisations work together in partnership – by establishing **Health and Wellbeing Boards**; their lines of reporting are to clinical commissioning groups and local authorities who are involved in the planning, buying, delivery and review of services

5. Involve and consult individuals who access services and others involved in their lives such as health and social care professionals, i.e. representing their views through **Local Healthwatch organisations**; their lines of reporting are to Healthwatch England which operates at a national level

6. To plan and develop services based on individuals' needs that are required in the short term and in the long term to provide specific service provision, i.e. to better reflect and predict individuals' needs in relation to residential care, community care and **rehabilitation**

Figure 8.3 Supporting an individual's needs

Functions that are common to both national and local health and social care provision

Functions that are common to both national and local health and social care provision include:

1. Promotion of health and well-being to prevent ill-health and improve long-term health and well-being
2. Improvement of the quality of care, support and treatment provided, i.e. to respect individuals' rights and promote the values of the health and social care sector
3. Provision of services that are high quality and cost effective
4. Provision of services that reflect individuals' current and future needs, i.e. to ensure individuals' views are heard and to enable the use of health and social care professionals' specific areas of expertise

 Key terms

NHS England oversees the funding, planning and delivery of the NHS

Health Education England oversees the education, training and workforce development in the health sector

National Institute for Health and Care Excellence (NICE) provides information, guidance and advice based on current research and best practice to the health and social care workforce

Public Health England provides advice and support on public health to local government, local authorities and the NHS

Voluntary not-for-profit organisations such as charities

Private non-government-led organisations that run for profit such as independent organisations

Care Quality Commission (CQC) the regulator of health and social care services in England

Healthwatch England the national consumer organisation for the health and social care sector

Monitor the regulator of health services in England

Health and Wellbeing Boards where representatives from the health and social care sector work together to improve the health and well-being of their local populations

Local Healthwatch organisations local consumer organisations for the health and social care sector

Rehabilitation a specialised service that aims to improve or maintain an individual's independence after an accident or during an illness

Take it further

For more information on the functions of national and local health and social care provision you will find it useful to refer to LO1 of this unit.

Command word activity

Explain (AC 3.1)

1. Write an account that includes a clear and detailed rationale, supported with examples of the roles of national and local health and social care providers. Be sure to include details of the roles that are common to both.
2. Discuss your account with a partner. What similarities and differences were there between your accounts?

3.2 Describe factors that influence national and local service delivery

As you will have learned there are some functions that are common to the roles of both national and local health and social care provision. There is also a range of factors that can have an influence on both national and local service delivery of health and social care.

Resources

The resources available will affect the types and numbers of services that can be provided both nationally and locally. For example, if the Government's priority is for funding services that lead to the improvement of healthier lifestyles then it will be these types of preventative and educational services that will be prioritised nationally for funding. Where voluntary and independent organisations provide services in local areas to meet individuals' specific needs they may require funding from the Government to do so effectively, that is, for specialist training for staff, type of support or care required by individuals who may have a range of both health and social care needs.

Services that are needs led involve identifying individuals' specific needs and planning how best to meet their needs and preferences irrespective of the services that are available. This means that health and social care delivery must be able to reflect the diverse needs of communities and individuals.

Accessibility

The accessibility of health and social care services, i.e. the information made available to those who access health and social care services both nationally and locally will impact on how many people access health and social care services. For example, if information is restricted to specific types of media or locations then individuals and practitioners may not be aware they exist. Similarly, if services are not accessible to individuals or designed with their needs as the focus, such as to meet individuals' physical and/ or mental health needs, then they may not be used by different groups of individuals.

Demand

The demand for health and social care services can vary and fluctuate depending on the needs of the population. For example, local populations that have children, young people, older adults, health inequalities, i.e. such as substance misuse, poor access to health education, individuals with specific conditions, will require services during different life stages, some more often than others. This may mean that when demand is high, i.e. during winter time there may be an increase in individuals accessing healthcare services due to infections and illnesses, services have difficulties meeting individuals' needs.

Location

The location of health and social care provision will be affected by the resources available such as the costs of premises, the availability of skilled and experienced care practitioners and the proximity to transport links. This may mean that services need to be located away from the areas where they are most needed. For example, a hospital that specialises in providing care and treatment for children may need to be located in a central location; individuals and their families may have to travel long distances to access it.

Figure 8.4 Working closely together

Liaison

Liaison with all those involved including individuals, care practitioners, colleagues, parents and carers will also affect the quality and provision of health and social care services, that is, the nature of the liaison that takes place, its effectiveness and how it is used to meet individuals' needs.

Partnerships

Partnerships between statutory, public, private, voluntary and independent organisations can affect the resources available, that is, resources could be pooled, the levels of skills and expertise available to provide better care, support and treatment to individuals.

Person-centred practice

Person-centred practice will influence national and local service delivery because it provides an opportunity for the individuals who access health and social care services to become experts and work in partnership with health and social care professionals and organisations by being involved in all aspects of service delivery, that is, planning, delivering, reviewing.

Service autonomy

Service autonomy will also influence national and local service delivery because enabling services to be less dependent on, for example, funding, over which they have no control, can mean for some that they will be more in control of their functions and the costs associated with these and for others that they are no longer able to provide all of their services to individuals who need them.

 Classroom discussion (AC3.2)

Does service autonomy benefit the people who use services? Discuss the pros and cons.

Community

Community involvement will impact on national and local service delivery as it can influence local and national needs as well as be a measure for establishing which services are required to meet the current and future needs of communities all over England.

Command word activity

Describe (AC 3.2)

Research one national and one local health or social care service. For each one produce an information factsheet about its functions and the factors that influence the services it provides. Exchange your factsheets with your peers in small groups. What did you learn?

Check your understanding

1. What is your understanding of national and local health and social care provision?
2. State two functions of national health and social care provision.
3. State two functions of local health and social care provision.
4. Name two factors that influence both national and local health and social care provision.

LO4: Understand the roles and responsibilities of practitioners within health and social care

4.1 Explain the roles and responsibilities of health and social care practitioners

A wide range of national and local health and social care provision exists to be able to meet the diverse and specific needs of individuals throughout their lives. Skilled, knowledgeable and competent health and social care practitioners are required across a variety of services to be able to provide the high-quality, safe and effective care, support and treatment.

Although health and social care practitioners' day-to-day work duties will vary depending on their roles, for example, nurse, care assistant, physiotherapist, optician, they will all have job descriptions that set out clearly the work duties that they are contracted to undertake and person specifications that state the personal qualities that they must possess and that are essential or required for their role. Associated with practitioners' roles are responsibilities that refer to how they carry out their duties and that will impact on the quality of care, support and treatment provided, that is, duty of care, the care they provide when carrying out their duties including accepting accountability. The level of competence that care practitioners have in carrying out their roles will depend on the knowledge, skills and experience they have that they will have developed through

carrying out their job roles, working alongside more experienced colleagues and completing training, courses and qualifications.

All health and social care practitioners are required to:

1. Work in ways that have been agreed with their employer, by following the work setting's policies and procedures and the duties and responsibilities outlined in their **job descriptions** and **person specifications**
2. Have a duty of care not only to the individuals they provide care, support and treatment to, but also to individuals' families, advocates, their colleagues, other professionals they work with and the public, by addressing conflicts that may arise between rights and the duty of care and handling complaints and comments professionally
3. Safeguard by recognising and responding to danger, harm and abuse using agreed lines of reporting
4. Risk manage by taking account of their own, individuals' and others' health and safety at all times
5. Work in partnership by taking into account the views of individuals and their representatives, by seeking information and advice from more experienced colleagues and professionals
6. Practise in ways that are person-centred by promoting individuals' rights to privacy, dignity, choice and independence and promoting their health and well-being
7. Plan individuals' care and support by planning with individuals and others involved in their lives how to meet their unique and specific needs
8. Record and report, handling information in agreed ways, communicating effectively both in writing and verbally
9. Undertake personal development, ongoing continuous professional development such as mentoring, coaching, supervision, training, qualifications to contribute to their development in their work roles, the use of **reflective practice** to evaluate and improve their working practices

Figure 8.5 Working in health and social care – what roles interest you?

Command word activity

Explain (AC 4.1)

Research two job roles in healthcare and two job roles in social care. Develop a job description for each one that explains their specific roles and responsibilities.

4.2 Describe different working relationships in health and social care settings

Working in partnership requires health and social care practitioners to work alongside others as equal partners:

1. **The individual who accesses health and social care services:** when planning their care, support and treatment, it is important that practitioners use their expertise such as their knowledge of local services and their personal qualities such as honesty and empathy. Individuals require the services provided by health and social care practitioners to meet their individual needs

2. **The manager:** when reporting information about the care, treatment or support provided to individuals, when participating in training and professional development. Managers provide leadership and support to health and social care practitioners

3. **The practitioner:** when liaising with and seeking advice from other practitioners who may have specialist areas of expertise, i.e. nutritionists, occupational therapists, psychologists. Practitioners provide skills, knowledge and experience

4. **Colleagues:** when communicating with colleagues over aspects of individuals' care and support. Colleagues are the source of peer support and expertise

5. **The team:** when meeting the specific health and social care needs of individuals. All health and social care practitioners working in teams of people with a range of skills and knowledge; the team informs practitioners' professional development and the improvement of working practices

6. **External agencies:** when sharing information with other services and organisations in relation to the provision of health and social care services such as Social Services, the Care Quality Commission, the police. These agencies are useful sources of information and advice and can also provide guidance when difficulties and/or conflicts arise

7. **Internal partners:** when discussing the effectiveness of health and social care services in terms of their delivery approaches and costs. Internal partners are essential for ensuring best practice and identifying areas for improvements

8. **Families:** when assessing their needs, providing them with information about the services available in their local area, involving them in individuals' plans for care, support and treatment. Families are important for providing individuals with the emotional and practical support they require

9. **Parents/carers:** when getting to know the individual accessing services including information about their background, their personality and preferences. Parents and carers are valuable sources of experience and expertise

Command word activity

Describe (AC 4.2)

For one of the job roles you researched in the explain activity for AC4.1 develop a poster to show your understanding of all the different working relationships that will be involved in that person carrying out their day-to-day work activities; you should also identify a specific health or social care setting relevant to the job role.

4.3 Explain the need for health and social care practitioners to adhere to the boundaries of their job role

The working relationships you learned about are focused around health and social care practitioners' job roles; they involve following policies and procedures and codes of conduct as well as maintaining boundaries. The quality of these working relationships with individuals and others will influence the quality of care, support and treatment provided.

Health and social care practitioners' job descriptions indicate the level and type of work activities that they are contracted to do; this will depend on their experience, knowledge and skills. For example, some job roles may require leading a team, working on their own or providing specialist care and treatment such as in relation to dementia care, diabetes care or administering medication.

As health and social care practitioners are accountable for their actions they must only carry out the tasks that have been specified in their job descriptions, that they have been trained to do and feel competent to carry them out safely i.e. are in their sphere of competence. Not doing so may not only mean that they are in breach of their contracts with their employers but they may also be placing themselves, individuals and others at risk with respect to their health, safety and well-being.

All health and social care practitioners will also be expected to carry out their duties and responsibilities to a high standard, professionally and in line with the organisation's culture and priorities that are set out in the work setting's policies, procedures and working codes of practice so as to avoid any conflicts of interest that may interfere with the practitioner's ability to meet individuals' needs while carrying out their duties.

Following their employer's policies and procedures is a legal requirement and part of their responsibilities; it is essential to ensuring the provision of safe, effective and high-quality care and support.

✔ Check your understanding

1. Name two responsibilities of health and social care practitioners
2. Describe the role of the Manager in health and social care settings.
3. Describe the role of the Team in health and social care settings.
4. State two consequences of health and social care practitioners not adhering to their job roles.

Case scenario: Yanis (AC 4.1, 4.2, 4.3)

Yanis has been working for five years as a care assistant in a residential care service that provides care and support to older people. Yanis is thinking about gaining some more experience in another field and would like to perhaps work with adults with mental health needs, or with children who have disabilities. Yanis is meeting with his manager to discuss his personal development plan and will be seeking guidance from him as he has experience of working in both the mental health services and with children and young people.

After meeting with his manager, Yanis reflects on their discussion and decides that his skills, knowledge and personal qualities are more suited to working with adults rather than children or young people and decides to conduct some desk research about the different job roles available in the mental health field.

1. Why is it important that Yanis finds out about what different job roles involve before he works in another field?
2. What personal qualities do you think may be more suitable to working with adults rather than children or young people? Why?
3. What working relationships may mental health practitioners have?

Read about it

Care Quality Commission (2015) 'Guidance for providers on meeting the regulations, Health and Social Care Act 2008 (Regulated Activities) Regulations 2014 (Part 3) (as amended), Care Quality Commission (Registration) Regulations 2009 (Part 4) (as amended)', Care Quality Commission.

HCPC (2016) 'Standards of conduct, performance and ethics', London: Health & Care Professions Council.

Monitor (2013) 'Substantive guidance on the Procurement, Patient Choice and Competition Regulations', Monitor.

Morris, C., FerreiroPeteiro, M. and Collier, F. (2015) *Level 3 Health and Social Care Diploma*, London: Hodder Education.

National Development Team for Inclusion/ Helen Sanderson Associates *et al.* (2010) 'Personalisation: Don't just do it, co-produce it and live it!'. Available at **www.ndti.org.uk**

Schön, D. (1983) 'The reflective practitioner: How professionals think in action', Basic Books, 1983.

SCIE (2014) 'Fact sheet: Overview of the Care Act', Social Care Institute for Excellence.

Websites

Care Quality Commission – (guidance on how CQC inspect and regulate health and social care providers)
https://www.cqc.org.uk/content/how-we-inspect-and-regulate-guide-providers

Equality and Human Rights Commission – (information about the Equality Act 2010)

https://www.equalityhumanrights.com/en/equality-act/equality-act-faqs

Equality and Human Rights Commission – (information about the Human Rights Act 1998)

https://www.equalityhumanrights.com/en/human-rights/human-rights-act

Government publications – (Health and Social Care Act 2012: fact sheets) **https://www.gov.uk/government/publications/health-and-social-care-act-2012-fact-sheets**

Government publications – (information about the Data Protection Act)

https://www.gov.uk/data-protection/the-data-protection-act

Healthwatch – (information about the functions of Healthwatch)

http://www.healthwatch.co.uk/

NICE – (information about the functions of NICE)

https://www.nice.org.uk/guidance?unlid

NHS England – (information about the functions of NHS England)

https://www.england.nhs.uk/

NSPCC – (Child protection in England, legislation, policy and guidance)

https://www.nspcc.org.uk/preventing-abuse/child-protection-system/england/legislation-policy-guidance/

Public Health England – (information about the functions of Public Health England) https://www.gov.uk/government/organisations/public-health-england

Skills for Care – (information and resources about the Care Certificate Framework)

http://www.skillsforcare.org.uk/Documents/Learning-and-development/Care-Certificate/The-Care-Certificate-Framework.pdf

Skills for Health – (information and resources about the Care Certificate Framework)

http://www.skillsforhealth.org.uk/standards/item/216-the-care-certificate

The Health and Safety Executive (HSE) – (information about the Health and Safety at Work Act 1974)

http://www.hse.gov.uk/legislation/hswa.htm

Unit HSC CM8: How will I be graded?

The table below shows what the learner must do to achieve each grading criterion. Learners must achieve all the criteria for a grade to be awarded (i.e. criteria D1 to D3 must be achieved to pass this unit assessment at grade D). A higher grade may not be awarded before a lower grade has been achieved in full, although component criteria of a higher grade may have been achieved.

Grade		Assessment grading criteria	Assessment of learning / What you need to show
D1	1.1	Describe the relationship between legislation, policies and procedures.	The description must provide evidence of understanding: • the differences between legislation, policies and procedures • the relationship between legislation, policies and procedures. The description may include how one influences the other.
D2	1.2	Summarise legislation in relation to health and social care.	Provide a summary of current legislation in relation to health and social care.
D3		Show evidence of reading or use of sources.	There should be evidence of learners' reading or use of sources. Learners must use a minimum of two traceable references to support the discussion.
C1	4.1	Explain the roles and responsibilities of health and social care practitioners.	The explanation must show an understanding of the roles and responsibilities of health and social care practitioners. More than one of the possible roles and responsibilities must be considered in the explanation.
C2	4.2	Describe different working relationships in health and social care settings.	The description must show an understanding of different working relationships in the health and social care setting. More than one working relationship in the health and social care setting must be considered.
C3	4.3	Explain the need for health and social care practitioners to adhere to the boundaries of their own job role.	The need for boundaries must be explained in depth. The explanation must demonstrate: • an understanding of more than one boundary • the importance of adhering to boundaries within their job role.
C4		Show evidence of reading or use of sources with referencing relevant to the explanation or description. Good use of vocabulary and grammar.	Use of referencing should show evidence of reading or use of sources. Vocabulary and grammar should be appropriate and accurate for purposes.

Grade		Assessment grading criteria	Assessment of learning / What you need to show
B1	1.3	Analyse how legislation informs policies and procedures in health and social care provision.	Analysis must show an understanding of legislation and policies and procedures in health and social care provision. Analysis must demonstrate understanding of ways that legislation informs policies and procedures in health and social care provision. Examples may be given to support evidence of understanding. Links to D1.
B2	2.1	Explain reasons for professional standards and codes of practice within the health and social care sector.	Provide an explanation of the reasons why professional standards and codes of practice are in place within the health and social care sector. The explanation must demonstrate understanding of the differences between professional standards and codes of practice.
B3	2.2	Summarise requirements of professional standards and codes of practice.	Give a summary of the requirements for both professional standards and codes of practice to include: • regulations • public expectations • other requirements.
B4		Show evidence of reading or use of sources. Referencing supports the analysis, explanation or summary.	Use of reading or use of sources should be shown through a range of relevant referencing. Referencing should be used appropriately to support the analysis, explanation or summary.
A1	3.2	Describe factors that influence national and local service delivery.	The description should: • differentiate between national and local service delivery of health and social care • describe factors that influence both national and local service delivery of health and social care. Examples should be given to support evidence of understanding.
A2		Show evidence of wider background reading or use of sources. Referencing supports the description.	Wider background reading should be evident or a wide range of source material should be used.
A*1	3.1	Explain the functions of national and local health and social care provision.	Provide an explanation of functions of national and local health and social care provision. A detailed explanation must include: • understanding of the functions of national health and social care provision • understanding of the functions of local health and social care provision • functions which are common to both national and local health and social care provision.
A*2		Show evidence of a range of background reading or use of sources used selectively.	Learners should show the ability to consider or explore relevant issues which contribute to the explanation. An extensive range of background reading or use of sources should be used selectively and cited appropriately.
Current legislation as relevant to Home Nation.			

HSC CM9
Reflective Practice

Learning outcomes

LO1: Understand professional development

1.1 Identify standards relating to professional development in health and social care

1.2 Explain continuing professional development

LO2: Understand the role of reflective practice in professional development

2.1 Discuss theoretical perspectives on reflection in relation to professional development

2.2 Explain how reflective practice supports the professional development of the health and social care practitioner

2.3 Analyse how reflective practice supports positive outcomes for:
- individuals / parents / carers
- staff team
- other professionals

LO3: Understand how the health and social care practitioner's own values, beliefs and experiences can influence delivery of care

3.1 Analyse how the health and social care practitioner's own values, beliefs and experiences can influence delivery of care

LO4: Understand how to identify learning needs and plan for professional development in health and social care

4.1 Identify:
- sources of support for learning and development
- professional development opportunities

4.2 Discuss methods for identifying and planning for professional development needs

LO5: Be able to reflect upon and plan for own personal development

5.1 Reflect upon own learning using a model of reflection

5.2 Use outcomes from reflection to assess and plan for own development

About this unit

'Reflective practice' is concerned with thinking about practice and making improvements and positive change. In this unit you will learn what it means to be a professional in health and social care, what guidelines professionals must follow and how they must keep developing their skills and knowledge as part of a continuous professional cycle. You will learn how thinking about what you do improves practice, and how frameworks for reflection can help you develop as a practitioner so that those you care for and those you work with have a better experience. You will learn how your own values, beliefs and experiences influence how you care for others. Professionals are responsible for identifying their own learning needs, finding sources of support for this and planning their own professional development. This unit shows you how to do this. Finally, this unit will help you reflect on and plan for your own personal development using a model of reflection to assist you. Unit HSC DM5: Personal and Professional Development builds upon this unit.

LO1: Understand professional development

Becoming a member of any profession takes hard work and dedication. Years ago, once a person qualified as a nurse or a doctor or social worker that was where their training often ended. They continued to practise in the way they had been trained, even when research showed there was a better way of doing something. Imagine if social workers still took children into care because they had learning difficulties, or if nurses continued to keep people in bed for days after their operation. What if a surgeon continued to amputate limbs that now could be saved? Professionals can only give the best care by continuing to improve their skills and knowledge.

1.1 Identify standards relating to professional development in health and social care

Professional development is a requirement in many careers, not just in health and social care and there are standards and guidance to help professionals continue to develop.

Professional bodies provide guidance and set out the standards of what is expected in that profession. In health care the Nursing and Midwifery Council and the General Medical Council set standards for their professions. The Health and Care Professions Council regulates health, psychological and social work practitioners.

Social workers

The Health and Care Professions Council (HCPC) publish standards of proficiency for social workers in England, which set out what a social worker should know, understand and be able to do when they complete their training so that they can register with the HCPC. It is this registration which allows social workers to practise in the profession for which they have been trained.

In addition to the standards, social workers in England must also follow the Professional Capabilities Framework (PCF), a professional standards framework, which sets out what is

expected of social workers in their continuing professional development after qualification. Social workers in Wales, Scotland and Northern Ireland have National Occupational Standards (NOS) which fulfil the same function. The Government has announced that a new body will be set up to take responsibility for all social work standards, training and regulation of the profession by 2020.

Nurses and midwives

Nurses and midwives are regulated by the Nursing and Midwifery Council (www.nmc.org.uk). Once nurses and midwives pass their final exams they must register with the Council in order to practise in their profession. The Council sets out in the code of practice the professional standards that nurses and midwives must uphold and continue to uphold in order to be registered to practise in the UK. The code is organised around four themes – prioritise people, practise effectively, preserve safety and promote professionalism and trust.

Nurses and midwives must prove they are fit to practise and must revalidate every three years. As part of **revalidation nurses** and midwives must have evidence to show:

- 450 practice hours, or 900 if renewing as both a nurse and midwife
- 35 hours of continuing professional development (CPD) including 20 hours of participatory learning
- Five pieces of practice-related feedback
- Five written reflective accounts
- Reflective discussion
- Health and character declaration
- Professional indemnity arrangement
- Confirmation.

Key terms

Revalidation nurses, midwives and doctors in the UK must revalidate, which means prove they are fit to practise by providing evidence that their skills and knowledge are up to date. Nurses revalidate every three years

Independent regulator a public body that has authority to monitor and inspect a service

Care Quality Commission

The Care Quality Commission (CQC) is the **independent regulator** (see p. 197 for definition) of health and social care in England (www.cqc.org.uk). The CQC monitors, inspects and regulates services to ensure they meet standards of quality and safety. They publish their findings and the performance ratings. They do not regulate individual practitioners such as nurses, midwives or social workers, but if they found an individual practitioner in breach of the relevant professional code, the CQC would report them to the professional body unless a law was broken, in which case, the individual could be prosecuted.

Policies and procedures

Employers in health and social care have local policies and procedures, which deal with quality. Complaints and health and safety policies and procedures are just two examples of ensuring quality in care. Health and care professionals are expected to follow such policies and procedures.

Legislation

Laws may relate to professional development. The Care Act 2014 brought together a lot of previous laws relating to care and many professionals had to take further training in order to comply with this law. Social workers needed training in how to help individuals assess their needs, and how to administer the new personal budget system. Person-centred care and joint working required professionals to work in new ways, for which they required training. Safeguarding was given a greater emphasis under this Act, requiring professionals to be trained in their specific responsibilities.

The Health and Social Care Act 2012 brought in NHS reforms which many people including professionals must follow in their practice. For health and care professionals, trying to understand reforms and guidelines is part of professional development.

The Health and Social Care Act 2008 (Regulated Activities) Regulations 2014 set out the requirements that all providers must meet in order to be registered with CQC and they impose a duty of candour on practitioners to be open with individuals receiving care or with their representatives. These Regulations set out the minimum level of care CQC expects and the sanctions that will be imposed if basic standards are not met. Health and social care practitioners must be aware of these fundamental standards.

Take it further

For an overview of the Health and Social Care Act 2012 reforms, watch the King's Fund animation available at **http://www.kingsfund.org.uk/projects/nhs-65/alternative-guide-new-nhs-england**.

Command word activity

Identify (AC 1.1)

Which standards relate to professional development in health and social care? Research the codes of practice relating to social work, nursing and midwifery and then briefly explain how each relates to professional development. Start with the standards you have already met in the course, then add others as you read about them.

Classroom discussion (AC 1.1)

Should practitioners be expected to continuously develop in their profession?

1. Work in pairs. Person A gives three reasons why practitioners should develop, while Person B gives three reasons why they should not.
2. All As get together and pool ideas. All Bs do the same.
3. Hold a debate, with speaking time limited to one minute each.
4. At the end of half an hour, vote on 'Should practitioners be expected to continuously develop in their profession?'

1.2 Explain continuing professional development

Continuing professional development (CPD) implies that gaining the professional qualification is not the end of learning. CPD requires ongoing learning and staying up to date with sector developments.

Many professionals update their knowledge by reading professional journals, which provide up-to-date information on current professional issues and new research.

Social workers may read the *British Journal of Social Work* published by Oxford Journals or the *Journal of Social Work* published by Sage.

Nurses may read the *International Journal of Nursing Studies*.

Midwives may read *MIDIRS* (Midwives Information & Resource Service) which provides a summary of current research in the care of pregnant women, new mothers or infants.

Community Care, *Nursing Times* and *Nursing Standard* offer a less academic format.

Merely reading journals is not sufficient; CPD happens when you use the information to improve your own practice.

Conferences provide another way to keep up to date and may offer a perspective which can influence policy at national or international level. Practitioners share good practice and find ways to improve the quality of care across borders. The European Conference for Social Work Research and the International Conference on Cancer Nursing are just two examples of these. Both the Royal College of Midwives and the Royal College of Nursing hold annual conferences. These provide an opportunity for networking, meeting other professionals in the same field, and sharing good practice.

Independent research is yet another way to keep developing professionally. It is, however, difficult for practitioners in the field to conduct research while doing their day job. Reading research findings and informing others, perhaps as part of a staff meeting or when mentoring students,

contributes to CPD. Research may be undertaken formally, perhaps as part of further study, and such research will be subject to the requirements imposed by the institution or workplace. It is important that the relevant permission, for example, by the ethics committee, is sought before starting research.

Setting actions for yourself and recording your achievements in a learning journal is good evidence of continuing professional development. Examples of actions might be:

- to read and summarise an article from a professional journal once a week
- to present a summary of your reading to a staff meeting
- based on your reading, to suggest ways to improve practice.

Reviewing – looking back on what you have learned and how you have changed your practice – provides evidence of continuing professional development. Perhaps you have decided to improve your communication skills on the basis of some feedback received and actions you have set. Consider Case scenario: Kiran.

Continuing professional development is lifelong learning. It is about informing oneself about latest developments in practice such as new drug treatments or new ways of working with other practitioners. There is always something new to learn and new ways of doing things, whether it is keeping records or taking a temperature. CPD

Case scenario: Kiran (AC 1.2)

Kiran was shy when she started work at a care home. Her manager reviewed her performance after a month and suggested Kiran become proactive in communicating with residents.

As a result of this feedback Kiran:

- greets each resident individually when she arrives
- makes a point of talking with each one during her shift
- learned a few words of Hindi from Mrs Raj, a long-time resident.

1. Which methods of CPD did Kiran use?
2. What should she do next?

is positive and helps professionals to keep up to date in their practice. CPD is not optional; the practitioner who does not develop professionally jeopardises the quality of care they offer and in many professions also risks losing their professional qualification.

Command word activity

Explain (AC 1.2)

What is meant by continuing professional development? Research this term then write a clear explanation, giving examples of how a practitioner such as a nurse or social worker can continuously develop their professional skills. Use at least two sources to help you and reference each source.

Key term

Standards guidance and rules regulating a profession or institution, including codes of conduct and practice, Regulations, registration requirements, National Occupational Standards and the Human Rights Act

Case scenario (AC 1.2)

Ahmed has been working in Accident and Emergency since he qualified as a nurse one year ago. He is very busy, often works longer than he should and gets home exhausted. He is worried that as yet he has no evidence of continuing professional development in his portfolio for revalidation.

1. Think of at least three things he can do towards continuing professional development.
2. Consider the advantages and disadvantages of each of your suggestions.

Take it further

Read the codes which apply to health care practitioners on these websites:

www.nmc.org.uk/standards/code/

www.hpc-uk.org/aboutregistration/standards/cpd

Check your understanding

1. Give three examples of standards that relate to professional development in health and social care.
2. How long does continuing professional development last?
3. Which sources could a practitioner use for continuing professional development?
4. How might a practitioner use these sources as continuing professional development?

LO2: Understand the role of reflective practice in professional development

Reflective practice involves thinking about what you do, analysing the decisions you made and the actions you took, in order to improve. Reflective practice is not new but various people have devised theories to help people reflect. In this section we discuss four theories, but there are many more.

2.1 Discuss theoretical perspectives on reflection in relation to professional development

Kolb's Experiential Learning Cycle

Kolb's is a straightforward model that shows how learning is cyclical – it never stops. Below are the parts of the cycle followed by some examples of how it works in practice.

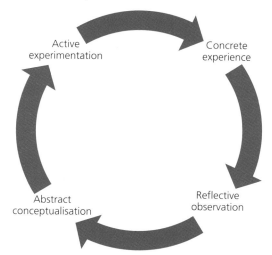

Figure 9.1 Kolb's Experiential Learning Cycle

Concrete experience: Bartek meets Mr Z who is deaf. Bartek greets Mr Z with 'Hi, how are you today?' Mr Z does not respond.

Reflective observation: Bartek thinks back to the interchange and realises Mr Z did not respond because he did not realise Bartek was talking to him. Is it because of where he was standing?

Abstract conceptualisation: Bartek thinks of various ways he can change the situation such as shouting louder, waving and changing his position.

Active experimentation: Bartek positions himself so the light falls on his face and Mr Z can see him. He repeats the greeting and this time Mr Z replies. Bartek realises that Mr Z lip reads and needs to be able to see the speaker's lips. Next time he speaks to Mr Z, Bartek makes sure Mr Z can see his face.

Concrete experience leads on to reflection about the incident, which leads to Bartek thinking about communication skills and experimenting with a different approach.

Honey and Mumford's learning styles

Honey and Mumford's theory was a development of Kolb's learning cycle. Honey and Mumford identified four learning styles, and suggested most people use two of these. See Table 9.1.

Honey and Mumford's learning style theory has many similarities with Kolb's theory and the two theories are often combined.

- Activists are associated with Concrete Experience
- Reflectors with Reflective Observation
- Theorists with Abstract Conceptualisation
- Pragmatists with Active Experiment

Understanding the learning cycle and knowing your preferred learning style may help you to identify your strengths and areas for improvement. You may have to learn to use other learning styles to become a competent practitioner. If you are keen to jump into a new project you may be an activist or a pragmatist, but perhaps you may need to look into the underpinning theories a little more. Sometimes a new approach will have more far-reaching consequences than initially realised; for example, when surgeons began using laparoscopic techniques for day surgery, it changed nursing. Individuals were no longer expected to be in hospital for a week or two but were often home on the same day. Nurses had to learn not just the new way of working with a higher turnover of patients, and greater liaison with other professionals about discharge planning, but they had to understand the theory of keyhole surgery to monitor surgical complications.

As another example, when many children's homes were closed and there was a move to fostering looked-after children, social workers too had to change their ways of working. Instead of placing children in residential homes they had to recruit and train more foster parents and take time to match the child with foster parents. They had to understand the theory behind changes, a change from an institutional perspective meeting the needs of social services, to a perspective that put the child at the centre of the process, a person-centred approach. Reflective practitioners adapt to change; sometimes they lead change!

Table 9.1 Honey and Mumford's learning styles

Learning style	They like	They do not like
Activists learn by doing	Problem solving New challenges Being the centre of activity	Following through with the detailed implementation ideas
Reflectors learn by listening, thinking, observing	Gathering all the information before coming to a decision	Being forced to make a decision without the full information
Theorists want to understand why things happen	Logic, certainties and facts, following a step-by-step approach	Emotions, subjective opinions, thinking outside the box
Pragmatists learn by trial and error	Finding practical solutions to problems	Taking time to consider all the different approaches

Take it further

You can read more about this on Rosewell, J. 'Technology: Level 1 Networked living: exploring information and communication technologies', available at **http://www.open.edu/openlearnworks/pluginfile.php/69355/mod_page/content/1/learning_styles.pdf**

Gibb's Reflective Cycle

Gibb's Reflective Cycle is another model which shows that the process of reflection is continuous. See a summary of the cycle in Figure 9.2.

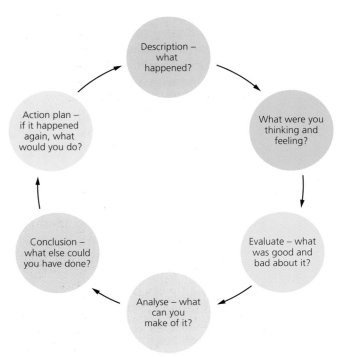

Figure 9.2 Gibb's Reflective Cycle

Gibb's cycle includes an analysis of thoughts and feelings, whereas the previous models focus on actions. It starts with a factual description of what happened but then proceeds to examine the practitioner's thoughts and feelings at the time. The situation is evaluated, weighing up the good points and bad points, then trying to interpret the situation. This leads to a conclusion which assesses the possible alternatives. Finally, an action plan is made so that if the situation happens again, the practitioner has alternatives ready. One issue with this model is that it views the situation primarily from the viewpoint of the practitioner, focusing on their emotions and experiences. The viewpoint of others in the situation is not considered.

Reflection in action/reflection on action (Schön)

Schön developed a theory of reflection in action and reflection on action.

Reflection in action occurs when the event is happening. For example, an individual collapses in front of you. You might panic at first and consider whether to shout for help or check he is breathing and has a pulse. Reflection in action happens quickly. You might ask 'Am I doing the right thing?' as you do it.

Later, when the situation has been resolved, you might think back to what you did and how you felt. This is reflection on action. As a result of reflection on action you might decide that you need to learn how to do emergency resuscitation in case the situation happens again.

 Classroom discussion (AC2.1)

Check back that you understand theories by
- Kolb
- Honey and Mumford
- Gibbs
- Schön
1. Divide the class into four equal groups. Each group is assigned one theorist and discusses the strengths and weaknesses of their theorist.

2. For each theoretical perspective, give at least one example from health and social care of how the theory may be applied. In your discussion, show how these perspectives can assist in professional development.
3. Come together as a whole class and decide which theories are similar and where theories are different.

2.2 Explain how reflective practice supports the professional development of the health and social care practitioner

Reflective practice supports professional development and positive outcomes in several ways.

It provides an ongoing review of practice and outcomes which the practitioner can record in their personal development journal. They can then look back and see how they have learned to tackle difficult issues.

Reflective practice provides a means of analysis. A learning styles analysis helps the practitioner to understand how they learn best and also the areas they need to work on. Gibb's cycle analyses feeling and emotions as well as events. Schön's reflection in action and on action helps practitioners to break down the component parts of an interaction so they can explore alternatives.

Analysis may lead a practitioner to form an action plan. It may be that, in the previous example, the person witnessing someone collapse might plan to refresh their resuscitation skills, or they may focus on managing their emotions and feelings when coping with an emergency.

Reflective practice encourages practitioners to explore alternative approaches and strategies, such as when Bartek reflected on his interaction with Mr Z and explored different approaches. A good practitioner explores different approaches and does not repeat the same mistakes.

Reflective practice helps practitioners to identify and plan for their learning needs, increasing personal and professional confidence and self-awareness. For example, Sue, a second year student nurse was on a surgical ward. She had never given an injection although in class they had practised on models and she knew the theory of how to give injections. She identified the gap in her skills and talked with her mentor. She planned that she would observe five injections while on the ward and then would give an injection under the supervision of a senior nurse. Once she had done this, she regularly gave injections on the ward and became confident in that skill.

Some nurses, midwives and social workers who mentor students choose to take teaching qualifications after they qualify. Other nurses may specialise in a specific area, for example diabetes or pain management, and take postgraduate qualifications in that field. Social workers may specialise in an area such as mental health.

Using a model for reflective practice helps practitioners to view situations from different perspectives, for example, from the viewpoint of an individual person receiving a service, or from the viewpoint of other professionals. You can see the importance of viewpoint in the following scenario.

Synthesising ideas is part of professional

Case scenario (AC 2.2)

Miss C was a sprightly 80 year old who used to sing in a choir before being admitted to residential care. Her friends are elderly and no longer drive so find it difficult to visit her in care home as it is in the country. Many of the other residents are deaf, which makes it difficult for Miss C to talk to them. Most days she sits in a chair in the lounge, looking out at the garden.

Jake, the health care practitioner, used Gibb's model of reflective practice. He saw very little happening for the residents and felt sad because physical care seemed to be all that was offered. Evaluating the situation, he saw that while residents were fed and kept warm, their social and emotional needs were unmet. Analysing it, he realised that routines were organised around the needs of the organisation rather than residents. Staff were busy, but making the beds was more important than a resident's personal engagement. He concluded that ignoring the social and emotional needs of residents such as Miss C was not good care and, in fact, Miss C had become depressed. Residents who sit around all day, with nothing to do, have poor circulation, little appetite for food and are unmotivated. Jake made an action plan – to organise a sing along. He was given permission to try it and found several residents joined in with the songs. This became a regular Tuesday afternoon activity which Miss C and other residents eagerly looked forward to.

In this case, Gibbs' model was used. Work through the case scenario and use Schön's model for reflection. Explain reflection in action and on action in this situation.

1. Look back at Unit HSC CM6 to remind yourself about Maslow's hierarchy of needs. How can Maslow's hierarchy of needs be utilised in this scenario?

development. In the case scenario above, Jake brought together the ideas of holistic care, Maslow's hierarchy of needs and reflective practice to improve the quality of care. By linking theory to practice he improved care, gained new skills and increased in confidence. Jake was a reflective practitioner so he did not leave it there, but gradually expanded the range of activities available to residents and involved members of the local community. Local scouts came to do gardening with the residents, and a local choir joined their singing group.

In the case scenario, we can see that Jake's experience was just one step in lifelong learning. His own professional development was supported in developing these activities. He will have had to consider health and safety; issues of consent; equal opportunities for all to join in; planning and organising time, people and resources. He had to ensure other aspects of care were not neglected too. He gained confidence, learned a range of communication skills and applied new learning to future practice.

Command word activity

Explain (AC 2.2)

1. Explain what is meant by reflective practice. Draw on your own experience where possible but ensure confidentiality by not naming people. Use examples from either a care home or hospital or other care setting to support your explanation.
2. How does reflective practice support the professional development of the health and social care practitioner in such a setting? Use examples to support your explanation.

2.3 Analyse how reflective practice supports positive outcomes

We saw in Jake's case scenario how reflective practice can support professional development, but practitioners do not use reflective practice just to benefit themselves. Reflective practice brings benefits for individuals, parents, carers, staff and other professionals.

For individuals / parents / carers

Consider the following case scenario to observe the positive impact that reflective practice can have on individuals and other carers.

Case scenario – part 1 (AC 2.3)

Evelina is a student nurse on placement in a nursing home which caters for people with dementia. George, a seventy year old, has been admitted because his wife can no longer cope with his mood swings and violent outbursts. George is restless and walks up and down, trying to get out into the garden. As he does so, other residents become scared. George becomes more and more agitated, swearing at people and eventually becoming so angry he has to be taken to his own room.

Using Gibb's model of reflection, Evelina realises that George became agitated when he realised he could not get out. No one came to talk to him and he became even more agitated. Evelina analysed the situation and realised that neither George nor other individuals were getting safe care. George's violence made the situation unsafe for everyone.

Evelina considered what else could be done. She read about dementia and some examples of good-quality care. This helped her to understand that George's anger was in response to feeling trapped. She made an action plan to learn more about caring for people with dementia and at the same time she decided to find out if the garden could be made safe for people to go out into when they wished. Working with the manager and gardener, they made a safe outdoor space that could be accessed by George and other residents. George was much more settled when he could get out. He and some of the other residents grew vegetables and took pleasure in watching them grow. Evelina also arranged for the vegetables to be used by the cook in the kitchen, and the residents enjoyed having them prepared and served as part of their meals. Very soon, George's violent outbursts lessened.

George's wife visited every day. As George settled in and took up gardening again, she said it reminded her of how he used to be before he became ill. He had been a keen gardener.

1. Look back at Gibb's model of reflective practice and try to match the stages with Evelina's thoughts and feelings.

Figure 9.3 A dementia-friendly garden

For staff team

The use of reflective practice can also impact positively on other members of staff, as seen in the continuation of the case scenario below.

 Case scenario – part 2

As part of her action plan, Evelina contacted Dementia Friends and organised a training session for all the staff in the nursing home. The gardener and the cook were especially keen to attend as they had no care training and wanted to know more. The staff found that individuals who used to get agitated were much calmer if they went out into the fresh air. Now staff did not have to spend too much time managing disruptive behaviour; they could spend time talking with residents and offering more activities. The gardener and the cook now understand how to interact with people with dementia and no longer avoid talking to George.

1. How does reflective practice benefit members of the staff team who are not carers?

For other professionals

It is not just the practitioner themselves who can benefit from reflective practice. There are various other health and social care practitioners who can experience professional development and positive outcomes as a result.

 Case scenario – part 3

The local GP and the pharmacist found that since the residents had more to do with their time, and had the garden where they could take some gentle exercise, less medication and fewer interventions were needed. The exercise improved both their physical and mental health; for example, some individuals experienced reduced blood pressure and many experienced improved mood, appetite, sleep habits and energy levels.

1. How does reflective practice benefit other professionals such as the GP and pharmacist?

Command word activity

Analyse (AC 2.3)

1. Using the above case scenario as an example, choose a different health and social care setting to produce a case study to analyse how reflective practice supports positive outcomes for:
   a. individuals/parents/carers
   b. staff team
   c. other professionals.
2. Use at least two different theoretical perspectives to support your analysis.

 Classroom discussion (AC 2.2, 2.3)

Consider the following statement as a class debate or discussion:

'Practitioners who do not prove they use reflective practice are a danger to the public and should be struck off their professional register.'

✔ Check your understanding

1. List three examples of theoretical perspectives on reflection.
2. How can reflection support professional development of practitioners? Give at least three ways.
3. How may reflective practice support positive outcomes for individuals? Give two examples.

LO3: Understand how the health and social care practitioner's own values, beliefs and experiences can influence delivery of care

Values are based on moral principles. For instance, we may value fairness, honesty, and treating people with respect.

Beliefs are opinions and are not necessarily based on facts; for example, some might believe that immigration into Britain is a new thing, but if we delve into history, we can see evidence that this is not the case.

Experiences are things that happen to a person during their life; for example, a child's experience of growing up is changed by significant events such as divorce.

Our values, beliefs and experiences influence our attitudes which in turn influence how we behave.

Own identity and belief systems

Our identity is shaped by our environment and by how we are socialised. A child absorbs the beliefs of those around them, whether it is that smoking is acceptable or whether their nationality/religion/football club is better than anyone else's. It is only when we experience secondary socialisation that we meet other beliefs and begin to question those we were raised with. Our identity changes as we change our beliefs. We may become more (or less) tolerant, more (or less) law abiding.

Personal and professional attitudes and behaviour: impact upon practice

Attitudes affect behaviour. A person whose attitude is prejudiced against others because of their skin colour, or their religion or their sexuality, will stereotype and label those they disapprove of. Their prejudiced attitude affects how they treat others. A prejudiced person might refuse to care for someone who is of a different religion or skin colour or might give them less or poor quality care.

Practitioners must learn to be aware of their prejudices, be prepared to question themselves and challenge their prejudices because their attitude may affect their behaviour and cause them to discriminate unfairly.

Professional attitudes in health and social care value diversity. Professional behaviour is to treat people fairly, according to their needs. Codes of practice make this clear. Practitioners must behave in a professional way, adhering to all policies and procedures within the setting. Person-centred practice places cultural and spiritual identity at the core of practice and practitioners need to be well informed of the personal needs of the individuals they are caring for in order to achieve this.

Following an evaluation of service delivery the NHS Constitution (2012) set out six values which health care professionals are expected to adopt and embed in practice. These values are:

- Compassion
- Respect and dignity
- Commitment to quality care
- Working together for patients
- Everyone counts
- Improving lives.

Sykes and Durham (2014) suggest using a framework to embed values. The framework is referred to as OPCE, where practitioners:

- Observe what happens
- Praise good practice
- Challenge poor practice and
- Escalate concerns using the organisation's procedures if poor practice does not improve.

Key terms

Values based on moral principles
Beliefs opinions not necessarily based on facts
Experiences things that happen to us

3.1 Analyse how the health and social care practitioner's own values, beliefs and experiences can influence delivery of care

Values, beliefs and experiences vary for each individual and help shape our identity. What follows is a case scenario that demonstrates how these differences can influence the practice of a health and social care practitioner.

Case scenario (AC 3.1)

Zak grew up in a multi-cultural city and went to school with friends from many different cultural groups. He was used to going round to friends for Hannukah, Eid, Christmas and Diwali.

Mary grew up in a small rural village and, although she learned about different cultures at school, she only met people from different cultures when she went to university. She was used to going to church on Sunday and celebrating Christmas.

Zak and Mary each had different experiences. Zak was already more culturally competent and able to understand differences and similarities between cultures, so when he trained as a social worker, he was able to cope with individual differences quite easily.

Mary lacked cultural competence and later as an adult, during her training as a nurse, she found it difficult to understand people who wore different clothes, spoke a different language and ate different food. It took her a long time to adjust to seeing people of colour and understanding their needs. She felt much more comfortable caring for people who were like herself and was anxious not to make mistakes with people whose culture she did not understand.

Zak learned the values of tolerance, fairness and justice early in life. He thought that everyone should be entitled to basic health and care, whatever their background, ethnic origin or religion. He believed that each person is an individual and should not be labelled or stereotyped because of their gender, or the colour of their skin or their disabilities. Zak's values influenced not only his personal life and friendships but his professional life too.

Mary made friends with Rani, an Indian nurse, and gradually learned to see Rani and her family as friends. She learned some of their customs and why they wore the clothes they did. Her journey to cultural competence was slower but she realised that as a practitioner she needed to see people as individuals.

One of Zak's placements as a student social worker involved working in a care home. Joe, a 90-year-old gentleman with dementia, held racist beliefs and when he first saw Zak, made some nasty comments. Zak was hurt, of course, but as a professional continued to treat Joe with the same respect that he treated others in the home. Joe had been a professional football player so Zak asked him about football. Joe came to look forward to their daily chats and forgot his racist comments. Zak's attitude of tolerance influenced his behaviour. His experience of getting on with others enabled him to behave in a professional manner and impacted on his practice. Zak put aside his own feelings. He knew that having dementia meant that sometimes Joe would say and do things that are socially unacceptable. Zak believed that Joe was entitled to have his own views, however different they were to his own; and instead of focusing on differences, Zak found something they both had in common, football, as a way to build a rapport with Joe. This rapport then helped as he encouraged Joe to maintain his interest in following a team.

1. Use the OPCE model below and apply it to what happened between Zak and Joe:
   - Observe what happens
   - Praise good practice
   - Challenge poor practice, and
   - Escalate concerns using the organisation's procedures if poor practice does not improve.
2. How might Mary have benefited from gaining cultural competence earlier?

Command word activity

Analyse (AC 3.1)

Choose one area which you feel has been influenced by your own experiences. How could this impact on your professional practice in health and social care?

Consider this from more than one perspective. How could your practice impact on individuals and their carers, on other staff and other professionals? How could you relate to or perceive others you work with, colleagues and individuals.

Use examples to support your points. Read around this and refer to what you have read in your analysis. Reference your sources and aim to use three different sources.

Classroom discussion (AC 3.1)

Should transgender treatment be available on the NHS?

First, find out about gender dysphoria by reading the NHS pages here: www.nhs.uk/Conditions/Gender-dysphoria

1. Consider three arguments in favour of this treatment being available on the NHS and three arguments against treatment on the NHS.
2. What does your opinion tell you about your values and beliefs? You may have to analyse your thoughts and feelings.
3. How might these values and beliefs influence your practice?
4. Should these values and beliefs influence your delivery of care?

Check your understanding

1. What is the difference between values and beliefs?
2. Give three examples of experiences that may change you as a person.
3. Give three examples of how attitudes may influence the delivery of care.

LO4: Understand how to identify learning needs and plan for professional development in health and social care

Take it further

This section links closely with the Unit HSC DM5. You may find evidence in your personal development plan which is useful for this section.

4.1 Identifying sources of support and professional development opportunities

When a person qualifies as a health and social care practitioner they are competent and up to date at that point, but things change. New ways of working, new ways of dealing with health and social care situations emerge. This means that a practitioner's knowledge can quickly become out of date. In order to ensure they are delivering the best possible care, they must continue to learn and develop their practice.

Sources of support for learning and development

Sources of support may be formal or informal. For example:

1. Formally you can take advantage of any mentoring schemes available in your organisation.
2. Informally you can observe others and learn how they manage situations.

Sources of support can include the following:

- **appraisal:** a formal method of getting feedback from your manager about what you do well and where you can improve.
- **supervision:** an opportunity to discuss issues that you may feel uncertain about how to handle.
- **feedback:** such as from individuals who you care for, is especially valuable. If it is positive, you know what to continue doing. If it is negative, you know you need to change what you do.
- **mentoring:** where a more experienced person meets with you regularly to offer support and advice, is useful when you are new to an organisation.
- **shadowing:** where you observe another practitioner, is especially useful if you shadow someone who has a different role.
- **independent study:** e.g. by taking an open learning course to extend your knowledge and understanding of dementia.
- **research:** often in collaboration with a university.
- **placement:** a good way to find out if you would like to work in a particular area before you apply for a job in that field.
- **volunteering:** gives you an opportunity to gain more skills and to understand how care spans more than just hospitals or care homes.

- **peer observations:** where you observe others and then they observe you, can help you learn new ways of managing situations and identify any skills gaps you may have.
- **external agencies:** such as Age UK, run befriending schemes for which you can volunteer. Befriending someone not only helps them but also is a good way to develop your own communication skills.

In some parts of the country, the police shadow community psychiatric nurses as part of their training. This helps them to understand mental health issues and the role of the community psychiatric nurse. This scheme has positive outcomes for those individuals with mental health issues cared for in the community, as they are often the victims of crime.

As a professional, you are responsible for your own continuing learning and development.

Professional development opportunities
Professional development opportunities include:

1. Training courses offered by your own organisation, or a university. There are distance learning opportunities and online programmes that may offer a more flexible approach to formal learning and work. Postgraduate courses are available at many universities to teach the skills of research, enabling practitioners to go on and pursue a career in this field.
2. Reading journals and then having a professional discussion with colleagues.
3. Shadowing other team members gives a greater insight into how their role fits with your own.

Awareness of the media is essential for practitioners. Individuals now have access to much more information and many are fully aware of latest developments in the field. A carer for someone with dementia may ask you about gene therapy to prevent the onset of dementia. If you are a health and social care practitioner, individuals expect you to know the latest developments in the news and health and social care research.

Command word activity
Identify (AC 4.1)
1. Choose a job role in health and social care. Identify the range of support, learning and professional development opportunities available for a practitioner in that job role.
2. Look back at the section on learning styles.
   a. Which development opportunities would suit activists?
   b. Which might suit reflectors?
   c. Which might suit theorists?
   d. Which might suit pragmatists?

Self-evaluation is perhaps the most difficult and yet the most rewarding way of developing professionally. Only you really know your own strengths and areas for improvement. Others may give feedback about what they see but they have only a partial understanding of what makes you tick. Analysing your own areas for development, planning to meet those needs and carrying out your plan is how you develop.

4.2 Discuss methods for identifying and planning for professional development needs
Methods for identifying professional development needs have been discussed earlier in the chapter. Obtaining feedback, reviewing your knowledge, skills and understanding against relevant professional standards such as the codes of practice or the NHS values will help you to establish development needs.

Think too about where you want to be in five years' time. Make sure that your development does not just focus on your current role but that you identify skills you will need in a future role, perhaps as a specialist practitioner or a teacher or manager. Shadowing is an excellent way to help identify development needs if you shadow someone in the role you aspire to.

Learning styles
Take the time to understand your own learning style. Are you a reflector but need to learn to be an activist for the role you are in? If so, this is a

development need. Competent practitioners do not just stay with their preferred learning style. For instance, they may know that at times they need to be a pragmatist while at others they must be a reflector. Sometimes they need to be a theorist and other times an activist. Learn to use all the styles at the appropriate time.

Setting goals

SMART goal setting is one way of writing a plan in order to maximise success. The following case scenario is an example of a SMART plan in action.

Evaluation

Ongoing evaluation is essential. It is not enough to have mastered one new skill or learned one new thing. The new skill or new knowledge is a first step on the road to professional development. Experience, skills and knowledge improve practice but it is important to maintain records to show how you have developed. Nurses and midwives have to revalidate every three years; other health and care practitioners have to sign a declaration every two years that they are still competent to practise. Records are needed for this.

Nurses and midwives are required to keep a record of professional discussion and verbal feedback received. According to the Royal College of Midwives, records should show who the feedback is from, maintaining confidentiality by using job titles or service user, rather than

---

 Case scenario (AC 4.2)

Sam, a nurse on the discharge ward, wants to know why it takes so long to organise an occupational therapy assessment before an individual is allowed home. Some of the individuals in her care wait for weeks. She wonders if there is anything she can do to speed up the process and decides to find out what occupational therapists (OTs) do. She makes a SMART plan:

Specific goal – work shadow an occupational therapist for a morning.

Measureable – yes, it is either done or not done.

Achievable – Sam knows she will have to do this in her own time, not work time. She will have to get permission and find an OT willing to let her shadow them. She thinks these things are possible.

Realistic/relevant – work shadowing an OT is relevant because it will help her to understand the delays in getting an assessment, and realistic because she has easy access to OTs.

Timed – this is be done before the end of the month.

Sam had already spoken to the OT Kay who visited the ward and was successful in getting permission to work shadow her.

Sam wrote up her experience as part of her professional development portfolio and observed the following:

Kay started the day by checking referrals which came from consultants, medical and nursing staff on the wards. Sam was a bit surprised to find how few OTs there were. Kay explained there was a national shortage and vacancies had been advertised several times. Kay then made ward visits, the first to the orthopaedic ward where an 80-year-old man was recovering, following an operation for a fractured femur. He had fallen at home. Kay had to assess his mobility and then arrange a home visit so that she could see how he could cope at home. Kay made two more ward visits and then had to do a home visit with a 90-year-old lady who was awaiting discharge. Unfortunately, when they arrived at the lady's home, it was obvious she could not cope with the stairs up to the toilet and bathroom. Kay explained that they would have to make adaptations to the home and meanwhile the lady would stay in hospital.

Sam made a note of key points she had learned from the visit:

- OTs were extremely busy and received referrals from a variety of sources.
- Most of the individuals needing assessment were elderly and lived alone.
- She saw good practice. However busy Kay was, she ensured that individuals were not rushed and that their views were heard.

As a result of this experience, Sam decided to include information on the referral form about whether an individual had support at home, and whether they had a toilet upstairs and downstairs. She also ensured that to avoid delays, any individual going on a home assessment visit was ready for this.

1. Who benefited from Sam's work shadowing experience?
2. How did they benefit?
3. Could Sam have gained this insight any other way?

real names. Records should show what the feedback was about and can be either positive or critical. Reflective accounts can be on theory or practice but should explain what has been learned from the topic and how this relates to the NMC code. The NMC provides a form to be used for the five reflective accounts required (www.rcm.org.uk).

Take it further

Now you know about personal development plans you can develop your own. Look back at the plan you made for the unit 'Personal and professional development' to help you.

Command word activity

Discuss (AC 4.2)

1. Why is professional development important?
2. Discuss three ways you may identify professional development needs.
3. How could you plan to meet these needs? Include a range of methods.
4. Read around this topic and use these sources to support what you say.

Case scenario: Nisha

Nisha works part-time as a care assistant at a residential care home. The manager, Mrs Day is a registered nurse. She gets the Nursing Times and Community Care for the staff room. Most of the staff have worked at the care home for several years. They are experienced carers, enjoy their work and are fond of the residents. Some of the older residents are showing signs of dementia. Nisha has been there a few months and is due for an appraisal with Mrs Day. In preparation for her appraisal she decides to look at her own strengths and weakness, the opportunities she has for improvement and what might hold her back.

1. How could she find out what are her strengths and areas for improvement?
2. What could she do to fill in some of the gaps in her knowledge?
3. Suggest an area she could focus on to improve the quality of care.

Activity (AC 4.1, 4.2)

Some people are visual learners and learn best with diagrams, flowcharts and pictures. Other people learn best by listening to others, whether in a lecture or online. Some people learn best by reading and then writing out what they have learned. Yet others learn best by doing; these are Kinaesthetic learners. These learning styles are often referred to as VARK learning styles: Visual, Auditory, Read and write, Kinaesthetic.

1. Divide the class into four groups, one for each style and give each group a learning style to focus on: Visual, Auditory, Read and write, or Kinaesthetic.
2. Ask each person to make a professional development plan to meet the needs of a person with the learning style for their group. Each member of the group should choose a different need; for example, in the Visual group, one person may plan to improve communication skills, another may plan to increase knowledge of dementia, and yet another may plan to learn how to communicate with a person with dementia. People in the Visual group should focus on visual methods of learning. Those in the Auditory, Read and write, and Kinaesthetic groups should each choose individual targets and make individual plans focusing on their group's learning style.
3. After twenty minutes the class should post their plans on a wall display, look at each other's work and decide which style and which plan is closest to their own needs.

Check your understanding

1. Give three examples of learning needs.
2. Give three ways to identify learning needs.
3. How may a professional development plan benefit a practitioner?

LO5: Be able to reflect upon and plan for own personal development

Reflection and personal development are part of maturing as a person. Applying the same process of reflection to professional development ensures that practitioners develop into experienced competent practitioners.

5.1 Reflect upon own learning using a model of reflection

Learning is more effective when structured using a model such as Kolb's cycle or Gibb's cycle, and based on reflection in action and on action. Knowing whether you are primarily an activist, pragmatist, reflector or theorist and learning to use other styles improves learning. There are many opportunities for learning as shown throughout this unit. See Figure 9.4 for a summary of these.

Figure 9.4 Sources of learning

Command word activity

Reflect (AC 5.1)

1. Reflect upon your own learning using a model of reflection.
2. Why did you use that model?
3. Have you used other models previously?
4. What is the benefit of using a range of models?

5.2 Use outcomes from reflection to assess and plan for own development

You may have already assessed your own learning needs and produced a plan for your own development. If you have, revisit it and update it, noting what you have achieved and what is still to do and by when.

If you have not yet produced a plan for your own development, identify three learning needs based on feedback from others and your own reflection. Plan how you are going to meet those needs using a framework such as the SMART outline shown earlier in the unit. Use this plan as the basis for your next tutorial or supervision session. Remember to update it as you achieve each outcome.

Activity (AC 5.2)

Use outcomes from your own reflection to assess and plan for own development. Your plan should use SMART targets and include a space for evaluation and reflection for each action.

Case scenario (AC 5.2)

Tess was on placement at a care home. She was a bit nervous when she first arrived. Everyone seemed so busy and nobody spoke to her after the first few introductions. The health and social care practitioners were busy getting everyone to the table for breakfast, and it was a noisy environment. Tess felt like hiding in a corner and texting her friend to see how she was getting on at her placement.

1. What learning needs would you suggest that Tess has?
2. Where may she find support to meet her needs?
3. What could Tess do to feel more at ease in her placement?

Check your understanding

1. Explain three ways to reflect on personal development.
2. Why is it necessary to record personal development?
3. Explain one way to write a personal development plan.
4. Where might you find help in writing a reflective account?

Read about it

Honey, P. and Mumford, A. (1986) *The Manual of Learning Styles*, London: Peter Honey Associates.

Sykes, C. and Durham, W. (2014) 'Embedding the NHS values: An OPCE framework and learning tool to support practice', *Nursing Management*, February, 20, 9, pp. 31–7.

Websites

British Association of Social Workers

www.basw.co.uk

Dementia-friendly environments: Gardens

www.scie.org.uk/dementia/supporting-people-with-dementia/dementia-friendly-environments/gardens.asp

Health and Care Professions Council

www.hcpc-uk.org.uk

'Learning to teach: becoming a reflective practitioner'

www.open.edu/openlearn/education/learning-teach-becoming-reflective-practitioner/content-section-2.1

Nursing and Midwifery Council

www.nmc.org.uk

'Police and mental health; how to get it right locally'

www.mind.org.uk/media/618027/2013-12-03-Mind_police_final_web.pdf

The Care Quality Commission

www.cqc.org.uk

The King's Fund

www.kingsfund.org.uk

Video 2 The Lodge from Open Learn 'Designing space for dementia care'

www.open.edu/openlearn/health-sports-psychology/social-care/designing-space-dementia-care/content-section-2

Unit HSC CM9: How will I be graded?

The table below shows what the learner must do to achieve each grading criterion. Learners must achieve all the criteria for a grade to be awarded (i.e. criteria D1 to D3 must be achieved to pass this unit assessment at grade D). A higher grade may not be awarded before a lower grade has been achieved in full, although component criteria of a higher grade may have been achieved.

Grade	Assessment criteria number	Assessment grading criteria	Assessment of learning / What you need to show
D1	1.1	Identify standards relating to professional development in health and social care.	Outline current standards that underpin professional development in health and social care. Examples of recognised standards may be provided.
D2	1.2	Explain continuing professional development.	Provide an explanation that shows understanding of continuing professional development in relation to health and social care.
D3	4.1	Identify: • sources of support for learning and development • professional development opportunities.	Provide information to accurately identify: • sources of support for learning and development • professional development opportunities.
D4		Show evidence of reading or use of sources.	There should be evidence of learners' reading or use of sources. Learners must use a minimum of two traceable references to support the explanation.

Grade	Assessment criteria number	Assessment grading criteria	Assessment of learning / What you need to show
C1	2.2	Explain how reflective practice supports the professional development of the health and social care practitioner.	Provide an explanation to show: • understanding of reflective practice • how reflective practice supports the professional development of the health and social care practitioner.
C2		Show evidence of reading or use of sources with referencing relevant to the explanation. Good use of vocabulary and grammar.	Use of referencing should show evidence of reading or use of sources. Vocabulary and grammar should be appropriate and accurate for purpose.
B1	2.1	Discuss theoretical perspectives on reflection in relation to professional development.	Discussion must focus on reflective practice to demonstrate understanding of more than one relevant theoretical perspective. How theoretical perspectives on reflection support professional development.
B2	4.2	Discuss methods for identifying and planning for professional development needs.	Discussion must focus on professional development and demonstrate understanding of: • the importance of professional development • a range of methods used to identify professional development needs • a range of methods used to plan for professional development.
B3		Show evidence of reading or use of sources. Referencing supports discussion.	Use of reading or use of sources should be shown through a range of relevant referencing. Referencing should be used appropriately to support the discussion.
A1	2.3	Analyse how reflective practice supports positive outcomes.	Analysis must accurately demonstrate how reflective practice supports positive outcomes for: • individuals/parents/carers • staff team • other professionals. Information must be given from more than one perspective to support the analysis.
A2		Show evidence of wider background reading or use of sources. Referencing supports analysis.	Wider background reading should be evident or a wide range of source material should be used. Referencing supports analysis.
A*1	3.1	Analyse how the health and social care practitioner's own values, beliefs and experiences can influence delivery of care.	Analysis must include an appraisal of the health and social care practitioner's role to demonstrate: • understanding of personal values and beliefs • how personal values and beliefs can influence practice in delivering care • consideration from more than one perspective.

Grade	Assessment criteria number	Assessment grading criteria	Assessment of learning / What you need to show
A*2		Show evidence of a range of background reading or use of sources used selectively.	Learners should show the ability to consider or explore relevant issues which contribute to the analysis. An extensive range of background reading or use of sources should be used selectively and cited appropriately.
D4	3.2	Summarise legislation, policies, procedures and codes of practice relating to the management of information.	Information must focus on management of information and summarise: relevant legislation, more than one relevant policy, more than one relevant procedure, more than one relevant code of practice.
Skills	5.1	Reflect upon own learning using a model of reflection.	
	5.2	Use outcomes from reflection to assess and plan for own development.	

Empowerment in Health and Social Care

About this unit

Empowerment in health and social care involves practitioners enabling individuals to fulfil their capacity to achieve their life's goals. Empowering individuals to gain control of their lives, care and support can promote their health and well-being and develop their strengths and abilities to make their own vision for their life and future a reality and one that is shared and understood by everyone.

In this unit you will find out about the meaning and importance of empowering individuals, including how legislation and standards inform current and best working practices. You will also learn more about the barriers that can arise to empowerment and the strategies that practitioners can use to overcome these. Understanding the risks involved when empowering individuals is integral to effective risk management and balancing the rights of individuals with the duty of care, roles and responsibilities of health and social care practitioners.

LO1: Understand empowerment of individuals in health and social care

1.1 Explain the importance of empowering individuals

Empowering individuals is at the heart of the values and principles that underpin good-quality, safe, compassionate and effective care and support. The EMPOWERING acrostic below is a useful way for remembering the many different aspects that this concept involves:

- Encouraging working approaches that build individuals' confidence and **self-esteem** (see p. 218 for definition)
- Meaningful support that ensures individuals feel in control of their lives, care and support
- Providing information and guidance for individuals to make their own choices and decisions
- Opportunities for individuals to improve their health and well-being
- Wider participation and involvement of others in individuals' lives
- Enabling individuals to develop their own personal skills and knowledge
- Resource-building to enable individuals to plan for their future
- Individuals increasing control over their lives, care and support
- Negotiating environments to reduce **discrimination** in individuals' lives

Greater involvement of individuals in their local communities

Activity (AC 1.1)

In pairs, discuss the values and principles that underpin the provision of safe, effective and good-quality care. Give examples of how these values and principles can be promoted in health and social care settings when empowering individuals with their day-to-day living, care and support.

Take it further

For more information on the values of care and individuals' rights you will find it useful to read the following: Unit HSC CM1: (LO1); Unit HSC CM4: (LO1 and LO2); and Unit HSC CM8: (LO1 and LO2).

You may also find it useful to read more about the values in care in *Standard 5 of the Care Certificate: Work in a Person-centred Way*, available at http://www.skillsforcare.org.uk/Documents/Learning-and-development/Care-Certificate/Standard-5.pdf

Empowering individuals is important for ensuring that individuals' unique needs, views and preferences are respected and met. Empowerment can enable individuals to:

Gain control of their lives: Empowerment not only means that individuals gain control of their lives but also that they feel in control of their lives. For example, a support worker in a **supported living scheme** could involve an individual who has learning disabilities in completing a **choices map** to empower the individual to take more control over the decisions made in his life in relation to how he spends his day and the support he needs.

Fulfil their capacity: Empowerment can enable individuals to recognise their personal preferences, strengths and abilities and achieve their life goals, aspirations and hopes. For example, a senior carer in a residential care home providing support to an older individual to talk about their interests and family traditions to empower the individual to book a holiday to visit her relatives who live abroad.

Become self-reliant: Empowerment can reduce individuals' dependency on others and enable them to become more independent and more reliant on themselves. For example, a mental health worker empowering an individual who has mental health needs to better manage their mental health so that they can develop more helpful and positive ways of responding to difficult feelings and situations.

Participate in decisions: Empowering individuals to participate in decisions enables individuals to be active participants in the decisions that are made about them. For example, **an advocate** supporting an individual who has dementia to access information about the services available in the local community that offer opportunities to meet with other people so that an informed decision can be made of the services that best meet the individual's preferences.

Have dignity: Empowering individuals in all aspects of their lives promotes their dignity. For example, a senior home carer visiting an individual in their own home to ask the individual's permission to replace the **hoist** being used with a new one, and explain the benefits of doing so, will promote the individual's self-respect, by enabling the individual to feel that they are still in control of their home and understand the benefits of changing this piece of equipment.

Have respect: Empowerment involves taking account of individuals' unique abilities, rights, feelings and preferences; doing so can promote respect. For example, a nursing home that respects that individuals have their preferred times to eat and drink and therefore ensures that the kitchen can be accessed 24 hours a day.

Have a sense of belonging/contribution: Empowerment can ensure individuals have a sense of belonging and that their contributions matter. For example, a care worker who supports an individual with physical disabilities to volunteer with a local charity can provide the individual with opportunities to have a role within their community.

Improve their self-esteem: Empowerment can lead to the development of confidence in one's own worth or abilities. For example, a community care worker who encourages an individual to apply for a range of jobs that interest them can improve the individual's confidence that they have the required skills and qualities to be able to carry out the range of duties and responsibilities that these jobs require.

Build their self-confidence: Empowerment can lead to the development of individuals' belief in their own capabilities. For example, a health worker who empowers an individual who is

recovering from major surgery by explaining that they have made very good progress with their walking can improve how the individual feels about themselves, including their potential to regain their ability to walk.

Improve their health and well-being: Empowerment can lead to the improvement of individuals' physical and emotional health and well-being. For example, involving individuals through their local communities in the buying, planning and delivery of health and social care services will enable individuals to feel positive in themselves and in control of the types of services that are being developed and will be made available.

Command word activity

Explain (AC 1.1)

Write down three examples of individuals being empowered by health and care practitioners. In pairs, take it in turns to discuss each example and provide a verbal account of how the individuals are being empowered, as well as the reasons why this is important. You could also discuss the consequences for the individual, the care practitioner and the service if the individuals were not being empowered in these chosen examples.

Key terms

Self-esteem the value or confidence individuals place on themselves

Discrimination the unfair or unequal treatment of an individual or a group

Supported living scheme a scheme where individuals own or rent their own home and have control over the support they get and how they live their lives

Choices map a tool used to describe decisions that are made by the individual and the decisions made by other people

Advocate an independent person that represents an individual's views and wishes

Dignity self-respect

Hoist a piece of equipment that enables an individual to move from one position to another

1.2 Explain how legislation and standards inform practice when empowering individuals

Legislation is guided by current government policy and sets out the requirements that health and social care settings, including all those who work in them, must comply with. Standards in the health and social care sector reflect the national minimum levels of performance that care practitioners are expected to achieve and the principles that they must adhere to in order to carry out their roles and responsibilities effectively.

Take it further

For more information on the differences and purposes of legislation and standards you will find it useful to read the following: Unit HSC CM3: (LO2) and Unit HSC CM8: (LO1 and LO2).

Table 10.1 provides some examples of how health and social care legislation and standards can inform working practices when empowering individuals in their day-to-day lives. For information on current legislation and standards you will find it useful to reference www.gov.uk

Take it further

You can find more details about the legislation given in Table 10.1 in the following units: HSC CM1; HSC CM3; HSC CM4; HSC CM9; HSC DM1 and HSC DM2.

Table 10.1 Legislation and standards relating to empowerment

Legislation and standards	Examples of informing practice when empowering individuals
Care Act 2014	An older individual with both physical health and social care needs will be able to have their holistic needs addressed through the care and support being provided in their own home. This will not only safeguard and promote the individual's health and well-being, but will also empower the individual to maintain their independence
	The family of a child with autism will be able to take the lead in selecting the services that are the most suitable to meet their needs and provide the support they require as a family
	An individual with learning disabilities being recognised by care practitioners as the expert of his own support in terms of how effective it is in promoting his independence
Health and Social Care Act 2012	An individual who has used an outpatients' clinic can share their experiences of doing so with their local participation group for patients through attending one of their meetings or by completing a questionnaire. The information gained through the individual's involvement will in turn help the local CCG when reviewing this service
	An individual who has recently moved to a new area and wishes to know the health and social care services that are available in their local area can call Healthwatch, an independent service that can provide them with information about the options available so that they can make an informed choice
	An individual requiring health and social care services will be supported by care practitioners who have been trained in line with national standards to provide safe, high-quality, effective care and support which will promote the individual's health and well-being
Health and Social Care Act 2008 (Regulated Activities) Regulations 2014	A new home care provider who wishes to register to provide services to adults who have learning disabilities and dementia will require a manager who is qualified, and experienced in managing health and social care services thus enabling high-quality care and support to be provided
	People who are on adults or children barred lists will not be able to manage health and social care services which can safeguard individuals who use health and social care services and minimise the risk of them being abused and neglected by people in positions of authority
	Individuals who access both health and social care services will be able to expect the same high-quality standards of care and support that will enable individuals to become more confident and self-reliant

Legislation	Examples of informing practice when empowering individuals
Equality Act 2010	Individuals with physical disabilities can have improved access to services through reasonable adjustments having to be made to, for example, buildings (i.e. installation of a ramp and accessible welfare facilities)
	Employers taking positive action and encouraging individuals to apply for jobs where older people, for example, are under-represented
	Health and social care services taking account of individuals' beliefs and lifestyles to promote individuals' identities and self-esteem
Health Act 2009	Improved NHS care and services will enable the promotion of individuals' health and well-being
	Preventative services will enable individuals to retain their independence and health for longer, thus reducing their dependency on services
Putting People First 2007 (Personalisation Agenda)	Enabling individuals to use **individual budgets** and make their own choices over how they want to be supported and by whom
	Providing individuals with opportunities to become employers through the use of **direct payments** to employ their own carers
Mental Health Act 2007	Providing individuals with mental health needs the right to have their views heard and respected in relation to their care and treatment
	Enabling individuals to appoint a named person to make decisions about their care and treatment if they are unable to
Children's Act 1989	Health and social care services working together to safeguard children and taking into account the 'best interests' of the individual
	Health and social care services taking into account the views and feelings of the child during the safeguarding process; the child remains the focus
Children's Act 2004	The child's 'best interests' remaining of central importance when decisions are being made about their welfare
	An advocate can ensure that a child's views and feelings are represented and heard
Data Protection Act 1998	All personal information contained within an individual's health care records will be kept secure at all times and will only be accessed by those who need to see it which promotes respect for individuals
	Health and social care services will be responsible for ensuring that all information held about individuals is accurate and reflects individuals' current needs which will promote individuals' dignity
Sector Skills Standards	Individuals will receive high-quality care and support from care practitioners who are trained and knowledgeable in how to work in a person-centred way to meet their needs which in turn will promote their health and well-being
	Individuals will benefit from care practitioners' expertise and knowledge in for example dementia, mental health and learning disabilities

 Key terms

Clinical commissioning groups (CCGs) are NHS organisations responsible for planning, agreeing and monitoring NHS services in England

Protected characteristics refers to the nine characteristics protected from discrimination under the Equality Act

Data protection principles refers to the eight principles that govern the use of personal information under the Data Protection Act

Individual budgets refers to the funding that is allocated to an individual for their eligible care and support needs

Direct payments cash payments made to individuals to buy the care and support services they have been assessed as needing

1.3 Analyse how factors affect the empowerment of individuals

Empowering individuals to be in control of their lives and make informed decisions can be affected by different factors:

Discrimination

The term discrimination refers to treating people unfairly and unlawfully because of making assumptions about the differences present in an individual or group such as in relation to their age, disability, religion or sexual orientation.

Read through the different types of discrimination detailed in Fig 10.1:

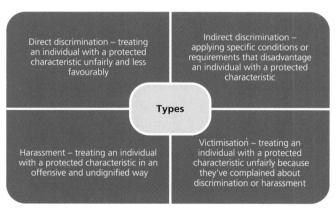

Figure 10.1 Types of discrimination

Discrimination can lead to individuals' needs remaining unmet. If, for example,

- an older adult is refused support to live independently because the service provider thinks that the individual is too old to develop their independent living skills, or assumptions

are made about the type of treatment an individual who has religious beliefs will prefer, without asking them first, or

- offensive comments are made about a child who has a physical disability; this can mean that these individuals are excluded and denied the care and support they require.

Communication

The effectiveness of communication with individuals and others involved in their lives including their families, other care practitioners and services will impact on the extent that individuals are empowered in their lives. Positive communications will instil mutual trust, respect, confidence and self-belief that can enable individuals to make decisions and choices about how they want to live their lives as they wish. Negative communications can lead to individuals feeling undermined and not worthy of respect and therefore unable to make decisions and choices; this can have a detrimental effect on their health and well-being.

Resources

The availability of resources can also impact on the empowerment of individuals. The funding allocated to an individual for the care and support services they require to have their needs met may not be sufficient to buy the preferred care and support chosen by the individual. Empowering individuals to live their lives as they wish may require access to specific resources that may not be available in all areas, for example the availability of care practitioners with specific expertise such as in relation to children who are deafblind or adults who have autism. The lack of resources can undermine the potential benefits of empowerment.

Health and safety

Health and social care practitioners have a duty of care to promote an individual's health and safety; this in turn has the potential to impact on an individual's rights to make their own choices and decisions. For example, an individual who has dementia and coronary heart disease and wants to smoke but is prevented from doing so by healthcare workers to promote both their health and their safety can be experienced by the individual as being restrictive, negative and abusive.

Risk

Empowerment involves working closely with individuals to make informed choices and decisions even when care practitioners may not agree with these or believe these mean that the individual will be taking a risk. Empowering individuals to take risks while ensuring their safety is central to promoting their dignity and well-being. A failure to do so can mean that the individual is prevented from fulfilling their capacity. A decision to involve others such as an advocate who can represent the individual's views and interests can ensure that the individual's rights are upheld and their safety promoted, for example when an individual who is prone to regular falls insists on continuing to cook for themselves and not have a home service delivery of frozen ready meals.

 Classroom discussion (AC 1.3)

Discuss the meanings and links between health, safety and risk in relation to the empowerment of individuals. Give examples to support your understanding of each term and how they are linked to empowerment.

Needs

Individuals' needs are diverse and can change. The empowerment of individuals will therefore be dependent on the flexibility of health and social care services to adapt to individuals' needs. This in turn will impact on the support available for individuals to be able to have greater control and involvement over decisions related to different aspects of their lives, care and support. For example, an older couple who are married and have lived together in their own home for over 60 years are unable to continue to live together because their health and social care needs are different; the wife requires residential care and the husband needs nursing care.

Command word activity

Analyse (AC 1.3)

Research a range of factors that can affect the empowerment of individuals in health and social care settings. For each of the factors that you have researched, produce a written report of their main characteristics and include examples of how and why they can impact both positively and negatively on the empowerment of individuals; ensure your report compares and contrasts the factors and includes a clear rationale.

Command word activity

Evidence (AC 1.3)

Produce a 3-minute presentation about how to balance the positive and negative effects of factors that can affect the empowerment of individuals.

Use the Harvard referencing system to produce an easy-to-follow list of all the sources of information that you've read and referred to in relation to the empowerment of individuals in health and social care.

You must use a minimum of two references that are accurate so that they can be easily tracked to confirm their validity and can support the presentation.

Resistance

Refusing to believe or accept that individuals who use health and social care services are the experts of their own care and support needs, rather than care practitioners, can prevent individuals from being supported in their right to be in control on their care and support. Individuals who have experienced discrimination, harassment and/or victimisation and have been profoundly and negatively affected may not have the self-belief that they have the ability to improve their health and well-being or make their own choices and decisions.

1.4 Discuss strategies used to empower individuals

Reducing the negative factors that can affect empowerment can be achieved by care practitioners putting into practice one or more of the following strategies:

Person-centred practice involves supporting the individual to lead a lifestyle that they value by identifying the individual's strengths and abilities and what is important to them. For example, a support worker could spend time with an individual and learn about their life including how they like to spend their day, their friendships and relationships, their hopes for the future; doing so can enable the focus to be placed on the individual and the support worker to see the individual as a unique person. *Communication* is another useful technique that when used effectively can empower individuals to become self-reliant; you will find more details about effective communication in Unit HSC CM4: communication in health and social care.

Figure 10.2 Communication, a two-way process

Positive use of verbal and non-verbal communication can enable an individual's confidence and self-esteem to improve thus enabling the individual to feel able to, for example, make their own views clear when their plan of care is being discussed, or share their feelings about a situation that they are not happy with in a constructive manner.

Verbal skills that demonstrate empathy are more likely to provide reassurance to individuals and build their confidence. Non-verbal skills such as body language and facial expressions reflecting that a genuine interest is being taken in the individual are more likely to make the individual feel that they are being respected and treated with dignity. Writing a daily care report that uses professional, easy to understand and clear language is likely to encourage the individual to want to participate in the decisions related to their care. Adapting communication through, for example, the use of sign language or Makaton will provide the individual with an opportunity to gain control of the communication and be able to actively participate in it.

Inclusion refers to every person being accepted for who they are, that is, irrespective of their individual and/or group differences. It involves care practitioners providing care and support to individuals in a way that recognises their differences to enable them to fulfil their capacity. For example, a care assistant who ensures that an individual's difficulties with mobilising does not prevent them from going to the places they enjoy, by making arrangements for the individual to use a taxi instead of public transport, or discussing the option of the individual using a wheelchair.

Decision making is an important part of empowering individuals. For individuals to be able to make their own decisions they or their representative, that is, a family member who knows them well or someone independent, such as an advocate that represents their best interests only must be given the opportunity to actively participate in decisions about them. Information-sharing is part of the decision-making process, as it involves individuals and/or their representatives being provided with full and accurate information, in a format that they can understand and that is suitable for their needs including the options available and the pros and cons of decisions made; in this way, informed decisions can be made.

Activity (AC 1.4)

In pairs, discuss how each of the strategies you've learned about so far could be used to empower the individuals described in the two case profiles below:

Martin has panic attacks during the day that can last up to 10 minutes; these usually happen when his wife leaves to go to work and he is at home on his own. During his panic attacks Martin feels very shaky all over and is unable to breathe.

Eva is 4 years old, has cerebral palsy and uses a wheelchair. Eva is very active and enjoys playing outdoors. At the children's centre that she attends Eva does not like to go outside to play with the other children because she feels embarrassed that she is the only child in a wheelchair.

Information-sharing also involves individuals and/or their representatives sharing accurate and honest information about themselves with care practitioners including, for example, their abilities, preferences and choices. The *recognition of individuals' abilities, preferences and choices* involves not only hearing them, but also taking positive action to ensure that these are respected and promote individuals' health and well-being.

Complaints procedures can be an effective way of enabling an individual to have their views and feelings heard and respected. They can also empower the individual to raise any issues that they are not happy with or that they feel require improvement. Having complaints listened to and taken seriously can also provide individuals with a sense of contribution (particularly if aspects of a service are changed as a result) as well as with an opportunity to build their self-esteem and self-confidence.

Access to relevant services will not only promote individuals' health and well-being but will also develop their self-reliance while reducing their dependency on services that may have been required had their needs not been met. *Advocacy* can be used to support individuals to not only access the services that they require to have their care and support needs met, but can also encourage individuals to gain control of their life

by making informed decisions and choices and by ensuring that their views, feelings and preferences are not only heard by others but are taken account of and form the basis of their care and support.

Self-directed support involves individuals gaining control of their support by being able to choose how their support is provided. It also involves individuals gaining control over how they spend their *budget allocation* by deciding how much of the personal budget allocated to them should be spent on different aspects of their support. Self-directed support is at the heart of empowerment as it means that individuals have the potential to make real decisions about their lives.

 ## Classroom discussion (AC 1.4)

In small groups discuss the role of the following strategies that can be used by care practitioners to empower individuals in health and social care. Ensure you include examples to support your views of how they can empower individuals:

- Complaints procedures
- Access to relevant services
- Advocacy
- Self-directed support
- Budget allocation.

 ## Key terms

Body language the movements of your body that express to others how you are feeling

Makaton a language programme that uses signs and symbols to help children and adults to communicate

 ## Check your understanding

1. What is your understanding of the meaning of empowerment in health and social care?
2. Explain the differences between legislation and standards.
3. Can you give three examples of factors that affect the empowerment of individuals?
4. Define the term inclusion. Why is it important?

LO2: Understand risk management when empowering individuals in health and social care settings

2.1 Describe risks involved when empowering individuals

Using effective strategies to overcome the factors that may prevent the empowerment of individuals may also result in risks occurring. Empowerment does not prevent individuals from taking risks but does promote their safety and security while taking the risks, with the aim of individuals fulfilling their capacity and achieving what they set out to do. Figure 10.3 includes some examples of the different risks that could be involved in empowering individuals in different situations.

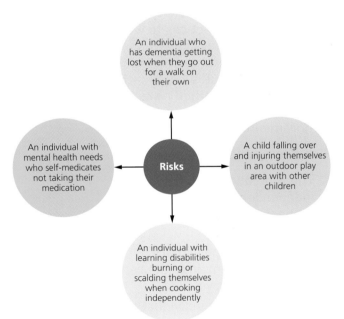

Figure 10.3 What are the potential risks of empowerment?

Potential risks not only affect the individuals being empowered but could also potentially impact on the care practitioners supporting the individuals, others who know the individual such as their family and friends, as well as the organisation through which the care and support is being provided.

2.2 Explain tensions when balancing the rights of the individual against the health and social care practitioner's duty of care

Empowering individuals involves supporting and promoting their rights, health and well-being. Empowering individuals also involves promoting individuals' safety and ensuring that individual's risk-taking does not place them, or others, at risk of danger or harm and that all that can be done to reduce the risk of danger and harm from occurring has been done.

Balancing the rights of the individual against the health and social care practitioner's duty of care can be a challenge because of the following reasons:

The identified risks may not be understood by the individual or the individual may feel that the potential benefits of their wishes outweigh the danger and harm associated with the identified risks.

The identified risks may conflict with the individual's wishes and rights. The individual has a right to take a 'bad' risk and if they can understand the potential consequences of the risks then they have made an informed decision.

The expectations that individuals have may conflict with the resources available. For example, an individual who has a physical disability may decide that they would like to take a cruise for three months and be supported while doing so by their personal assistant. Discussions with the individual will need to establish when and where the individual would like to take a cruise, the availability of the personal assistant, whether it would be practical or safe to be supported by only one personal assistant, the costs involved, i.e. to the individual, the personal assistant/s.

Care practitioners have a duty to not only safeguard the individuals they are empowering to take positive risks, but also to safeguard all those others they work with, i.e. other individuals who use health and social care services, their colleagues and other professionals. If an individual's risk-taking places others in danger or harm then care practitioners have a duty to care and to prevent this from occurring.

Take it further

For more information on the tensions when balancing the rights of the individual against the health and social care practitioner's duty of care you will find it useful to read Unit HSC CM1 (LO1).

 ## Case scenario: Gill (AC 2.2)

Gill is 76, has the onset of dementia, lives on her own and smokes heavily, a pastime which she thoroughly enjoys. Gill's family have stopped buying her cigarettes because they are worried that she may fall asleep while she is smoking and cause a fire to start. Gill has therefore asked the care practitioners who visit daily to buy her cigarettes as her family have stopped doing so.

The care practitioners who support Gill at home cannot agree on whether they should get involved in buying Gill cigarettes. Although they have a duty to promote Gill's well-being and right to smoke, they also have a duty of care towards Gill in terms of ensuring her safety and protecting her from danger and harm. The practitioners have also, up till now, always worked in partnership with Gill's family.

1. How could Gill's right to smoke and her safety be promoted at the same time?
2. What could be the potential consequences of the care practitioners and Gill's family not reaching a shared understanding about this situation?

Command word activity

Explain (AC 2.2)

In small groups discuss other examples of where empowering an individual in a health care or social care setting can result in tensions between the individual's rights and the care practitioners' duty of care. For one of these scenarios that you have discussed, provide a verbal account of the reasons for the tensions and their effect on both the individual and the care practitioners in the setting

2.3 Explain how to manage risks when empowering individuals

Risk management supports the empowerment of individuals by finding different ways of managing the identified risks rather than preventing the individual from gaining control over their life, making their own choices and decisions. Working practices that use a positive approach to risk management use person-centred practices to work with the individual and others involved in their life to identify and understand the risks involved and agree together on the best method to use for managing any identified risks that will reflect the individual's wishes and preferences without compromising their own or others' safety.

Risk management and positive outcomes:

1. The promotion of the individual's rights, independence and inclusion when identifying, managing and reviewing actual and potential risks
2. To ensure the individual's needs and preferences remain at the centre of the care and support provided
3. To safeguard the individual and others from danger and harm
4. To ensure that all information provided in relation to the individual is accurate and up to date
5. The provision of opportunities to explore the risks identified with individuals and others involved

6. To be able to act on the risks identified and achieve the best possible outcome for the individual

7. To agree on strategies that can be used that promote the individual's rights and maintain their safety and well-being

The risk-management process is also supported by current legislation and health and social care settings' policies and procedures. Both of these set out the requirements and agreed working practices that care practitioners must follow when empowering individuals in different health and social care settings in relation to, for example, the promotion of health, safety and well-being, the safeguarding and protection of individuals from danger, harm and neglect.

Take it further

For more information on current legislation you will find it useful to access **www.gov.uk**. Also read Unit HSC CM3 (LO2); Unit HSC CM8 (LO1 and LO2); and Unit HSC DM2 (LO1).

As well as the risk-assessment process, the care planning process can also be used to support individuals to manage the risks associated with their care and support. The care planning process sets out how an individual's needs will be met, including how the support required will be provided and how any risks identified will be managed. The care planning process is undertaken with individuals and therefore empowers them to be in control of their care and support, promotes their independence and involves them in all decisions that are taken in relation to their care and support. The extent that the care planning process empowers individuals will depend on the extent of their involvement in agreeing on what their needs and preferences are, the accuracy and relevance of the information collated about the individual and their unique and personal characteristics, the support and services available to the individual. The care planning process involves care practitioners working in partnership with individuals and others involved in their lives, with a range of services and other professionals. It also involves

Figure 10.4 Promoting independence together

being committed to supporting the individual and having the courage to speak up when aspects of the process are not working or have been applied incorrectly or unsafely; care practitioners' awareness of the whistleblowing procedures that are available in health and social care settings is essential to ensure that individuals' rights are upheld and they are protected from danger, harm and neglect.

Command word activity

Explain (AC 2.3)

Research the following procedures that occur in health and social care settings: complaints and whistleblowing.

Develop a leaflet that provides information, advice and guidance to care practitioners in health and social care settings about how complaints and whistleblowing procedures can minimise the risks of danger, harm and neglect to individuals being empowered to gain control of their own life.

Case scenario: Leanne (AC 2. 1, 2.2, 2.3)

Leanne is 26 years old, has a learning disability and **epilepsy**. Leanne is no longer in a relationship with her partner and lives alone in her flat with her 5-year-old daughter. Leanne's parents are concerned that Leanne will not be able to manage to live on her own and look after her daughter due to her epilepsy.

Leanne thinks that she is capable and can manage without her partner but has agreed to meet with the social worker to discuss her situation.

What are the potential risks of Leanne living on her own? What are the tensions that have arisen? How could any potential risks be managed?

 Key term

Epilepsy a neurological condition that is characterised by the individual having seizures that start in the brain

 Check your understanding

1. Define risk management.
2. Name three potential risks involved in supporting an individual with mobility difficulties to go out shopping.
3. For one of these risks, explain how to manage it.
4. Why can balancing the rights of individuals cause tension with practitioners' duty of care?

LO3: Understand the roles and responsibilities of the health and social care practitioner when empowering individuals

3.1 Critically evaluate the roles and responsibilities of the health and social care practitioner when empowering individuals

Empowering individuals in health and social care involves practitioners being able to overcome the barriers and challenges that may be faced when doing so, while carrying out the roles and responsibilities that are required of them in their day-to-day working activities:

Policies and procedures: being aware of their work settings' policies and procedures that are related to empowering individuals will ensure that practitioners carry out all care and support activities in line with legal and organisational requirements, for example recording an individual's risk assessment, including the discussion that took place that involved the individual and where decisions were made.

Agreed ways of working: each health and social care setting will have in place agreed ways of working that will reflect the setting's purpose as well as individuals' specific needs; these will vary between different health and social care settings. It is the care practitioner's responsibility to know what these are, ensure they understand what they mean for their working practice and clarify any areas they do not understand with their employer to ensure that individuals continue to be empowered throughout their whole care and support journey.

Person-centred practice: working in ways that are person-centred is integral to care practitioners' practices and ensures that they are adhering to the professional standards that are in place for all health and social care practitioners.

Promoting participation: promoting participation of individuals and of all others involved in their lives underpins the empowerment of individuals. Promoting participation not only involves care practitioners actively involving individuals in their care and support, but also in their wider communities so that empowerment is promoted in all aspects of an individual's life.

Communication: effective communication underpins all delivery of high-quality health and social care. For care practitioners, it involves being able to communicate with:

- the individual about their wishes and preferences
- the individual's family about their backgrounds and cultures
- the individual's advocates about their views and feelings
- their colleagues about the health and safety aspects that may be important to consider
- their managers about the decisions taken to empower an individual to risk-take positively
- so that they can achieve their goals, with other professionals and services to share understanding, knowledge and experience.

Consultation: consultation by care practitioners must be meaningful and must be led by the needs of the individual rather than the needs of the service. Consultation requires care practitioners to plan the information they would like to find out, the reasons for this and how this will improve the care and support provided to the individual. Consultation can only be effective when it is undertaken using methods that reflect individuals' needs and preferences such as small forums or one-to-one interviews or informal discussions.

Collaboration: collaboration involves care practitioners working in partnership with the individual and all those others that are required for the empowerment of the individual. Collaboration involves mutual respect, honesty and being able to actively listen and take account of differing views and opinions. Collaboration involves health and social care practitioners working together to achieve the same shared goal – the empowerment of the individual.

Observation: observation of working practices, the impact of decisions made on individuals and others are all important and central to the effectiveness of empowering individuals in their day-to-day lives.

Figure 10.5 Effective supervision

Monitoring: monitoring the progress made by individuals with their life goals, the success of the strategies applied when empowering individuals, the risks involved in enabling an individual to take control of different aspects of their life is part of the care practitioner's duty of care and responsibilities when safeguarding and protecting individuals and others from danger, harm and neglect.

Review: reviewing the care and support in place, how individuals feel about how they are being supported to live their lives must be undertaken by care practitioners at regular intervals to ensure that all agreed working practices remain effective, safe and up to date in terms of reflecting and meeting individuals' current needs, wishes and preferences.

Risk management: managing risks enables care practitioners to support individuals to take risks that promote their own and others' safety, health and well-being. Risk management can only be completed effectively by care practitioners when they undertake it with individuals. Risk management can enable care practitioners to fulfil their responsibilities for upholding the rights of individuals while balancing their own duty of care towards them.

Care planning: care planning with individuals is about ensuring that individuals are leading how they want their care and support to meet their needs and recognising that they are the true experts in deciding on the best type and level of support they require to have their needs fully met.

Resourcing: resourcing availability underpins the practicalities and reality of putting individuals' plans of care and support into action. Solutions to resourcing can be achieved by care practitioners looking beyond their own health and social care settings and working in partnership with other services and professionals.

Training: training in current best practice approaches and the impact of current legislation and standards underpins all care practitioners' working practices; and ensures that they are empowering individuals safely and in line with legislative requirements and professional standards of all health and social care practitioners working in the health and social care sector.

Command word activity

Evaluate (AC 3.1)

Choose one health and social care practitioner. Research their role and responsibilities when empowering individuals.

You will need to:

- provide reasoned opinions or judgements from more than one perspective to demonstrate the roles and responsibilities of the health and social care practitioner
- assess the opportunities that exist for empowering individuals as well as the barriers and challenges that may be faced
- assess the effectiveness of the health and social care practitioner to empower individuals.

Develop a class presentation about your findings and the research evidence available that supports your views.

Read about it

DOH (2011) 'Improving care for people with long-term health conditions. Information Sheet 1. Personalised care planning. An "at a glance guide" for healthcare professionals', Department of Health

Morris, C., FerreiroPeteiro, M. and Collier, F. (2015) *Level 3 Health and Social Care Diploma*, London: Hodder Education.

Moss, B. (2015) *Communication Skills in Health and Social Care*, 3rd edition, Sage Publications

National Development Team for Inclusion/Helen Sanderson Associates *et al.* (2010) 'Personalisation: don't just do it, co-produce it and live it!'. Available at **www.ndti.org.uk**

SCIE (2014) 'Fact sheet: Overview of the Care Act', Social Care Institute for Excellence

Skills for Care (2015) 'The Care Certificate workbook. Work in a person-centred way. Standard 5', Skills for Care

Websites

Equality and Human Rights Commission – (information about the Equality Act 2010)

https://www.equalityhumanrights.com/en/equality-act/equality-act-faqs

Equality and Human Rights Commission – (information about the Human Rights Act 1998)

https://www.equalityhumanrights.com/en/human-rights/human-rights-act

Government publications – (Health and Social Care Act 2012: fact sheets) **https://www.gov.uk/government/publications/health-and-social-care-act-2012-fact-sheets**

Government publications – (information about the Data Protection Act)

https://www.gov.uk/data-protection/the-data-protection-act

Government publications – (information about current legislation and standards)

www.gov.uk

Healthwatch – (information about the functions of Healthwatch)

http://www.healthwatch.co.uk/

MIND – (information about the legal rights of individuals who have mental health needs)

http://www.mind.org.uk/information-support/legal-rights/

Skills for Care – (information and resources about the Care Certificate Framework)

http://www.skillsforcare.org.uk/Documents/Learning-and-development/Care-Certificate/The-Care-Certificate-Framework.pdf

Skills for Health – (information and resources about the Care Certificate Framework)

http://www.skillsforhealth.org.uk/standards/item/216-the-care-certificate

The Health and Safety Executive (HSE) – (information about the Health and Safety at Work Act 1974)

http://www.hse.gov.uk/legislation/hswa.htm

Unit HSC DM1: How will I be graded?

The table below shows what the learner must do to achieve each grading criterion. Learners must achieve all the criteria for a grade to be awarded (i.e. criteria D1 to D3 must be achieved to pass this unit assessment at grade D). A higher grade may not be awarded before a lower grade has been achieved in full, although component criteria of a higher grade may have been achieved.

Grade	Assessment criteria number	Assessment grading criteria	Assessment of learning / What you need to show
D1	1.1	Explain the importance of empowering individuals.	The explanation must demonstrate: ● an understanding of empowerment ● the importance of empowering individuals.
D2	1.4	Discuss strategies used to empower individuals.	The discussion must provide more than one appropriate strategy used to empower individuals. Relevant examples of the use of strategies from health and social care may be given to support the discussion.
D3		Show evidence of reading or use of sources.	There should be evidence of learners' reading or use of sources. Learners must use a minimum of two traceable references to support the discussion.
C1	1.2	Explain how legislation and standards inform practice when empowering individuals.	The explanation should demonstrate an understanding of both legislation and standards in relation to empowerment and of the differences and purposes of legislation and standards. The explanation should show how legislation and standards inform practice when empowering individuals. Relevant examples may be included to support the explanation.
C2	2.1	Describe risks involved when empowering individuals.	The description should demonstrate an understanding of risks which may occur when empowering individuals in health and social care. More than one risk should be described. Links to B2.
C3		Show evidence of reading or use of sources with referencing relevant to the explanation or description. Good use of vocabulary and grammar.	Use of referencing should show evidence of reading or use of sources. Vocabulary and grammar should be appropriate and accurate for purposes.

Grade	Assessment criteria number	Assessment grading criteria	Assessment of learning / What you need to show
B1	2.2	Explain tensions when balancing the rights of the individual against the health and social care practitioner's duty of care.	The detailed explanation should show an accurate understanding of both: • the rights of the individual • the health and social care practitioner's duty of care. The detailed explanation should demonstrate an understanding of tensions that may occur when balancing the rights of the individual against the practitioner's duty of care. More than one tension may be linked to a particular situation arising within the explanation.
B2	2.3	Explain how to manage risks when empowering individuals.	The explanation should demonstrate an understanding of: • the possible risks when empowering individuals • ways to manage the possible risks when empowering individuals in health and social care. More than one approach to managing risks must be considered. Examples may be given to demonstrate understanding of how to manage risks. Links to C3.
B3		Show evidence of reading or use of sources. Referencing supports explanation.	Use of reading or use of sources should be shown through a range of relevant referencing. Referencing should be used appropriately to support the explanation.
A1	1.3	Analyse how factors affect the empowerment of individuals.	Identify relevant factors that affect the empowerment of individuals. An analysis should balance the effects of the identified factors and show the consequences of the effects of the identified factors on the empowerment of individuals. Examples may be given to support the analysis.
A2		Show evidence of wider background reading or use of sources. Referencing supports analysis.	Wider background reading should be evident or a wide range of source material should be used.
A*1	3.1	Critically evaluate the roles and responsibilities of the health and social care practitioner when empowering individuals.	Provide reasoned opinions or judgements from more than one perspective to demonstrate the roles and responsibilities of the health and social care practitioner when empowering individuals. Learners will need to be able to demonstrate the barriers and challenges that may be faced and consider how effectively practitioners empower individuals.
A*2		Show evidence of a range of background reading or use of sources used selectively.	Learners should show the ability to consider or explore relevant issues which contribute to the evaluation. An extensive range of background reading or use of sources should be used selectively and cited appropriately.

HSC DM2

Protection of Children, Young People and Adults in Health and Social Care

About this unit

The unit links to HSC CM3: Safeguarding in health and social care. It aims to provide knowledge and understanding of how to protect children, young people and adults in health and social care. Children and some adults are vulnerable for a variety of reasons; they may not be able to communicate as well or may be dependent upon others for care. They therefore require additional protection from **abuse** and harm. This builds on what has been learned in HSC CM3 by focusing on how to respond to suspected harm and abuse. Within this, legislation, guidance, policies and procedures are explored to provide the legal framework that underpins health and social care practice. It will explore how to respond to suspected harm and abuse and the role of different practitioners within this. Finally, additional sources of information and support, including serious case reviews are explored.

LO1: Understand legislation, policies and procedures in relation to safeguarding and protection

1.1 Explain protection in relation to safeguarding

Protection is one element of safeguarding. It is about promoting the health, well-being and human rights of individuals. It is also about identifying and taking action to prevent abuse and **neglect**.

Safeguarding is a term which extends to include protecting children, young people and adults from abuse and maltreatment. It is about valuing an individual's unique needs. Safeguarding also underpins the provision of a high-quality service and is an essential part of a health and social care practitioner's role.

To identify abuse, staff must be aware of signs and indicators and contexts in which abuse may take place. To be able to take action, policies and procedures must be in place and legislation must be followed. All organisations that come into contact with children, young people and vulnerable adults must adhere to safeguarding legislation and have specific safeguarding policies and procedures in place. All professionals that work in these organisations need to be aware of their own responsibilities and where they can access additional support and advice.

Key terms

Abuse action by another individual that causes significant harm

Neglect failing to provide care that causes or is likely to cause harm to an individual

Protection detecting and preventing harm and abuse

Command word activity

Explain (AC 1.1)

Obtain a safeguarding policy from a health and social care organisation. Explain how protection of children, young people and adults is covered within this policy

1.2 Summarise legislation, policies and procedures in relation to the safeguarding and protection of children, young people and adults

There are numerous pieces of legislation, policies and procedures that relate to safeguarding and the protection to children, young people and adults. Some of the legislation relates to all age groups, and some is aimed specifically at children and young people or adults.

Take it further

For more details on safeguarding, go to Unit HSC CM3, Section 1.1.

Take it further

The relationship between legislation, policies and procedures can be found in Unit HSC CM3, Section 2.2.

Table 11.1 Legislation and guidance relating to health and social care provision for children, young people and adults

Legislation	How it relates to safeguarding and protection	Who does it relate to?
Working Together to Safeguard Children 2015 A government publication that provides statutory guidance for all practitioners and organisations that work with children	Applies to statutory, private, voluntary and faith-based organisations States providing early help is more effective in promoting the welfare of children Assists professionals to fully understand what they need to do, and what they can expect other people to do, to protect children Places a strong emphasis on how organisations should work together to promote welfare of children Emphasises that safeguarding and therefore protection is the responsibility of every practitioner Promotes the need for a clear understanding of the needs and views of children Requires practitioners with concerns about a child to make a referral and follow it up if not satisfied with the response States an advocate should be available in: an early help assessment confirmed concerns of harm child protection conferences.	All children under 18 years of age
Care Act 2014	Sets out a legal framework for local authorities and other parts of the health care system to protect adults at risk of abuse or neglect Requires local authorities to set up a Safeguarding Adult Board, bringing together teams and organisations involved in keeping 'at risk' adults safe Requires safeguarding adult reviews to take place when there has been a failure in safeguarding Requires local authorities to find out information when they think an adult with care or support needs might be at risk of abuse or neglect to identify if any action is required Requires organisations to share information about abuse or neglect to address issues quickly	Some provision for children and parent carers in transition/s Mainly adults over 18 years who have care and support needs and their carers
Children and Families Act 2014	Protects children in care from becoming vulnerable Gives children option to stay with a foster family until they are 21 Creates a new legal duty to improve the care given by schools in support of children with medical conditions Provides clearer rights for young carers and parent carers	All children and young adults in care until 21 years
Health and Social Care Act 2012	Set up CCGs Commissioned some public health care services Provides that CCGs and the NHS Commissioning Board (now **NHS England**) will be members of Safeguarding Boards	Children and adults
Mental Capacity Act 2005	Designed to protect individuals who are unable to make some or all decisions about their care and treatment for themselves due to reasons such as dementia, learning disabilities or a brain injury Recognises that not everyone who has these conditions will lack capacity Protects individuals as it is assumed that an individual does have capacity unless it is proven otherwise Protects those that do not have capacity as any decisions must be in the individual's best interests Includes Deprivation of Liberty Safeguards (DoLS) which allows restriction of activities, such as using locks or key pads to stop a person going out of a building or requiring a person to be supervised when out – but only if in the best interests and appropriate Recognises that as restrictions take away a person's freedom (contrary to the Human Rights Act 1998) any decision should be the least restrictive and a last resort	Young people over 16 years and all adults

Legislation	How it relates to safeguarding and protection	Who does it relate to?
Children Act 2004	Strengthens the 1989 Act and places a stronger emphasis on agencies working together in partnership Created the post of Children's Commissioner in England Requires a clear line of accountability for those who commission or provide children's services to safeguard and promote the welfare of children Requires that there should be: ● clear whistleblowing procedures ● safe recruitment strategies ● supervision ● support for staff including safeguarding training.	All children under the age of 18 years
No Secrets (2000)	Defines vulnerability and abuse Explains how health and social care services should work together to implement policies and procedures for protecting vulnerable adults It has since been repealed by the Care Act 2014	All vulnerable adults
Children Act 1989 A major piece of legislation that worked to safeguard children	The fundamental premise is that 'the child's welfare shall be the court's paramount consideration' when making any decisions about a child's life. It introduced the concept of parental responsibility and placed responsibility on the local authorities to identify children in need who require safeguarding	All children under the age of 18 years

Figure 11.1 How does the Care Act protect vulnerable individuals?

Activity

Create a guide for new members of staff on the Care Act 2014 and how it protects individuals.

Take it further

Remind yourself about Commissioning Groups and Safeguarding Boards in Unit HSC CM3 3, Section 2.1.

 Key term

NHS England regional teams who work with organisations and cover healthcare commissioning and delivery

Activity

Describe how the Mental Capacity Act 2005 protects an individual with late stage dementia in a nursing care home.

Activity

Create a list of activities that relate to everything an individual may do in a day that could be affected under DoLs. Identify which Articles they relate to under the Human Rights Act 1998.

Table 11.2 Other general legislation and how it relates to protection of children, young people and adults

Legislation	Relation to protection	Who does it protect?
Protection of Freedoms Act 2012 developed a number of measures aimed at reducing government intrusion into the lives of individuals. It applies to a number of areas including biometric data, surveillance, protecting property, counter-terrorism, safeguarding and data protection (see p. 239 for more information on DBS)	Merged the Criminal Records Bureau (CRB) and the Independent Safeguarding Authority to create the **Disclosure and Barring Service (DBS)** Made DBS checks a requirement for over 16s that work with vulnerable individuals Provides that job applicants will see the results of the DBS check before their employers so mistakes can be corrected Enhanced disclosures will display any criminal record and cautions, reprimands and warnings	A DBS check is required for anyone working with children or vulnerable adults
Domestic Violence Crime and Victims Act 2004 and Domestic Violence Crime and Victims (Amendment) Act 2012	Individuals can be prosecuted if they were aware or ought to have been aware that the victim was at risk of significant physical harm, they failed to take steps to prevent that harm and the person subsequently died Provided a new definition of domestic violence to include intimate partners or family members regardless of gender or sexuality Applies to scenarios where a child or vulnerable adult dies as a result of abuse and it is not clear which member of the household was responsible for the death In 2012, the 2004 Act was amended to include a new offence of causing or allowing *serious physical harm* (i.e. not just causing death) to a child or vulnerable adult	A child or vulnerable person
Equality Act 2010 legally protects people from discrimination in the workplace and wider society	There is responsibility in the workplace and wider society such as education and public services to eliminate discrimination which then protects individuals from harassment and harm The Equality Act 2010 also provides rights for people such as carers or parents to not be discriminated against because they have an association with an individual with disabilities	Children, young people and adults
Forced Marriage Act 2007	Offers protection from physical, financial, emotional or psychological pressure (such as telling an individual they are bringing shame on a family by not consenting) The courts can issue a Forced Marriage Protection Order (FMPO). This order will protect the individual who is being forced into marriage by legally preventing the behaviour or conduct of those forcing the marriage There can be a power of arrest attached to the order, especially if violence or threats of violence have been used, so if ignored an individual can be arrested by the police	Both adults and children
Anti-social Behaviour, Crime and Policing Act (2014)	Made it a criminal offence to: Take someone abroad to force them to marry (even if the marriage does not take place) Marry someone who lacks capacity to consent Breach an FMPO	Both children and adults

Legislation	Relation to protection	Who does it protect?
Sexual Offences Act 2003 aimed to make new provision about prevention of sexual offences and protecting children from sexual offences	Provides that a child under the age of 13 years is incapable of giving consent to any form of sexual activity Aims to prevent and protect children and young people from sexual exploitation Aims to clarify what constitutes a crime of a sexual nature against children, young people and adults Included new measures to protect children from offences including sex trafficking and paedophiles grooming children on the internet Makes it an offence to give someone a substance (for example spiking a drink) without their consent and with the intention of overpowering them for sexual activity	Both children and adults
United Nations Convention on the Rights of the Child contains 54 rights. Adults and governments must work together to make sure all children can enjoy all their rights	Many of the rights offer protection to children and cover protection from abuse and neglect	Applies to children up to the age of 18 years
Human Rights Act 1998 builds on the rights and freedoms within the European Convention on Human Rights. It applies to all aspects of daily life and details a number of 'rights' that all people in the UK are entitled to	Protects individuals and gives them the power to challenge discrimination, protecting vulnerable individuals. The most relevant articles include: Article 3 Freedom from torture and inhuman and degrading treatment (for example being abused) Article 4 Freedom from slavery and forced labour Article 12 Right to marry and start a family (for example, someone with learning disabilities who has capacity to consent has the right to marry) Article 15 Protection from discrimination in respect of these rights and freedoms	Applies to both children and adults
Data Protection Act 1998	Protects individuals by keeping personal details and information (which includes health and social care records) safe and secure Aims to prevent information from being misused or sold on to people who use it to take advantage of individuals Covers the collection, use, storage and disposal of personal data and information Permits the sharing of information where it is critical and necessary to prevent serious harm or distress or in life-threatening situations	Applies to both children and adults
Public Interest Disclosure Act 1998 created to protect whistleblowers from being unfairly treated at work or losing their job	Whistleblowers are protected in the following circumstances: A criminal offence has been committed or is likely to be committed There has been a failure to comply with any legal obligation A miscarriage of justice has occurred or is likely to occur Where someone is endangering or is likely to damage the health and safety of an individual Where a person is damaging or likely to damage the environment Where someone is concealing or likely to conceal information	Applies to protecting both children and adults

Key term

DBS checks check, carried out to identify any criminal record

Forced marriage when pressure or abuse is used to make a couple marry

Take it further

Information on the Equality Act 2010 can be found in Unit HSC CM1, Section 3.1.

Take it further

You can read about the UN Convention on the Rights of the Child at: **https://www.unicef.org.uk/what-we-do/un-convention-child-rights/**

Take it further

Details of the principles of privacy and data protection are covered in Unit HSC CM4, Sections 3 and 4.

Take it further

Legislation can change. Go to **http://www.legislation.gov.uk/** to keep up to date.

Forced marriage

A forced marriage is different from an arranged marriage where the couple is still consenting. It is a current and contentious issue and it is therefore a developing area of law.

The Forced Marriage Unit is a government group that provides help, advice and support to victims or potential victims of forced marriage. According to the Home Office, in 2015, advice or support was given to 1,220 individuals relating to a possible forced marriage and ages ranged from very young children to people post-retirement age.

Whistleblowing

A whistleblower is someone who discloses illegal or dangerous activity in an organisation or workplace. Whistleblowers are protected by the Public Interest Disclosure Act 1998.

To be protected by the law, any disclosure made must be in the public interest, which means that it must have the potential to affect other people.

Take it further

Read about whistleblowing in Section 2.3 of this unit.

Activity

Whistleblowing can be difficult to do. Explain why this is the case, the importance of doing so and how you could support a colleague wishing to disclose poor practice.

Local multi-agency safeguarding policy and procedures

Following the 'No Secrets' government guidance, statutory, voluntary and independent sector agencies were required to work together to produce policies and procedures on adult safeguarding. Since the introduction of the Care Act 2014 Safeguarding Adults Boards were set up. Part of their remit is to ensure that policies and procedures are able to work and lead to effective safeguarding practice. Multi-agency policies and procedures support this and meet other requirements of the Care Act such as information-sharing and a duty to work of co-operation.

Local Safeguarding Adults Boards

Safeguarding Adults Boards were set up in response to the 'No Secrets' report. They are multi-agency boards who are responsible for protecting and safeguarding vulnerable adults in a local area. A number of agencies are involved such as local authorities, Health Trusts and the police.

Under the Care Act 2014, all local authorities must have a Safeguarding Adult Board. The overarching purpose is to help and safeguard adults with care and support needs by preventing abuse and neglect occurring and stopping it quickly when it happens.

The board leads safeguarding arrangements across its area, sharing and implementing strategies and monitoring their effectiveness. It must publish an annual report detailing how effective its work has been. The board should also consider issues that contribute to the well-being of the community and prevention of abuse and neglect, such as quality of local care and support services and the effectiveness of interventions for adults who self-neglect. It also commission, safeguarding adult reviews.

Key term

Safeguarding Adults Reviews involve different agencies reviewing and deciding how agencies and individuals involved could have worked differently to prevent harm or a death from taking place

Safeguarding Adult Principles

The following principles underpin all safeguarding work (Department of Health 2011). These are:

Empowerment: individuals should be supported to make their own decisions so they are person-led and informed consent should be gained.

Prevention: an emphasis on preventing harm before it occurs.

Proportionality: the least intrusive responses to risks should be put into place so that professionals work in the best interests of individuals and only get involved as much as needed.

Protection: support should be offered for those in greatest need.

Partnership: solutions should involve working with wider communities and recognising the community has a role in preventing, detecting and reporting abuse and neglect.

Accountability: taking responsibility for decisions and being transparent so others can see how decisions are made.

Local Safeguarding Children Boards (LSCBs)

LSCBs were set up under the Children Act 2004 and must be established in each local authority area. As well as the local authority, a number of other organisations are represented, for example the police, health services, probation services and youth offending team. Their aim is to improve the overall well-being of children in the local area. The board develops and agrees policies and procedures for safeguarding and promoting the welfare of children, taking actions where there are concerns about a child's safety and monitoring and evaluating the effectiveness of activities undertaken by the board. They also have a major role in serious case reviews.

Safe recruitment

Safe recruitment is about preventing the employment of a worker who may pose a risk to vulnerable adults, young people and children. Staff involved in recruitment should ensure that they send a clear message to potential new members of staff about how they work to protect individuals to help deter unsuitable workers:

1. Application forms should be used as it is easier to identify any gaps in employment history.
2. Interviews and selection techniques should be carried out by a trained selection panel to assist in identifying prospective employers that should be rejected.
3. A safeguarding question during the interview process will help to identify the knowledge and skill base of prospective workers.
4. Checks should be carried out prior to employment, for example DBS checks and references.
5. Staff should be provided with training on safeguarding, and given a handbook containing policies and procedures that relate to safeguarding.
6. Each organisation should have a policy on how to report concerns that practitioners may have about another.

Activity

Find a job advertisement for working with children, young people or vulnerable adults. Identify any checks or methods that the organisation is taking to help safe recruitment.

Table 11.3 Legislation and guidance for Wales, Scotland and Northern Ireland

Wales	Scotland	Northern Ireland
Social Services and Wellbeing (Wales) Act 2014 Violence against Women, Domestic Abuse and Sexual Violence (Wales) Act 2015 Children and Young Persons Act 2008 Children and Young People: Rights to Action Framework	Adults with Incapacity (Scotland) Act 2000 Public Bodies (Joint Working) (Scotland) Act 2014 Children and Young People (Scotland) Act 2014 Getting it Right for Every Child (GIRFEC)	Mental Capacity Act (Northern Ireland) 2016 Carers and Direct Payments Act (2002) Safeguarding Board Act (Northern Ireland) 2011 Children (Northern Ireland) Order 1995 Our Children and Young People: Our Pledge

Related policies and procedures

Aside from safeguarding, each organisation will have their own policies and procedures relating to protecting individuals. Some examples include Data Protection Policy, Whistleblowing Policy, and Equality Policy.

Activity (AC 1.2)

Identify two policies that your placement or your school or college have that protect individuals and identify two ways that each policy protects individuals.

Command word activity

Summarise (AC 1.2)

Create a fact file on legislation. Include one piece of legislation that is specific for children, one specific for adults, and two that relate to both children and adults.

✔ Check your understanding

1. What is the difference between protection and safeguarding?
2. Describe how the Care Act 2014 relates to protecting individuals.
3. Identify two rights under the Human Rights Act that relate to protecting individuals.
4. Identify three articles under the UN Convention on the Rights of the Child that can protect the rights of children.
5. Explain the role of either Local Safeguarding Children Boards or Local Safeguarding Adults Boards.

Legislation specific to home nation

Although some of the legislation is for all of the UK, Scotland, Wales and Northern Ireland have legislation and guidance specific to that nation. Some examples are shown in Table 11.3.

LO2: Understand how to respond to suspected harm or abuse

2.1 Explain actions to take if harm or abuse is suspected and/or disclosed for children and young people and adults

A number of actions should be taken if harm or abuse is suspected or disclosed. This is important to ensure that individuals can be prevented from further harm. The steps involved recognise that the priority of any disclosure is to ensure the safety and care of the vulnerable individual as well as steps to maintain confidentiality, identifying any need for investigation and who may be involved.

Adherence to policies and procedures

Policies and procedures should be easy for everyone to access. Every practitioner, when working in health and social care, must be aware of their policies and procedures so they know what action needs to be taken in the event of a disclosure of abuse and who to report to. Following policies and procedures is important because as well as providing consistency, it should ensure that actions meet the legal framework, which is essential when disclosure of abuse or suspected abuse is made. Furthermore, by reporting concerns to the right person this will ensure that time is not wasted and maintains confidentiality of the information. It is good practice to be aware of safeguarding contacts, as this will save time in the event of a disclosure or an emergency situation when you are concerned for the welfare of the child, young person or adult.

> **Activity**
>
> Identify the policies and procedures in your work placement for the protection and safeguarding of individuals. Where can these be found?

Roles and responsibilities

Everyone who comes into contact with children or vulnerable adults has a responsibility to protect individuals. These roles and responsibilities are not just limited to any disclosure of abuse, but there is a wider context of safeguarding such as following risk assessment to keep individuals safe. However, in order for protection to be effective, it is important that each practitioner knows their role and responsibility for protection and their role in relation to other individuals. In the event of disclosure the main role is to listen to the child, young person or adult, and not to question the individual unless the practitioner needs to clarify any points they do not understand. It is the responsibility of the practitioner to whom the disclosure has been made to pass the information on to the safeguarding officer.

> **Activity**
>
> Identify the protection and safeguarding officer at your work placement. Find out their name and job title and the best way to contact them.

Maintain safety

The safety of the individual making the disclosure is the most important consideration. If a practitioner is concerned for their immediate well-being, then steps must be taken to ensure the safety of the individual. The safeguarding officer should be immediately contacted. There may be the need for immediate medical care or for contacting external agencies, such as the police and local safeguarding team to find an emergency place of safety, for example a refuge.

Lines of reporting

Lines of reporting refer to the process by which concerns are raised. Specifically, this means identifying the most relevant people to contact when raising concerns about the safety of an individual. There will be a practitioner who acts as safeguarding officer to whom concerns can be raised directly. In larger organisations, there may be more than one. The safeguarding officer will then determine the process and actions to be taken. Ofsted state a safeguarding lead practitioner should be on duty in an early years setting whenever the setting is open.

If a practitioner feels their concerns have not been fully acted upon by the safeguarding officer, there will also be another person, perhaps more senior, by which a practitioner can make a further report or follow up. There will be a formal process for the practitioner to report any concerns raised if these are about the safeguarding officer themselves.

Recording

Accuracy of information is essential in cases of abuse or suspected abuse. This is because the report might form part of legal or disciplinary action and therefore part of the evidence.

The practitioners should record the following:

1. What the child or adult has said, using their own phrases or words.
2. Anything that the practitioner notices, for example any signs of injuries.
3. Whether the individual appears emotionally upset should also be noted, but it must be clear which words are the individual's own and which are the practitioner's inferences or impressions.
4. The circumstance of the disclosure should be noted, the setting where the disclosure was made and anyone else who was there at the time.
5. The information if written should be clear, factual and legible covering information such as what happened, where and how long ago.
6. It might need to be photocopied so black ink is preferable.
7. The report should end with the practitioner's name, along with it being signed and dated.

Preservation of evidence

Key term

Forensic evidence evidence that can be used in a court, especially DNA

The priority in a disclosure is to ensure the safety of the individual. However, it may also be important to obtain forensic evidence to be used as evidence for prosecution where a crime has been committed. Forensic evidence can be transferred easily, but also is easily destroyed; therefore steps should be taken to preserve evidence.

Evidence could include financial records or receipts in the case of financial abuse, or clothing and underwear in the incidence of sexual abuse, as DNA evidence of the offender may be present on these items.

If the evidence is written, such as case files or notes, it should be preserved and secured to avoid being tampered with or altered. Any fabrics such as clothing or bedding should not be washed and anything used to comfort the individual, for example a blanket or coat, should be preserved.

If a sexual offence is thought to have occurred, try to discourage the individual from washing or cleaning themselves. Any physical marks should be documented and body maps can be used as indicators of where the marks occurred on the body. The evidence must be factual and include details such as size, shape and colour of the injury, whether the skin is broken as well as if the individual reports pain. Body maps are useful in court to assist with giving live evidence. Young children, in particular, may lack the vocabulary needed to give accurate evidence and can use a body map rather than having to point to their own body, which could be traumatic or embarrassing for them.

Safeguarding alert form body map

Please complete all sections			
Details of the vulnerable adult			
Title	**First name**	**Surname**	**Client identification no. (if known)**

Please indicate position on body of marks or injuries, note any colour of any injury, whether skin is broken or anything else of relevance.

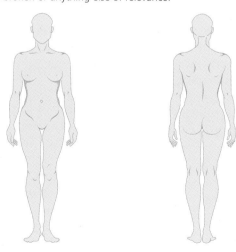

Date of incident		Time of incident	Location of incident
About you - person completing this form			
Title	**First name**	**Surname**	**Relationship to vulnerable adult**
Email :		Telephone number: Mobile number:	

Figure 11.2 Example of a body map

Key term

Body map an outline of the human body, which can be used to document and illustrate visible signs of harm or injury

Boundaries of confidentiality

In the event of disclosure, the practitioner should never promise to keep anything a secret as there is a legal obligation to act on the information. However, confidentiality should be maintained outside those involved in acting on the information; this includes colleagues. Informed consent should be obtained to share information where there is a safeguarding risk; the individual's preferred method of communication should be used. However, if the individual lacks capacity or informed consent is not possible and individuals are at risk, it may be necessary to override this, but only if it is in the public interest or best interests of the individual.

Listening

Listening skills and being attentive will help the child or adult to make their disclosure. The practitioner should remain calm, not panic and listen sympathetically. The practitioners should demonstrate concern, but not any emotions such as shock, disbelief or embarrassment. Questions should be kept to a minimum so that it is not deemed that the practitioner has been leading the child or adult in their disclosure or response. This is important as a leading question may be seen to be guiding the child or adult to answer in a specific way and this might affect whether the testimony can be used in any court proceedings. It is important to be aware of the different ways in which children or vulnerable adults may disclose the abuse, as this might not always be in a verbal way.

Non-judgemental

If harm or abuse is disclosed it is important that a non-judgemental approach is taken. This means that a practitioner will not impose

Activity

Describe how a judgemental approach may affect the child or adult making a disclosure about domestic abuse.

Classroom discussion

As a group, think of as many reasons as possible why a victim of domestic abuse would want to stay in that situation. Then think of the reasons they would want to leave. Using a whiteboard or flipchart, have a member of the class record these in two columns. Which column has more reasons?

their own values, beliefs or standards. A practitioner should not allow their personal feelings to impact on what is being disclosed and affect their interpretation of what is being said. By remaining objective, the practitioner avoids jumping to conclusions about what has occurred and ensures that the individual making the disclosure feels they are being listened to. For example, sentences such as 'Why didn't you say something sooner?' or 'You could have just said no or run away' should be avoided. This may make the individual who is disclosing abuse not want to say any more, feel that it is their fault, or that they are not being taken seriously.

Reassurance

Making a disclosure is incredibly difficult, especially if it is about a family member. Therefore, reassurance can be helpful as it means the individual will know that they have done the right thing in telling the practitioner and that it is not their fault the abuse has occurred. It will help and reassure the individual to know that they are believed and that they are going to be supported throughout the process. It should be noted again that the practitioner should not make promises because they may not always be able to keep them. When providing reassurance to the child or adult, phrases such as 'I promise this will never happen to you again' should be avoided.

Command word activity

Evidence (AC 2.1)

You are working in a day centre for adults with learning disabilities. One of the individuals, Jennifer, who attends the centre has recently been appearing very unkempt and today has bruising on the back of her arm. She appears distressed throughout the day and at the end does not want to go home, saying that someone will hurt her.

Copy and complete this table to explain the action that must be taken in response to Jennifer's

disclosure (for example, contact the safeguarding officer), and the consequences of not completing this step.

The evidence should come from wider reading. Possible sources of information include the Care Act 2014 summaries, serious case reviews, policies and procedures on safeguarding and the Social Care Institute of Excellence.

Step to be taken	Why this is important	Supportive evidence or quote	What would happen if this step was not completed	Supportive evidence or quote

Take it further

As well as responding to suspected harm or abuse, health and social care practitioners have a duty to respond to recognise individuals who are vulnerable and may be susceptible to radicalisation by extremists or terrorists. Read about this here: http://www.safecampuscommunities.ac.uk/the-prevent-agenda

2.2 Analyse the role of agencies when responding to suspected harm or abuse of children, young people and adults

All organisations should work together and communicate effectively when suspected harm or abuse of children, young people and adults is disclosed. Some organisations have specific legal obligations and responsibilities. All organisations will have developed their own policies and procedures around protection and safeguarding and have a responsibility to monitor the individuals in their care. These will reflect legal requirements. They will be required to train staff on protection of individuals so that staff are aware of warning signs and indicators, and their roles and responsibilities.

All agencies have responsibility to report any concerns that they have about individuals in their care or poor practice and to take any unresolved issues further in reporting to an external body.

Table 11.4 Agencies and their role in responding to suspected harm or abuse

Agency	Role
Inspectorates including Care Quality Commission Ofsted	Taking action if care services do not have suitable arrangements to keep people safe Monitor the effectiveness of services
Local authorities	Will have a specialised team that deals with safeguarding (e.g. Safeguarding Children's Team) Will follow up any concern about harm or abuse with assessment Will be involved with working with families when abuse or harm is suspected Can apply to the courts for a legal supervision order to monitor a child's needs, whether at home or elsewhere Will carry out needs assessments to identify needs and how they impact upon an individual's well-being
Police	The investigation of alleged offences against children, young people and adults The exercise of emergency powers to protect children Have legal roles within safeguarding
Schools / colleges	Monitor and identify any concerns and act upon the information Work with multi-agencies to support children Attend case conferences
Medical staff	May be some of the first staff to be alerted to possible harm or abuse Can examine and treat. Records may be used as evidence

Analyse (AC 2.1, 2.2)

A community care worker visits Mrs Brown, who has dementia, twice a day. The community care worker visits one day and observes that Mrs Brown's grandson has moved in. On subsequent visits the grandson and his friends are found sitting in Mrs Brown's kitchen, or lounge, playing games or drinking alcohol. The grandson claims he is now helping with care for Mrs Brown and paying her bills. Since this has occurred, Mrs Brown is frequently short of money and is vague about the reasons.

1. Create a flowchart to analyse the different agencies that would be involved in this situation. In your analysis, consider:
   a. the role of each agency
   b. the key stages of any procedures that need to be followed
   c. actions to be taken by each agency involved.

2.3 Explain the responsibilities of the health and social care practitioner in relation to whistleblowing

The health and social care practitioner has a clear responsibility to report wrongdoing in practice. The practitioner should follow the policies and procedures of the setting, reporting these concerns in the appropriate way, which is often to report these to the line manager. If these concerns are not acted upon, or it is not appropriate to report them, then someone else should be informed (such as a more senior worker or a prescribed person). Reporting concerns may also prevent abuse occurring, for example if staff report doubts that they may have about a colleague's actions or behaviour.

Key term

Prescribed person independent bodies or individuals that can be approached by whistleblowers

Take it further

See the full list of prescribed persons at **https://www.gov.uk/government/publications/blowing-the-whistle-list-of-prescribed-people-and-bodies--2/whistleblowing-list-of-prescribed-people-and-bodies**

If the practitioner has repeatedly reported their concerns and they have not been acted upon or taken seriously or no action is taken, then the practitioner should 'blow the whistle' to external agencies. Examples of whistleblowing also include reporting on any practices that exist in the health and social care setting that are putting individuals at risk, such as repeatedly having insufficient staff on duty.

Whistleblowing can lead to a number of mixed emotions, such as the practitioner questioning themselves, or asking 'what if I'm wrong?', or feeling loyalty towards the workplace or management. However, the safety and well-being of individuals in the care of the practitioner is first and foremost and no team member should put their loyalty towards their colleagues over the protection of individuals at risk. Whistleblowers are protected by law and should not be disadvantaged for reporting poor practice.

Take it further

See p. 238 for more information about the legal protection available for whistleblowers.

Command word activity

Explain (AC 2.3)

Create an awareness poster on whistleblowing to explain what it is, why it is important and the process of whistleblowing.

Check your understanding

1. List three actions to be taken if abuse is suspected.
2. Outline the role of two agencies or organisations involved in responding to suspected harm or abuse.
3. Define whistleblowing.
4. Outline the procedure that should be taken by a practitioner if they feel there is poor practice within their organisations.
5. Explain why whistleblowing may be a dilemma for some practitioners.

LO3: Understand how to access additional support and information in relation to safeguarding and protection

In order to respond appropriately to safeguarding issues, health and social care practitioners must understand their role. There are a number of sources of additional support and information that can be accessed in relation to this role and safeguarding and protection.

3.1 Explain sources of support and information in relation to safeguarding and protection of children and young people, and adults

3.2 Describe how to access sources of support and information in relation to safeguarding and protection

There are numerous sources of support and information in relation to safeguarding and protection. Some sources are specific, according to whether it is children and young people or adults, and some are generic.

Policies and procedures

All organisations that come into contact with children and young people or vulnerable adults should ensure that they have safeguarding policies and procedures in place to ensure that everyone can be protected from harm. Policies and procedures can be accessed through the workplace. On induction, every member of staff should be shown where to find this information. If a staff member is not sure or has any questions about accessing these policies, they should speak to their manager.

Safeguarding policies generally:

1. Have a statement that says the organisation is committed to safeguarding
2. State who the policy applies to (for example, staff, volunteers)
3. Have identified risks of harm to individuals and indicators of safeguarding issues
4. Will state clearly what the organisation will do to keep individuals safe (for example, staff checks, training staff)
5. State how concerns raised will be responded to
6. Have links to procedures
7. Have a date valid from and a review date to ensure the information is still valid (although it can be reviewed prior to that date)

Procedures should contain a step-by-step guide on how to implement the policy in practice. For example, there are often contact details of safeguarding officers for the organisation and how to raise concerns.

There are other policies and procedures that have a role in protection and safeguarding, for example within a policy on managing challenging behaviour or a confidentiality policy. It is essential that all staff are familiar with policies and procedures of the organisation and know how to access the information. This normally forms part of an induction process.

Manager

Managers have a major role in protection and safeguarding and therefore are a key source of support and advice. Their role would include:

- answering questions that a practitioner may have or knowing where to go for the information
- recruiting in a safe way, for example taking up references to ensure applicants have the skills and abilities to do the job and that there has been no unsatisfactory previous performance
- complying with requirements set by CQC and Ofsted (see inspectorate bodies and registered manager)
- supporting staff by ensuring they are trained and the workplace is safe
- supporting staff in the event of disclosure of a safeguarding issue
- liaising with outside agencies regarding disclosure and whistleblowing concerns.

Key term

Registered manager a person appointed to have legal responsibility over the day-to-day running of any service regulated by the Care Quality Commission

Colleagues

Colleagues can offer support and information about policies and procedures and accessing other sources of information. They may be more experienced and offer insight and share their knowledge. They may have different skills and knowledge and by working together can promote well-being and prevent harm. Colleagues may also be able to help with emotions that a practitioner may be feeling. Colleagues are often easy to access as health and social care practitioners often work with others. A new member of staff may have a mentor which would be an experienced colleague that can aid the transition of the new member of staff into the organisation.

Training

Training provides staff with knowledge and understanding of how to use policies and procedures and how to protect and safeguard. Training can be face to face, online or via distance learning. Training will generally include information on types of abuse, signs and symptoms or indicators. It will explain procedures to take in relation to disclosure and support available. Training may also link to wider ways of how to keep individuals safe, for example challenging behaviour or equality. It is also useful to keep records of training and information obtained so that these can be referred back to for useful information. Training can be accessed through the employer. Some training such as safeguarding is mandatory for all staff and should form part of the induction with updates. Some health and social care practitioners may opt to undertake additional training or complete university courses that relate to safeguarding.

Take it further

Read about types of training and continuing professional development (CPD) in HSC DM5, Section 1.2.

Classroom discussion (AC 3.1)

Training is important in ensuring that you have the knowledge of how to act in the event of suspected harm or abuse. Evaluate how useful training is for this situation. What else might a practitioner require in these circumstances?

Inspectorate

Both the Care Quality Commission and Ofsted will provide sources of information and advice for protection and safeguarding. The Care Quality Commission provides two types of information: provider handbooks and guidance on how to meet the standards. These contain information on safeguarding and how organisations can work to keep people safe. This information can be obtained from visiting their website. The Ofsted website provides guidance on standards, handbooks and frameworks including safeguarding. As well as accessing resources online, both inspectorate bodies are available via telephone, fax, email or by writing to them. You can look up their details online.

Take it further

Visit the Ofsted website for additional information on protection and safeguarding here: https://www.gov.uk/government/publications/inspecting-safeguarding-in-early-years-education-and-skills-from-september-2015

Local authority

The local authority will have information on safeguarding and policies and procedures that comply with legislation. As they are responsible for local safeguarding boards, they can be a good source of information and advice. Contact details of the local authority can be found here: https://www.gov.uk/find-local-council. Local authorities can be contacted in person, via an online form, email, phone or post.

Police

The police have a key role in safeguarding and are able to support and provide information and advice on a range of safeguarding issues. The police can be contacted in a variety of ways. In an emergency situation dial 999; otherwise the non-emergency number 101 can be used. They can also be contacted in person by visiting the station and concerns about safeguarding will be passed on to the safeguarding teams.

Command word activity

Explain and describe (AC 3.1, 3.2)

Create a resource booklet aimed at a new health and social care practitioner. The booklet should explain three different sources of information and advice that can provide further support and information on safeguarding of either vulnerable adults or children and describe how to access these resources.

Check your understanding

1. Identify three areas a safeguarding policy will cover.
2. Identify the two main inspectorate bodies that can provide information on safeguarding.
3. Outline the support colleagues can offer.
4. Outline the role of the police and local authorities.
5. Describe the support a manager can offer.

LO4: Understand the purpose of serious case reviews

In England, a serious case review is an investigation conducted by Local Safeguarding Children Boards (LSCB) either following the death of a child from abuse or neglect or if a child is seriously harmed and concerns are raised about how agencies worked together. Serious harm is defined in *Working Together to Safeguard Children* (2015) Chapter 14, Section 7, p. 75 as any or all of 'a potentially life-threatening injury serious and/or likely long-term impairment of physical or mental health or physical, intellectual, emotional, social or behavioural development'.

Even if the child has recovered from any harm, the case must be reviewed as serious harm may still have occurred. Other incidents may be referred to the LSCB even if neither criterion are suspected, such as where a child dies in a young offender institution or a secure children's home. The procedure and name is different in Wales, Northern Ireland and Scotland.

Key term

Serious case review an examination that takes place after a child dies or is seriously injured and abuse or neglect is thought to be involved. It aims to provide lessons that can be learned to prevent a similar incident occurring again

4.1 Explain why serious case reviews are required

Serious case reviews are required to learn lessons from incidents. The cases that are reviewed have had significant detrimental impacts or resulted in the death of individuals. Many are high-profile cases that often reach the media and there is a need to provide explanations and be accountable about events that have occurred, by identifying strategies to prevent this occurring in future. Although carried out in hindsight, they seek to understand practice from the viewpoint of those involved at the time.

A serious case review will identify actions required to improve service delivery and work together; it is not about apportioning blame. It will draw together information about a case to identify where mistakes were made, the lessons that can be learned and how this can be acted upon, along with the expected changes so this can be monitored. The outcome of the review will inform professional practice, multi-agency working, and how those involved can work together to improve safeguarding practice.

Command word activity

Explain (AC 4.1)

All the results of children's serious case reviews are stored in the 'National Repository of Serious Case Reviews'. This can be accessed online at **https://www.nspcc.org.uk/preventing-abuse/child-protection-system/case-reviews/national-case-review-repository/**

Identify two serious case reviews from your local area and explain the reasons these took place.

4.2 Analyse how outcomes of serious case reviews inform practice

The outcomes of serious case reviews should inform practice, and the review process should be carried out with the aim of suggesting areas for improvement, rather than being just a 'tick box exercise'. A serious case review is different to any disciplinary action that may occur, which if required is a separate process carried out by individual agencies following their own policies and procedures. Once a review has been completed, a report will be published. Adult safeguarding reports are published by the local Safeguarding Adults Boards and children's are added into the National Repository. The report details what should happen in order to reduce the risk of reoccurrence. It should be easy to understand so that professionals or members of the public can understand what is being said. The report should detail the actions that have been agreed by those involved in the review and a timetable for the action to be taken. It should state how success will be measured so that improvements can be monitored. Some examples of how serious case reviews may lead to changes in practice are as follows:

1. Review of procedures: Procedures may need to be altered or adapted.

2. How information is collated: Some serious case reviews have highlighted an individual repeatedly missing health care appointments, but this was not followed up.

3. Improve local inter-agency practice, for example finding out what other agencies do and how they work, and how to work together.

4. Change the way in which information is shared between organisations.

5. Staff: being aware of the workloads of staff and how they are being managed and supervision that staff receive.

6. Training needs: such as awareness of how abuse may present (such as bruising on babies that are not yet mobile).

7. Support available to families or individuals in need.

8. Resources that may be helpful.

 Case scenario

Steven Hoskins was a 39-year-old man with learning disabilities who lived alone. He was targeted and subsequently tortured, resulting in his death. Following a serious case review, it was found that he had previously made contact with different agencies, and there had been numerous warning signs and opportunities for interventions. Agencies should have been aware of his circumstances and the risk. As a result of the findings of the serious case review, improvements were made in the local area in staff training, communication and sharing information. There was also an introduction of a system that raises an alert if there are a number of calls from the same person reporting similar problems. The lessons learned from this case could be useful for implementation in other areas.

Take it further

Watch a video about the case of Stephen Hoskins and the lessons learned at **http://www.scie.org. uk/socialcaretv/video-player.asp?guid=55e3a233-c880-4cb4-8701-4acb9d243d39**

1. Outline why Stephen Hoskins was targeted.

2. Outline a change that has been implemented by the police.

3. Outline a change that has been implemented by primary care.

4. Why is sharing information important?

The NSPCC have collated information about serious case reviews and grouped these into different areas such as health and housing. Choose one area and identify the issues for practice from the serious case reviews **https://www.nspcc.org. uk/preventing-abuse/child-protection-system/case-reviews/learning/**

There are challenges to analysing a serious case. It is easier to look back at something and identify what should have been done differently, than to put in place actions that can be implemented in practice to avoid a reoccurrence. Serious case reviews must seek to understand why mistakes and poor practice have occurred; however, individuals may feel that they are being blamed and seek to justify resulting actions. Actions that are to be put into place must be realistic and feasible within the time frame and resources available.

Command word activity

Analyse (AC 4.2)

Using the National Repository, read some of the summaries from two different years. Choose two summaries with a similar theme to analyse. Consider the following in your analysis:

1. What were the recommendations?
2. What suggestions were made to improve safeguarding procedures?
3. Were different perspectives provided?
4. Where any of the recommendations or suggestions conflicting?
5. If there were any similar themes, why might this have occurred?

Check your understanding

1. Define a serious case review.
2. Explain one reason why a serious case review might be required.
3. Where can you obtain previous serious case reviews?
4. Describe two ways in which serious case reviews can improve practice.
5. Give one weakness of serious case reviews.

Read about it

Department of Health (2011) *Statement of Government Policy on Adult Safeguarding*, London: Department of Health

HMSO (1998) *Public Interest Disclosure Act*, London: HMSO

HMSO (2014) *The Care Act 2010*, London: HSMO.

Home Office (2011) *Protection of Freedoms Bill*, London: HMSO

HM Government (2012) *Changes to Disclosure and Barring: What You Need to Know*, London: HMSO

HM Government (2015) *Working Together to Safeguard Children: A Guide to Inter-agency Working to Safeguard and Promote the Welfare of Children* (PDF), London: Department for Education (DfE)

Home Office (2016) *Forced Marriage 2015 Statistics*, London: Home Office.

NHS Commissioning Board (2012) *Arrangement to Secure Children's and Adults' Safeguarding in the Future NHS*, London: NHS Commissioning Board.

Websites

CQC (2016) http://www.cqc.org.uk/

Department of Health (2016) *Care Act Factsheets*. Accessed from

https://www.gov.uk/government/publications/care-act-2014-part-1-factsheets/care-act-factsheets#factsheet-7-protecting-adults-from-abuse-or-neglect

Home Office (2005) *The Domestic Violence, Crime and Victims Act 2004*. Accessed from https://www.gov.uk/government/publications/the-domestic-violence-crime-and-victims-act-2004

SCIE (2015a) *Deprivation of Liberty Safeguards (DoLs) at a Glance*. Accessed from http://www.scie.org.uk/publications/ataglance/ataglance43.asp

SCIE (2015b) *Roles and Duties of Safeguarding Adults Boards*. Accessed from http://www.scie.org.uk/care-act-2014/safeguarding-adults/safeguarding-adults-boards-checklist-and-resources/role-and-duties.asp

UNICEF (2014) *Rights Under the Convention on the Rights of the Child*. Accessed from http://www.unicef.org/crc/index_30177.html

Unit HSC DM2: How will I be graded?

The table below shows what the learner must do to achieve each grading criterion. Learners must achieve all the criteria for a grade to be awarded (i.e. criteria D1 to D3 must be achieved to pass this unit assessment at grade D). A higher grade may not be awarded before a lower grade has been achieved in full, although component criteria of a higher grade may have been achieved.

Grade	Assessment criteria number	Assessment grading criteria	Assessment of learning / What you need to show
D1	1.1	Explain protection in relation to safeguarding.	Provide information to explain protection in relation to safeguarding.
D2	2.3	Explain the responsibilities of the health and social care practitioner in relation to whistleblowing.	Information must explain the responsibilities of the health and social care practitioner in relation to whistleblowing.
D3	3.2	Describe how to access support and information in relation to safeguarding and protection.	Information must focus on safeguarding and protection to show understanding of a range of ways that relevant support and information can be accessed.
D4		Show evidence of reading or use of sources.	There should be evidence of learners' reading or use of sources. Learners must use a minimum of 2 traceable references.
C1	3.1	Explain sources of support and information in relation to safeguarding and protection of: ● children and young people ● adults.	Identify sources of support and information. Explain how these sources support children, young people and adults. More than one source should be considered.
C2	1.2	Summarise legislation, policies and procedures in relation to the safeguarding and protection of: ● children and young people ● adults.	Information must focus on safeguarding and protection of adults, children and young people to summarise: ● relevant current legislation ● more than one relevant policy ● more than one relevant procedure
C3		Show evidence of reading or use of sources with referencing relevant to the explanation or summary. Good use of vocabulary and grammar.	Use of referencing should show evidence of reading or use of sources. Vocabulary and grammar should be appropriate and accurate for purpose
B1	2.1	Explain actions to take if harm or abuse is suspected and/or disclosed for: ● children and young people ● adults.	Explanation must demonstrate an understanding of the relevant actions to take when abuse is suspected and/or disclosed in relation to: ● children and young people ● adults.
B2	4.1	Explain why serious case reviews are required.	Explain why serious case reviews are required. Examples of when serious case reviews are required and carried out may support the explanation.

Grade	Assessment criteria number	Assessment grading criteria	Assessment of learning / What you need to show
B3		Show evidence of reading or use of sources. Referencing supports the discussion.	Use of reading or use of sources should be shown through a range of relevant referencing. Referencing should be used appropriately to support the explanation.
A1	4.2	Analyse how outcomes of serious case reviews inform practice.	Provide a detailed analysis of serious case reviews to demonstrate understanding of: ● serious case reviews ● how outcomes of serious case reviews inform practice ● practice that relates to safeguarding. Information must be given from more than one perspective to support the analysis.
A2		Show evidence of wider background reading or use of sources. Referencing the analysis.	Wider background reading should be evident or a wide range of sources material should be used. Referencing supports analysis.
A*1	2.2	Analyse the roles of agencies when responding to suspected harm or abuse of: ● children and young people ● adults.	Analysis must include an appraisal of the roles of more than one agency in responding to suspected harm or abuse concerning: ● children and young people ● adults. The discussion must include the sequence of key stages of procedure of each agency analysed.
A*2		Show evidence of a range of background reading or use of sources used selectively.	Learners should show the ability to consider or explore relevant issues which contribute to the analysis. An extensive range of background reading or use of sources should be used selectively and cited appropriately.

Current legislation as relevant to the Home Nation.

HSC DM3.1
Anatomy and Physiology for Health and Social Care

Learning outcomes

LO1: Understand the structure and functions of the organ systems of the human body

1.1 Describe the structures and functions of the organ systems of the human body

1.2 Explain the relationship between the structure and function of the organ systems

1.3 Explain the relationships between the organ systems in maintaining healthy body functions

LO2: Understand homeostasis in the human body

2.1 Explain the process of homeostasis in the human body

2.2 Explain how homeostasis maintains the healthy functioning of the human body

2.3 Examine the relationship between the nervous system and the endocrine system in gaining homeostatic control

LO3: Understand factors which may affect changes in physiological measurements

3.1 Explain factors which may affect changes in physiological measurements

LO4: Understand how to obtain, record and report physiological measurements

4.1 Explain how to gain consent prior to obtaining physiological measurements

4.2 Describe how to use equipment for measuring:
- temperature
- blood pressure
- pulse
- respiratory rate
- oxygen saturation

4.3 Explain the reasons for accurate and timely recording of physiological measurements

4.4 Explain how to report physiological measurements that may be a cause for concern

LO5: Be able to obtain and record physiological measurements

5.1 Apply standard precautions for infection prevention and control

5.2 Use equipment accurately to obtain physiological measurements

5.2 Record physiological measurements accurately

About this unit

The human body is a complex machine made up of trillions of parts and components that are organised into **tissues, organs** and **body systems**. While each has a particular function, they work together to maintain healthy function over a lifetime.

When the function is interrupted this can have consequences for the individual, including for some premature death or a lifetime of discomfort. Similarly disease, lifestyle choices or accidents can have severe effects on the quality of life. Growing old can also affect the body's efficiency to varying degrees.

Anyone entering a career in health and social care must know about human physiology and anatomy. It is essential that you understand how the human body is made up and how it functions. You can then deliver care that is appropriate, and informed by your understanding of these areas.

The purpose of this unit is to provide a wide basic knowledge of body systems, their component parts, functions and interactions. We will examine and show how these interactions maintain our health. We will look at how the body self-regulates to maintain optimum conditions (homeostasis) and we will learn about the factors that may affect changes in physiological measurements. We will also learn about the skills used to obtain, record and report basic **physiological** data and measurements.

Anatomy and physiology can be a complex area that uses a great deal of specific terminology, and so this chapter is somewhat different to the others in this book. It is hoped that we have made it as accessible and interesting as possible.

LO1: Understand the structure and functions of the organ systems of the human body

Anatomy is the study and examination of the structures that make up the human body. These include everything from individual **cells** to organs and organ systems. This will, for example, include the digestive and respiratory systems.

Physiology is the study of how these cells, tissues, organs and systems work. It looks at their functions and the consequences if any of these components and systems fail.

1.1 Describe the structures and functions of the organ systems of the human body

1.2 Explain the relationship between the structure and function of the organ systems

The structures and functions of organ systems are best described together with an explanation of how their structures relate to their functions.

🔑 Key terms

Anatomical relating to the structures of the body

Physiological relating to the functions of the body

Cells are the individual building blocks of the body. There are about 200 different types in the body

Organelles are the microscopic structures (very tiny structures that you will need a microscope to see) found inside the cell, as well as the cell membrane that surrounds a cell

Tissues are groups of cells, sometimes identical, that perform a particular function, for example nerve tissue

Organs are structures that are made up of different tissues that perform a particular function, for example the heart

Body systems are made up of various organs that work together to fulfil a particular function, for example the digestion of food by the digestive system

Metabolism is the sum of all the reactions occurring in the body that keep us alive and is particularly associated with those of **cellular respiration**

Cellular respiration sometimes called internal respiration is the process that occurs in all cells. This is where glucose is changed into carbon dioxide and water, releasing energy. Oxygen is required for this process

Respiratory system

We need oxygen in the air to remain alive. This is brought into the body by the respiratory system (the lungs) before being passed to the blood for transport to our cells.

If we think of the body as a machine then as with all machines it requires a source of energy. This is provided by the carbohydrates and fats in our diet but to access this energy, a complex series of reactions must take place in every cell of the body. This is cellular respiration and it is this process that requires oxygen.

In this process:

● an energy-rich sugar such as glucose is gradually broken down in both the cytoplasm of a cell and within special structures in the cell known as mitochondria
● as the glucose is broken down into simpler components, the energy that was holding the molecule together is released
● some of this energy is released as heat.

The rest of the energy is trapped by a chemical called ADP (adenosine diphosphate) which uses this energy to become a molecule called ATP (adenosine triphosphate).

ATP can be compared to a mobile phone battery. Once ATP is produced it is used to power all the reactions and processes of the body as it is easily converted back to ADP releasing useable energy. Respiration is like recharging the battery as it results in the supply of ATP being built up again.

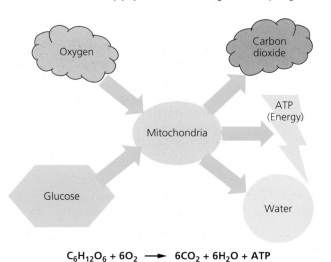

$$C_6H_{12}O_6 + 6O_2 \longrightarrow 6CO_2 + 6H_2O + ATP$$

Figure 12.1 Cellular respiration

The function of the respiratory system therefore is to supply us with oxygen and remove carbon dioxide. Carbon dioxide is a poison as it dissolves in water within the cells and blood to form carbonic acid. This for reasons we will explain later is dangerous and so carbon dioxide must be removed from the body.

To this end we have lungs and a mechanism for moving air into and out of them – breathing.

The lungs

It may help you to look at Figure 12.2 as you read the next section.

Our two lungs, situated within the chest, are made up of stretchy, microscopic, balloon-like structures called alveoli (alveolus singular). Each alveolus is made up of a single layered wall of very thin cells called pavement epithelia. The inner surface of this wall is lined with water while the outer one is covered by a network of small blood vessels known as capillaries which also have singled celled walls. Having very thin walls allows the rapid movement by **diffusion** of oxygen into the blood and carbon dioxide into the lungs and out of the body.

The alveoli of each lung are clustered at the ends of tubes that resemble the branches of trees. The finest are called bronchioles and they join a large tube – the bronchus that leads out of each lung connecting with the trachea. The trachea is a large tube also known as the windpipe that leads from the lungs to the throat, mouth and nasal passages. A swollen box-like structure near the top is the larynx and this contains the vocal cords that allow humans to speak.

Each lung is surrounded by two layers of membrane separated by a very thin layer of fluid that makes them stick together like a stubborn plastic bag at the supermarket vegetable section! These pleural membranes are attached on one side to the lung tissue and on the other to the ribcage and the

> ### 🔑 Key term
>
> **Diffusion** is the movement of molecules from a high concentration (many in the same volume of space) to a low concentration (fewer in the same volume of space)

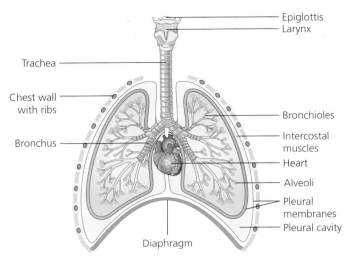

Epiglottis
Larynx
Trachea
Chest wall with ribs
Bronchus
Bronchioles
Intercostal muscles
Heart
Alveoli
Pleural membranes
Pleural cavity
Diaphragm

Figure 12.2 Structure of the respiratory system

sheets of intercostal muscles found between each rib as well as the muscular domed diaphragm that divides our chest from the abdomen.

The presence of these sticky membranes means that any movement up, out and down by the ribs and diaphragm results in the lung tissue following, therefore expanding the alveoli and allowing air into and out of the lungs.

Breathing or mechanical respiration occurs by the action of the intercostal muscles and the diaphragm. There are two sets of intercostal muscles: internal and external.

When the external muscles contract, the ribcage, which is hinged on the spine, lifts up and outwards.

At the same time the diaphragm contracts downwards. Both actions take the pleural membranes and the lungs with them.

The elasticated alveoli are pulled apart, making more space inside the lungs.

This lowers the air pressure within the lungs and so air from outside the body is drawn into the lungs, inflating them.

To breathe out the muscles relax, the diaphragm snaps back up and the ribcage drops down, due to gravity. This causes the air to be released as the lungs decrease in volume.

If a more forced exhalation is required, the internal intercostal muscles are used to pull the ribcage back down more forcibly.

Cardiovascular system

The cardiovascular system consists of the heart and blood vessels, which together move blood around the body.

Blood

Blood has a number of functions including transport, protection from infection, preventing blood loss, maintaining pH and regulating body temperature.

If a sample of blood is spun very fast in a machine called a centrifuge, it separates out into a straw coloured liquid – the plasma – and a solid pellet of cells and cell fragments.

Plasma is mostly water with many chemicals dissolved in it. It is the main transport medium. (See Table 12.1 for what it is made up of). Plasma also carries three main cell types – red blood cells, white blood cells and cell fragments known as platelets.

Red blood cells carry oxygen and remove carbon dioxide. They are unusual in that they do not contain a nucleus. This allows more room in the cell for haemoglobin – a protein that is used to absorb and carry oxygen.

There are many types of white blood cells which differ in appearance and function. Their common function is to deal with harmful organisms and protect us from disease. They contribute to our **immunity**.

Platelets are cell fragments that trigger the blood's **clotting** mechanism when they come into contact with air or a foreign body, such as a plastic tube used in kidney dialysis or a heart/lung machine.

Key terms

Immunity is our ability to detect and respond to possibly harmful chemicals and microorganisms like bacteria and viruses that have entered our bodies

Clotting is the process by which the body detects a leak of blood and triggers a response that results in a fine net being weaved across the hole which then traps red blood cells forming a clot that then seals it preventing further blood loss

Take it further

Follow the link to discover how blood clots:

https://www.youtube.com/watch?v=--bZUeb83uU

Blood is a means of transport. It carries gases, nutrients, salts, waste products, chemical messengers known as hormones, and heat around the body. This transport occurs in a series of tubes or blood vessels – arteries, arterioles, veins, venules and capillaries – pumped around the body by the heart.

Arteries and arterioles
Arteries and arterioles distribute or take blood from the heart to either the lungs or the tissues of the body. They carry blood under pressure and so have thick multi-layered walls. The larger arteries have elastic fibres in their walls so they can expand and recoil. This action is what forms the pulse.

The arterioles have muscle layers in them which can control how much blood flows through them so regulating or checking both distribution and blood pressure as we will see later.

Venules and veins
Venules and the larger veins return blood from the tissues to the heart at a lower pressure and therefore have thin walls. The internal space or lumen of a vein/venule is large to allow easy flow at this low pressure and because one-way valves are there, this ensures that blood only flows in the correct direction.

Table 12.1 Composition of blood

Component	Function
Plasma – 90% water Glucose Amino acids Vitamins Minerals Albumin Fibrinogen Antibodies Lipoproteins Carbon dioxide Urea Electrolytes	Transports the substances shown below: Nutrient needed for energy Nutrient needed to make proteins Nutrients needed for essential processes, for example vitamin D needed to absorb calcium Nutrients needed for essential processes, for example calcium needed for healthy bones and teeth Blood protein needed to remove excess water from our tissues Blood protein involved in the clotting of blood Proteins made by the immune system to fight bacteria Proteins that carry fats/cholesterol to and from cells A poisonous waste gas from respiration that could make our cells acidic A poisonous waste product from the breakdown of excess protein from our diet For example, sodium, needed to help maintain correct concentration of the blood
Red blood cells (Erythrocytes)	Carry oxygen and some carbon dioxide
White blood cells (Leucocytes) e.g. Neutrophils Lymphocytes – B-cell types T-cell types Monocytes Eosinophils	Produces chemicals to destroy bacteria and then 'eats' them B-cells produce antibodies that make bacteria easier to kill T-cells destroy viruses and cancer cells 'Eats' dead cells and dead bacteria Release chemicals to kill parasites, e.g. worms
Platelets	Triggers blood clotting

Activity

Use your imagination and any materials you have available to make models of the blood vessel types. Simple representations can easily be made from paper and card.

Capillaries

Capillaries as stated earlier are small microscopic vessels with thin one-celled walls. They are the diameter of a single red blood cell. Their role is to allow for exchange of materials within the tissues, dropping off useful substances and oxygen to the cells and picking up unwanted materials and carbon dioxide so that they can be removed from the cells.

The thin walls allow for a quick and easy transfer, and blood flow through capillaries is relatively slow allowing for this exchange. This is also helped by the fact that plasma leaks through the capillary walls forming tissue fluid that then bathes the tissues of the body before draining back into either venules or yet another type of tube called a lymph vessel. Lymph vessels make up a one-way system of tubes that eventually link up with large veins in the armpits. They form part of the lymphatic system that we will refer to in later sections.

The walls of all capillaries are covered by a very thin mesh-like covering called the basement membrane. This helps maintain the shape of the vessels as well as acting like a sieve, only allowing small molecules, for example salts and sugars, to leave the capillary.

The heart

The heart pumps blood around the body through the blood vessels. The heart is effectively two pumps joined together that are synchronised or co-ordinated to work together as one.

The right side receives blood from the body and sends it to the lungs to drop off carbon dioxide and to pick up oxygen.

The left side receives the blood back from the lungs and pumps it off around the body once more.

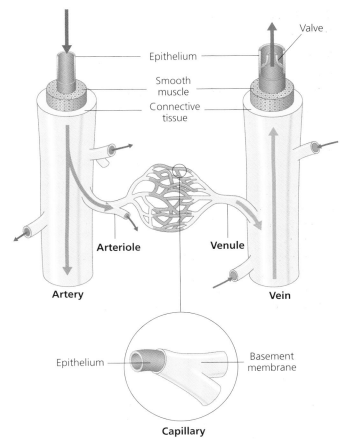

Figure 12.3 Types of blood vessel

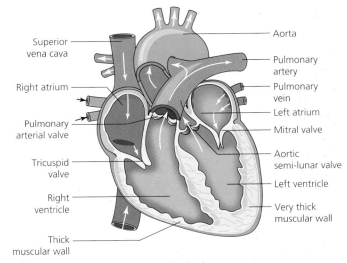

Figure 12.4 Blood flow through the heart

You may find it useful to look at Figure 12.4 as you read this section.

The heart is made of special cardiac muscle. This is an unusual muscle in that it can beat or contract by itself and does not get tired.

Both sides of the heart have upper thin walled chambers called atria (atrium singular) and more muscular thicker walled chambers below – the ventricles.

The right atrium receives blood from the head, arms and lower body through two large veins – the vena cavae. The tricuspid valve divides the atrium from the right ventricle and will only allow blood to pass downwards so filling the ventricle.

Blood leaving the right ventricle leaves via the pulmonary arteries that lead to each of the two lungs. As blood leaves the right ventricle it has to pass through another set of valves – the pulmonary arterial valves. These prevent blood from re-entering the ventricle.

The left atrium receives oxygenated blood from the lungs via the pulmonary veins and from here it passes through the bicuspid valve into the left ventricle, then through the aortic valve into the aorta, the body's biggest artery, and off around the body.

The events that occur during this filling and emptying of the heart is called the **cardiac cycle**. This takes place on average 60–80 times per minute. Each cycle causes the walls of arteries to expand. This we call our pulse. The time when the atria are filling and the ventricles are relaxing is known as diastole while the period during which the ventricles are contracting and blood is leaving the heart is known as systole.

The sound of the heart is often written as 'lub-dup'. The lub sound is caused by the tricuspid and bicuspid valves shutting as the ventricles contract. The dup sound is caused by the pulmonary and aortic valves shutting as the ventricles relax so preventing blood from being sucked back into the heart.

Key term

Cardiac cycle is the term given to the events occurring in the heart during one heart beat and includes the pumping of both the atria and the ventricles. The frequency of the cardiac cycle is known as our heart rate

Activity

Describe how the structure of the lungs, heart and blood vessels help to carry out their functions.

Take it further

Follow this link to check your understanding of how the heart works:

https://www.youtube.com/watch?v=H04d3rJCLCE

The British Heart Foundation provides useful and easy to understand information on both heart function and health. Try the link here:

https://www.bhf.org.uk/heart-health/how-your-heart-works

While cardiac muscle can beat automatically there needs to be a system that can regulate or control heartbeat. To ensure this happens, a special region on the top of the right atrium – the pacemaker – connects with nerves from the brain that speed up and slow down the heart. Special muscle cells called Purkyne fibres carry the message to beat down through the wall that divides the two sides of the heart to the bottom or apex of the heart. Thus the lower regions of the ventricles contract first so that blood is pushed up and out of the ventricles like squeezing a tube of toothpaste.

Like any muscle, the cardiac muscle requires a supply of nutrients and oxygen. It gets this by a special set of arteries that branch off the aorta just as it leaves the heart and spread out over the surface of the heart before plunging down among the cells of the heart branching into smaller and smaller vessels. These are the coronary arteries. If they become partially, or completely blocked, this can result in angina, heart attacks and death.

Digestive system

A healthy diet needs to contain carbohydrates, fats and proteins.

Carbohydrates are needed by all living organisms for a source of energy as well as to construct cell membranes and, in the case of plants, cell walls.

Fats are used for energy and are also a vital part of cell membranes. In addition some fats form the basis of important hormones used to regulate body activities and development.

Proteins are literally the basis for life as they make up the structure – cell membranes and components of tissues such as skin, bone and muscle; they carry out vital physiological functions and also control all the chemical processes that occur in cells.

Every living thing has its own unique set of proteins which are made using instructions carried by our genes that are found in the nucleus of cells. Genes determine which proteins the organism makes and hence what it looks like and how it behaves. This is because proteins are large complex molecules made up of sub-units called **amino acids** (see p. 262 for definition) of which there are approximately twenty different types arranged like letters in a word to make a particular protein. Genes dictate the sequence of these acids in a particular protein.

Carbohydrates and fats are also large molecules made of sub-units but with much less variation. When we eat we are doing so to get a supply of these nutrients.

In addition, we need a supply of chemicals called nucleotides that are the building blocks of our genes. As we produce new cells for growth and repair we need to make new copies of our genes from assembling the nucleotides that we get from the genetic material we eat – whether animal or plant.

We also need a supply of minerals and vitamins that are essential for the healthy structure and functioning of our bodies. These are shown in Table 12.2.

Digestion is the process by which we break down these food sources into those that we require. There are two types of digestion.

Mechanical digestion
In mechanical digestion we physically break the food down into smaller pieces so that it can be swallowed and so that the eaten food becomes pureed as in a blender. This makes it more accessible for the next stage.

Table 12.2 Minerals and vitamins

Mineral	Function
Iron	Transport of oxygen
Calcium	Bones, teeth, muscle contraction
Phosphorus	Bones, teeth, cell division
Sodium	Control of fluids, nerve action
Potassium	Cell metabolism, nerve action
Iodine	Hormone thyroxine
Vitamin	
A	Vision, skin
B	Cell respiration
C	Connective tissue
D	Regulates calcium and phosphorus levels
Folic acid	Production of nucleic acids
K	Blood clotting

This occurs in the mouth or buccal cavity and involves biting and chewing using teeth, jaws and tongue. Saliva is added to lubricate the food and make it easier to swallow. Further mechanical breakdown occurs in the stomach where its muscular walls churn the food around changing it into a fluid paste called **chyme** (see p. 262 for definition).

Chemical digestion
In **chemical digestion** (see p. 262 for definition), the large nutrients such as carbohydrates, fats, proteins and genetic material are changed into their sub-units so that they may pass from our gut into the blood and be transported to our tissues. In the case of proteins it is their amino acids that we require so that we can turn them into human proteins. The **nucleic acids** (see p. 262 for definition) supply us with nucleotides to build up into the genes that we will need to pass on to all our new cells as we grow.

One use of proteins in all living things is to work as enzymes. Enzymes are special proteins that catalyse or speed up a chemical reaction. In our bodies we have thousands of different enzymes all designed to do one specific job. They act rather like a lock and key with only one type of enzyme able to control one particular reaction by fitting precisely on to what is referred to as the

Table 12.3 Digestive enzymes: chemical digestion starts in the mouth, continues in the stomach and is completed in the small intestine.

Substrate (food component)	Enzyme	Result of action / Chemical change	Site of action
Carbohydrate (starch)	Salivary amylase	Starch to maltose	Buccal cavity
Carbohydrate (starch)	Amylase	Starch to maltose	Duodenum
Carbohydrate (maltose)	Maltase	Maltose to glucose	Duodenum
Carbohydrate (sucrose)	Sucrase	Sucrose to fructose and glucose	Duodenum
Protein	Pepsin	Protein to polypeptides	Stomach
Polypeptides	Peptidases e.g. trypsin	Polypeptides to peptides	Duodenum
Peptides	Peptidases	Peptides to amino acids	Duodenum
Fats	Lipases	Fats to **fatty acids** and glycerol	Duodenum
DNA/ chromosomes	Nucleases	DNA to nucleotides	Duodenum

substrate molecule. One group of enzymes bring about chemical digestion and these are identified in Table 12.3.

Enzymes are delicate molecules and their shape is easily distorted. If this happens then they will no longer function. Factors that can result in these changes include extremes of acidity (low pH) and alkalinity (high pH) as well as high temperatures – for humans this is about 42°C. All chemical reactions are slowed down at low temperatures. Thus for enzymes to work in the human digestive system or anywhere else in the body conditions need to be kept at a pH of approximately 7.5 (very slightly alkaline) and at 37°C – body temperature

The structure and function of the alimentary canal
Food moves through the digestive system, or alimentary canal, in stages as follows. You can see these parts of the system in Figure 12.5.

Buccal cavity: site of **mechanical digestion** when eating and chewing. Some initial chemical digestion of starch begins by the enzyme salivary amylase. Saliva is mainly water and is produced by three pairs of glands located in the sides of the

Key terms

Amino acids long chains of these make up proteins

Nucleic acids for example DNA (deoxyribose nucleic acid) are the chemicals we refer to as genes or chromosomes that determine our structure, appearance and behaviour by controlling the proteins we make in our cells

Nucleotides are the building blocks of nucleic acids. There are four types that are found in DNA and their sequence determines which proteins are assembled in a cell

Fatty acids and glycerol are the constituents of fats. There are many types of fatty acid

Simple sugars are the carbohydrates used for energy, the most familiar being glucose. Complex carbohydrates like starch are broken down into glucose molecules

Mechanical digestion is the physical breakdown of our food into smaller pieces or a puree. The food nutrients remain unchanged

Chemical digestion is the chemical change of proteins, nucleic acids, fats and carbohydrates from large insoluble molecules into smaller molecules that can be absorbed into and carried by the blood

Chyme is the name given to the pulverised or pureed food that is formed in the stomach and then passed on through the gut. It contains a lot of water and all the food nutrients in a digested, partially digested or undigested state

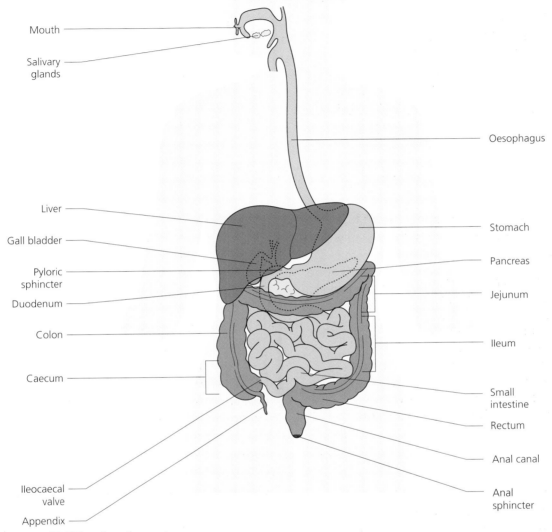

Figure 12.5 The digestive system

Labels (clockwise/left to right):
Mouth
Salivary glands
Liver
Gall bladder
Pyloric sphincter
Duodenum
Colon
Caecum
Ileocaecal valve
Appendix
Oesophagus
Stomach
Pancreas
Jejunum
Ileum
Small intestine
Rectum
Anal canal
Anal sphincter

cheek and beneath the tongue. They are called the parotid, sublingual and submaxillary glands and help lubricate the fluid ready for swallowing. Food is tasted by sensory cells in the tongue and by sensory cells in the nose!

Epiglottis: a flap of tissue that should cover the entrance to the trachea when swallowing.

Oesophagus: swallowed food is pushed by muscular contractions known as peristalsis down to the stomach.

Stomach: contains layers of muscle that churn the food resulting in further mechanical digestion. Glandular epithelial cells in the stomach wall produce a slimy fluid called mucus that protects the stomach wall from being digested itself. Other cells in the folds of the wall or gastric pits release an enzyme that begins the digestion of protein. This enzyme is very unusual in that it requires an acidic environment to work in and so hydrochloric acid is also released to provide this low pH. This means that the chyme leaving the stomach and passing into the small intestine will be acidic and will need to be neutralised if all the other digestive juices are to work.

Liver: this large organ has hundreds of functions but its main contribution to digestion is the production of bile which is stored in the gall bladder before being released down the bile duct when food leaves the stomach. Bile contains waste products and is poisonous if allowed to build up in the body but it contains a number of chemicals referred to as bile salts. Some of these are alkaline and help make the intestine less acidic. Others help in the digestion of fats as fat is not soluble in water and this makes chemical digestion difficult. The bile salts act like a detergent dispersing the fats as small droplets making it easier for the fat digesting enzymes to access them.

Pancreas: the pancreas also has several functions. In terms of digestion it too produces alkaline salts that pass down the pancreatic duct into the intestine making it slightly alkaline. Cells within the pancreas also produce a range of enzymes that work on carbohydrates, fats, proteins and nucleic acids. The pancreas is a dual function organ as it is also involved in the regulation of blood sugar levels as will be explored in a later section.

Small intestine: here most of the chemical digestion takes place due to the enzymes produced by the pancreas and also by special cells lining the wall of the intestine especially the first part which is called the duodenum. The further reaches of the small intestine, the jejunum and ileum have highly folded walls which are covered by very small projections called villi. These contain both blood vessels and a branch of the lymph system referred to as a lacteal. The outer surface of the villi have epithelial cells with further microscopic projections called microvilli which together results in a very large surface area. It is at the villi that the products of chemical digestion are absorbed along with minerals and vitamins. Fatty acids, glycerol and fat soluble vitamins enter the lacteal, everything else passes directly into the blood capillaries. Muscles within the walls of the small intestine continue to move the chyme along by peristalsis and small muscles in the villi cause them to waft about stirring up the food products.

Once absorbed by the villi the products of digestion are transferred to the liver along a special vein – the hepatic portal vein. The liver acts like a distribution centre, either storing some of the required nutrients or dispersing them through the blood to where they are required.

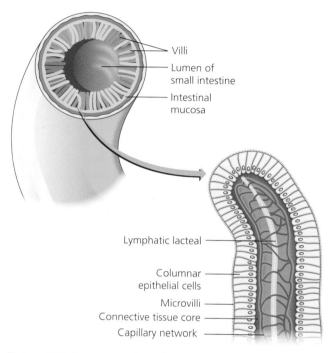

Figure 12.6 A cross-section of a gut villus

Large intestine: all the digestive juices released into the gut represents a lot of water that could potentially leave the body resulting in dehydration. As a land animal we cannot afford to lose this water and so the main function of the large intestine is to reabsorb this water back into the body. This is why severe diarrhoea can be very serious as this is caused by the intestinal muscles working too rapidly and the contents are ejected from the body before this vital water can be reabsorbed.

Also within the large intestine live billions of bacteria that normally do us no harm. They feed off our undigested food resulting in intestinal gases. They also provide us with certain vital vitamins as a by-product of their metabolism. These include vitamin K and folic acid.

Rectum: this receives the now 'dry' undigested material referred to as faeces and here it is compacted and stored before being released through the anus.

Activity

Use a search engine to obtain some un-labelled diagrams of the lungs, heart and digestive system. Print these off and working in pairs identify the structures.

Alternatively cut up a diagram of the digestive system and cut out the various organs. Test each other by putting them back in the right order!

Take it further

Try following the links identified to help you visualise the digestive organs and the process of digestion:

www.innerbody.com/image/digeov.html

https://www.youtube.com/watch?v=_QYwscALNng

If you are interested in the human diet and the role of nutrients you may wish to locate and refer to the following books:

Food Bible by Judith Wills (2007)

Nutrition for Life by Lisa Hark and Darwin Deen (2005)

Check your understanding

1. Summarise the process of cellular respiration.
2. Describe the functions of the diaphragm, intercostal muscles and pleural membranes of the respiratory system.
3. Identify four functions of blood.
4. Distinguish between arteries, veins and capillaries in terms of structure and function.
5. Describe the functions of the stomach, liver and large intestine.
6. Explain the presence of villi within the wall of the small intestine.

Excretory system

At any one time our diet usually contains more nutrients than we need. Any surplus is usually stored. Some excess sugars can be stored in the liver and muscle cells as a molecule called glycogen. Any further surplus is converted to fat and stored in cells under the skin called adipose tissue or around organs like the heart and kidneys. The same is true for excess fats from our food.

Key terms

Deamination is a process that occurs in the liver where excess amino acids from our diet have their amine component removed as ammonia. This is highly toxic and so is immediately converted to a slightly less poisonous molecule – urea. Urea is then transported by the blood and removed from the body in the kidney

Excretion is the removal of waste, usually poisonous, by-products of metabolism from the body. Examples are carbon dioxide from the lungs, components of bile from the liver and urea mainly from the kidney

Amino acids from the protein we have eaten are used as required but any that are not immediately needed cannot be stored. This is because amino acids all contain a structure called an amine group that contains nitrogen and hydrogen atoms in a similar way to the poisonous gas ammonia.

Excess amino acids are used to provide energy in cellular respiration but only when this potentially toxic amine group is removed in a process called deamination. This takes place in the cells of the liver. The amine group is converted into a less dangerous form called urea.

Though less poisonous it is still harmful if allowed to build up in the body and so it is removed by the kidney in a process called excretion along with some other toxic wastes produced by the body.

The anatomy of the kidney and excretory system

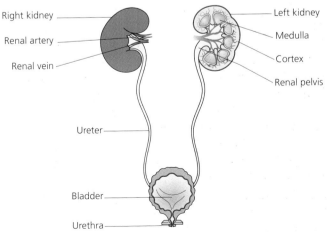

Figure 12.7 The excretory system

We have two kidneys lying towards the bottom and rear of our abdomen. Each is supplied with blood from the aorta by the renal arteries and blood is fed back into the inferior vena cava by the renal veins. A tube called the ureter links each kidney to the muscular bladder which in turn is linked to the outside by a tube known as the urethra.

The internal structure of the kidney reveals little to the naked eye. Each kidney is covered in a tough outer membrane and there is a lighter outer region referred to as the cortex and a darker inner region – the medulla. In the centre of this is a white fibrous sac called the calyx which leads to the ureter. The working units of the kidney – nephrons – are microscopic and not visible.

The structure of the nephron and its function
There are a million nephrons which are twisted folded tubes interconnected with blood vessels in each kidney. A simplified representation of one is shown in Figure 12.8.

Each nephron consists of a hollow sphere – the Bowman's capsule – attached to a tube. The side of the sphere opposite the tube is squashed in. (Imagine punching in the side of a deflated football!)

Within this indentation lies a group of specialised blood capillaries – the glomerulus. They differ from normal capillaries in that they have holes in their cells so that plasma can easily pass through into the capsule.

This movement of fluid is made even easier by the cells of the Bowman's capsule adjacent to the capillaries being spread out like fingers

of a hand with large gaps to allow the fluid through although escaping fluid still has to pass through the basement membrane of the capillaries. The cells of this inner wall are called podocytes.

The outer wall of the capsule is however made of tightly fitting epithelial cells which do not allow the fluid to pass through and so this fluid is funnelled into the tubule. This mass exit of fluid from the glomerulus is called ultrafiltration and the liquid that flows into each tubule is called glomerular filtrate.

Key terms

Ultrafiltration is the rapid movement of plasma through the walls of specialised capillaries found bunched within each Bowman's capsule of a kidney nephron. The basement membranes of the capillaries prevent large molecules such as blood proteins from leaving and so this modified filtered plasma is known as the glomerular filtrate. Ultrafiltration relies on a high blood pressure to work

Active reabsorption is a process that occurs in the first section of tubule that the glomerular filtrate enters on leaving the Bowman's capsule. This section is surrounded by capillaries and useful substances such as glucose, salts (minerals) and amino acids are pumped from the filtrate back into the blood using ATP generated during respiration. As energy is used to transfer these molecules it is known as active reabsorption

Osmosis is the diffusion of water through a semi-permeable membrane from a weak solution to a solution of a higher concentration

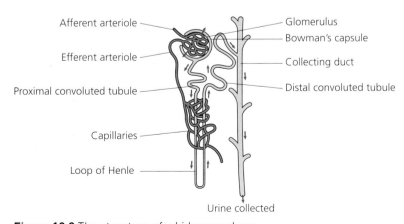

Afferent arteriole — Glomerulus
— Bowman's capsule
Efferent arteriole — — Collecting duct
Proximal convoluted tubule — — Distal convoluted tubule
Capillaries —
Loop of Henle —
Urine collected

Figure 12.8 The structure of a kidney nephron

As a result of **ultrafiltration** water, glucose, amino acids, salts and urea are filtered from the blood into the nephron. Larger molecules like the blood proteins together with blood cells are kept in the capillaries by the basement membrane.

The glomerular filtrate passes into the first section of the tubule – the proximal convoluted tubule. (The kidney tubules are often referred to as being convoluted as they are twisted and bent back on themselves.) The cells of this first convoluted region are designed to actively take back into the blood useful chemicals like glucose and amino acids. About 95 per cent of the water along with some of the filtered salts also passes back into the blood by diffusion. (The diffusion of water is known as **osmosis**.) To this end the proximal tubule is surrounded by blood capillaries into which these useful substances pass.

The remaining filtrate consisting of some water, some salts and urea is now referred to as urine. This now passes down a long hairpin structure – the loop of Henle and up into the distal convoluted tubule. At this point the excretory function of the kidney is over and the urine passes from the distal tubule into a collecting duct that links with the calyx. Many nephrons link to each collecting duct and so urine flows from the nephrons into the calyx and from there down the ureters to the bladder where it is stored until released through the urethra during urination.

Excretion is only one function of the kidney. Its other roles which involve the loop of Henle, the distal tubule and the collecting ducts will be dealt with in Section 1.3.

Activity

Use a search engine to obtain some un-labelled diagrams of the excretory system and kidney nephron. Print these off and working in pairs identify the structures.

Activity

If possible collect two kitchen colanders and a sieve. Create a mixture of water, penne pasta, rice, turmeric (or paprika/chilli powder), salt and pepper in a bowl/bucket. Stir well.

Arrange the sieve between the two colanders. Pour your mixture through. (Not over the floor!). Explain how this model represents ultrafiltration.

Take it further

You may find the following links useful in clarifying your understanding of kidney structure and function:

https://youtube/hiNEShg6JTI

https://youtube/8UVlXX-9x7Q

www.bbc.co.uk › Home › Science › Edexcel Triple Science Topics › Control systems

www.innerbody.com/image/urinov.html

Endocrine system

The endocrine system consists of organs referred to as glands. These may be separate structures like the thyroid gland in the neck and the adrenal glands above the kidneys or they may consist of tissues located inside other organs such as the brain, pancreas, ovaries and testes. A gland is any tissue or organ that secretes a substance or chemical. Endocrine glands produce hormones. Hormones are essentially chemical messengers that travel in the blood and have either immediate short-term or slower long-term effects. Some hormones are proteins, for example insulin; others like cortisol or testosterone are based on complex fats.

Like enzymes, hormones have specific shapes that allow them to be recognised by chemicals located on the walls of their target cells. It is tempting to think that hormones set out on a journey armed with specific directions. Obviously they do not – they randomly travel throughout the body, only having their effect on specific cells when they encounter them.

Key terms

Secretion is the release of a chemical from a cell or a specialised collection of cells – a gland – that serves a useful purpose, for example water from sweat glands, digestive enzymes from the pancreas and hormones from an endocrine gland

Hormones are molecules released from secretory cells that travel in the blood to a specific target organ where they bring about an effect or response. This response may be rapid as with the hormone adrenalin or gradual as with the growth hormone somatotrophin

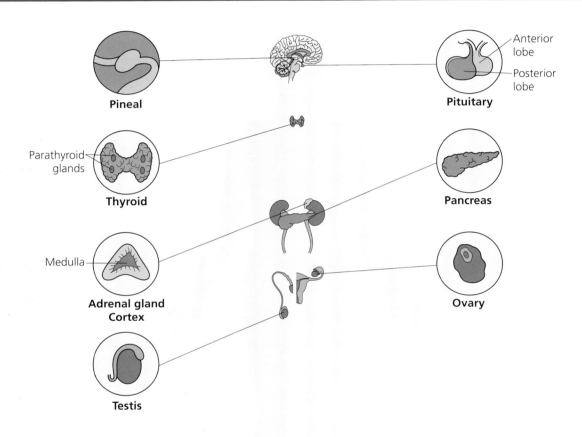

Figure 12.9 The location of the main endocrine glands

Table 12.4 Glands, hormones and effects

Endocrine gland	Hormone produced	Action of hormone
Adrenal gland	Adrenalin	Prepares body for action, e.g. increases heart and breathing rates, blood pressure and metabolic rate
Pancreas	Insulin	Promotes uptake of glucose by cells so lowering blood sugar levels
	Glucagon	Raises blood sugar levels by converting a carbohydrate store (glycogen) in muscles and the liver into glucose
Thyroid	Thyroxine	Regulates cell metabolism
	Calcitonin	Regulates calcium absorption and use
Pituitary	Somatotrophin	Growth hormone – promotes bone growth
	Prolactin	Initiates production of breast milk
	LH	Both involved in controlling the menstrual cycle
	FSH (follicle stimulating hormone)	
	Oxytocin	Initiates contractions of uterus
	ADH (anti-diuretic hormone)	Triggers uptake of water from the urine in the kidney, decreases urine production

Table 12.4 shows the main hormones and their effects. We will look at specific examples in detail in Sections 1.3 and 2.2.

Immune system

The function of the immune system is to combat organisms that gain access to our bodies and which could potentially do us harm or even kill us – collectively known as **pathogens**. These could include bacteria, viruses and **parasites**.

Unlike other body systems there are few organs involved with **immunity** but instead a multitude of different types of cell – usually loosely referred to as white blood cells or leucocytes. Some have their origins in our bone marrow found in the centres of our long bones.

During our development before birth and after, up to about the age of eight, some of these cells mature in a gland found near the heart that disappears as we progress into adolescence. This is the thymus gland and its role appears to be training the developing lymphocytes to recognise our own body cells and weeding out any that may react with them by mistake. This system is not foolproof and humans suffer from a number of autoimmune conditions such as diabetes, rheumatoid arthritis and multiple sclerosis where

Key terms

Immunity is our ability to detect and respond to possibly harmful chemicals and microorganisms like bacteria and viruses that have entered our bodies

Auto-immunity is when the immune system malfunctions and mistakes body tissues for invading organisms and so destroys or damages our own cells. Examples are diabetes, multiple sclerosis and nephrotic syndrome

Pathogen is a collective name given to any microscopic organism such as bacteria that can cause us harm, illness and/or death

Parasite is an organism that can live in or on another organism doing it harm in the process. Tapeworms, malaria causing microbes and viruses are examples

Antigen is a chemical – usually a protein or carbohydrate that results in the production of antibodies by the immune system thus triggering an immune response

Antibody is a specific protein produced by the B-cell lymphocytes in response to a particular antigen. It results in causing the microbes to clump together making them an easier target for phagocytic white blood cells

Phagocytosis is when a cell takes in solid matter by flowing around it and engulfing it. Phagocytes are cells of the immune system that engulf and digest dead bacteria and body tissues

the immune system gets it wrong and attacks body structures in error.

The cells of our immune system circulate around the body travelling in the plasma and in the lymph. The lymph system contains many swellings or lymph nodes in which these cells are temporarily stored. We have particularly large concentrations of these nodes in our neck, armpits and in the groin. These regions become active and enlarged during an infection. We tend to say that our 'glands are up or swollen'.

Immunity is very complex and is still being unravelled by scientists. Put very simplistically there are two main types of cell involved – lymphocytes and phagocytes. Lymphocytes are divided into B-cells and T-cells; the former produce special proteins known as antibodies. These lock onto specific target molecules referred to as antigens, which are usually proteins or carbohydrates found on the surface of bacteria. These are very specific and immobilise the foreign invaders clumping them together and providing an easy target for the phagocytes to engulf them and destroy them. This takes a while to happen but at the same time some B-cells are turned into memory cells so that any future infection will be recognised earlier and dealt with faster.

The T-cells act differently. Viruses are the ultimate parasite – they cannot reproduce on their own but need to invade our cells and use them to make more viruses. This invasion results in subtle changes to our cells, which the T-cells recognise. They then destroy our infected cells, wiping out the virus at the same time. It is T-cells that react to foreign tissues after a transplant, resulting in organ rejection.

Some antibodies are passed passively to us across the placenta before birth but the majority we produce during our life when exposed to the particular organism that has invaded us.

We can also acquire immunity through vaccinations where we are exposed to possible pathogens that have been made harmless but that will still trigger our immune system to produce antibodies. Circulating antibodies are one example of 'blood proteins'.

Phagocytes are cells that engulf and 'eat' invading bacteria and/or dead tissue. Some phagocytes produce toxic chemicals that kill the bacteria directly; others eat those already immobilised by antibodies.

Integumentary system

The integumentary system consists of the skin and all its associated structures including hair, nails, glands and nerve endings. The skin is the largest organ of the body and its functions include protection, temperature regulation, sensation and excretion, secretion of sebum, vitamin D synthesis.

The skin is made up of three layers – the epidermis, dermis and, at the bottom, the subcutaneous layer.

The epidermis consists of many layers of cells that become progressively flatter as they age and move to the surface. Cells at the bottom of this layer are constantly dividing, forming new layers while the outer ones die as they become coated and filled with a protein called keratin. This protein

Key terms

Vasodilation is the term used to describe when blood vessels open up and increase their diameter so allowing more blood through. It is brought about by muscles in their walls contracting

Vasoconstriction is the opposite of vasodilation. Muscles in the walls of blood vessels contract to narrow the vessel so restricting blood flow

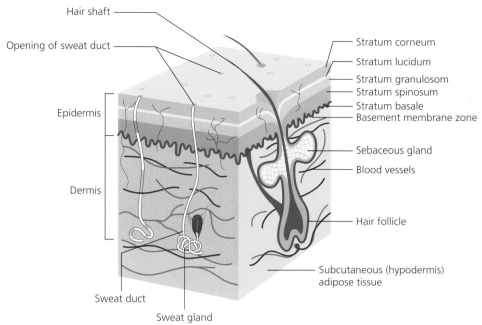

Hair shaft

Opening of sweat duct

Stratum corneum

Stratum lucidum

Stratum granulosom

Stratum spinosum

Stratum basale

Basement membrane zone

Epidermis

Dermis

Sebaceous gland

Blood vessels

Hair follicle

Subcutaneous (hypodermis) adipose tissue

Sweat duct

Sweat gland

Figure 12.10 The skin seen in section

also makes up nails and hair. This outer dead layer offers protection from invasion by pathogens unless broken by a scrape or cut. Within the lower epidermis cells produce a pigment called melanin that absorbs UV radiation and so reduces the risk of the skin being burnt by the rays of the sun.

Cells at the base of the epidermis contain a chemical that under the influence of UV radiation changes into an inactive form of vitamin D. This then becomes the active form in the kidney and is used to help absorb calcium from our food, promoting healthy bones and teeth.

Within the dermis lie blood vessels, muscles, nerve endings, glands and hair roots.

Hair, when erected by muscles, helps keep us warm by trapping a layer of insulating air. It also shades the skin from some UV radiation.

Nerve endings and sensory receptors give us sensation allowing us to respond to temperature, pressure, touch and pain. This enables us to detect changes in our environment, pick up and identify objects and protect us from harm.

Blood vessels in the skin can alter their internal diameter – either dilating or constricting. If we

feel cold vasoconstriction occurs, less blood flows through the skin, we go pale and less heat is lost from the body. At the same time muscles in the skin are activated and we shiver as they contract, releasing heat through cellular respiration.

On the other hand, if we are too hot vasodilation occurs and more blood flows through the skin, making us appear red and losing heat to the air.

Under these circumstances water is also extracted from the blood by the sweat glands and passed on to the skin surface through pores. The water evaporates, in the process using heat and so cooling the body. Some waste products, for example urea and excess salts especially sodium and chloride, are also excreted from the body in this water.

The sebaceous glands also secrete a fluid called sebum on to the skin which helps keep the skin supple and waterproof.

Beneath the dermis within the subcutaneous layer are the previously mentioned adipose cells. These not only act as a store of potential energy but offer us some mechanical protection from knocks.

While our skin is protecting us against possible pathogenic invasion there are internal spaces that are also exposed to the exterior. These include the ear passages, the tubes of the lungs and, of course, the gut.

Special gland cells in the external ear passage produce wax that traps and drains away dirt and microbes.

Within the respiratory tubes special glandular epithelial cells produce mucus that traps any dirt particles along with bacteria. Also within the walls of the trachea and bronchii are ciliated epithelia that have microscopic projections called cilia that beat in an organised way, moving the mucus with its dirt and bacteria up to the throat where it is swallowed. The action of these cilia is inhibited by nicotine leading to a smoker's cough.

Mucus produced in the stomach and intestines protects the gut from being digested and while primarily for digestion the acid of the stomach does destroy or inhibit most bacteria.

Activity

Describe how the structure of the skin is related to their functions. You could try and make either a 2-D or 3-D model of the skin. Card, wire, and Styrofoam could all be used.

Check your understanding

1. Explain what is meant by the terms ultrafiltration and reabsorption.
2. Explain what is meant by osmosis.
3. Describe how the kidney performs its function of osmoregulation of body fluids.
4. What is meant by the term hormone?
5. What hormones are produced by a) the pancreas, b) the adrenal gland and c) the thyroid gland; Give a function for each named hormone.
6. Identify three types of cell involved in the body's immune response and describe the function of each.
7. Distinguish between the terms antibody and antigen.
8. Describe four different functions of the skin.

Nervous system

The nervous system is a collection of nerve cells that receive, transmit and respond to information concerning both the external environment and the internal one of our body. Detectable changes in both are referred to as stimuli. These changes can result in immediate responses or the information can be analysed before initiating any reaction. These stimuli can also be stored as memories. Any responses are carried out by either muscles or glands.

The main component is the central nervous system (CNS) which consists of the brain and spinal cord. Branching out from both are nerves of two systems – the peripheral and autonomic. Peripheral nerves tend to link the muscles we use in movement and the major sense organs with the brain.

The autonomic system is associated with muscles and glands that on the whole we have no conscious control over. It consists of two sub-systems the sympathetic that tends to prepare the body for action and the parasympathetic system which returns the body to normal function. The sympathetic system has nerves that are interlinked allowing a very fast response throughout the body.

Take it further

Help your understanding of the autonomic nervous system by following these links:

www.scholarpedia.org/article/Autonomic_nervous_system

www.sciencemuseum.org.uk/howdoesyourbrainwork/howdoesyournervoussystem

Nerves are made up of mainly two types of elongated cells called neurons – motor neurons that link the CNS to muscles or glands and sensory neurons that link sense organs to the CNS. There are other types, for example, association neurons, that can link neurons within the brain and spinal cord.

Nerve transmission is a complicated process but a nerve impulse is basically a wave of electrical activity that flows along the neuron

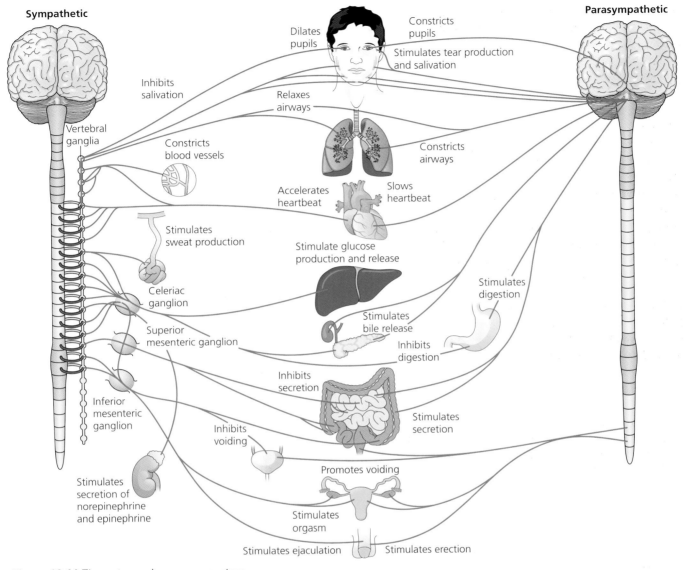

Figure 12.11 The autonomic nervous system

through the cytoplasm. A nerve cell at rest has a difference of charge across its membrane. The outside of the cell is more positive than the inside due to negatively charged proteins in the cytoplasm and positively charged sodium ions outside.

When a **stimulus** is applied at one end above a certain **threshold value** special channels in the membrane open and the sodium ions flow into the cell, making the inside at that point of entry positive. This causes a small localised electric current to flow through the cytoplasm which causes more sodium channels to open up and repeat the process. Meanwhile the original channels close and sodium ions together with potassium ions are pumped out restoring the original situation of the outside being more positive than the inside.

This change in charge can be detected on special equipment and is referred to as an **action potential.** An action potential is generated if the threshold value is exceeded. Above that, an increase in the level of stimulus will still only produce a similar action potential, not a larger one. This is known as the **all or nothing rule** (see p. 273 for definition).

Key terms

Nerve transmission is the term given to the process by which nerve cells carry information (an impulse) along their length

Stimulus this is the event that makes a nerve cell likely to transmit an impulse. It may, for example, be pain, pressure, sound, light or a rise or fall in temperature

Threshold value a stimulus has to be above a certain level for a nerve cell to fire an impulse. This value is its threshold

Action potential is the name given to a difference in electrical charge that is generated by the stimulus and which then travels along a nerve cell

All or nothing rule a nerve cell will either fire an impulse or not. A stimulus will not create a weak impulse or a strong one

Saltatory conduction is a leap-frogging effect where an action potential is only generated at particular points along a nerve making the speed of transmission faster

Reflex is an automatic response involving a pathway of usually only two or three nerve cells. It is an immediate response that requires no conscious thought and is usually associated with avoiding danger or harm

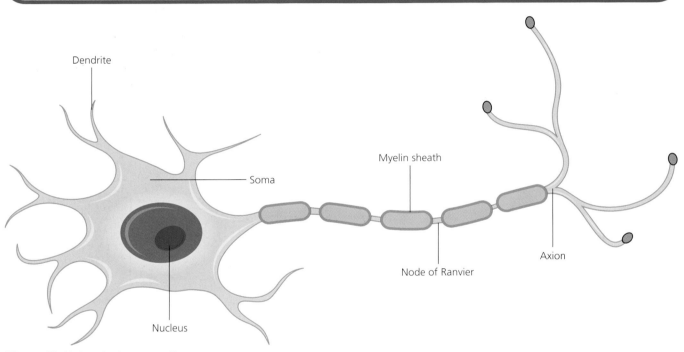

Figure 12.12 A typical nerve cell

All this can be visualised if the analogy of dominoes is used.

Dominoes are placed on their ends at a distance apart that if the first is knocked over it strikes the next causing the third to fall and so on. A wave of falling dominoes continues to the end of the row. The force just needed to knock over the first domino is equivalent to the threshold value. Either the dominoes fall or they don't – the all or nothing rule. If the dominoes each picked themselves up after they were knocked down the comparison would be complete!

Now imagine there are two parallel rows of dominoes set up crossing a room. One row is 'normal' the other is a 'magic' one!

The first dominoes in each row are knocked over but in the 'magic' row it is not the second domino that falls after the first is pushed but number 20. This then causes number 40 to fall then number 60, and so on, until the last domino falls. The last domino will obviously fall over in the magic row long before the last one in the conventional row. This leap-frogging effect is found in the majority of human neurons and is known as **saltatory conduction** (see p. 273 for definition).

This is brought about by special cells called Schwann cells that wrap themselves around the neurons. They form an insulating layer like the plastic coating of electrical wires. This layer is referred to as the myelin sheath. Unlike wires this coating is not continuous but is made up of many neighbouring Schwann cells with microscopic gaps between them – nodes of Ranvier. The exchange of sodium and potassium ions described earlier can only occur at these gaps and so the electrical current flows from node to node, rather than 'dribbling' through all the cytoplasm of the neuron. This leap frogging action potential means the nerve impulse arrives at the end of the neuron faster, making the nerve cell more efficient.

The importance of the myelin sheath can be seen in the debilitating condition multiple sclerosis (MS) when the body's immune system randomly attacks the myelin sheath by mistake, causing

Take it further

You may wish to use the links below to help you visualise the events occurring in a nerve cell during the transmission of an impulse:

https://www.youtube.com/watch?v=nIojqRFJWbM
https://youtube/l0EwpHbTLu4
https://faculty.washington.edu/chudler/auto.htm

numerous failures in the activity of both motor and sensory neurons.

Nerve cells do not make direct contact with each other. Instead there is a microscopic gap between neighbouring cells – the synapse.

When an impulse arrives at the end of a neuron it results in special chemicals called neurotransmitters (there are many types) being released. These diffuse across the synapse.

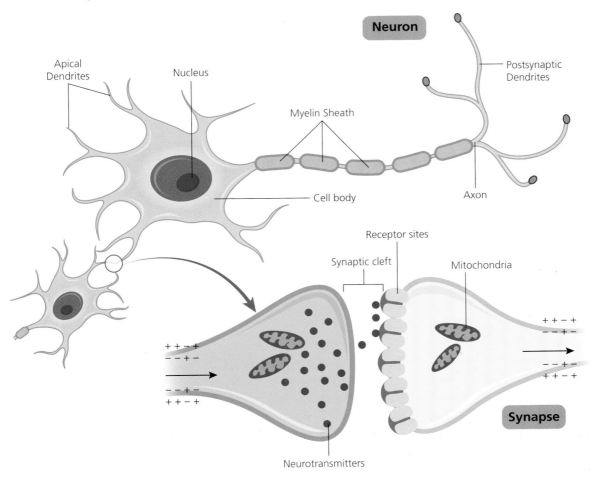

Figure 12.13 A synapse

Depending on how much neurotransmitter is released the threshold value of the next cell may be exceeded and an action potential generated. Certain drugs, for example painkillers, act by suppressing these neurotransmitters and so blocking neural transmission. The ends of neurons have many branches each with their own synapse and so multiple 'connections' are the norm.

All neurons connect to or originate from the CNS. In most instances the brain is involved but there are occasions when an immediate response is required usually to prevent harm or damage. A spinal reflex involves usually just two neurons, possibly three, which while linked via other connections to the brain does not rely on information sent or received from the brain. Thus this automatic response is very fast. An example is the knee jerk reflex and this is shown in Figure 12.14.

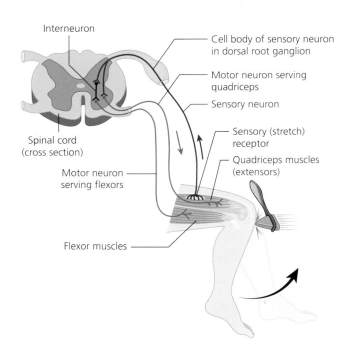

Figure 12.14 The knee jerk spinal reflex

The brain
The brain is part of the CNS and is a very complex structure that is still little understood. Some major regions are listed below:

● Cerebral cortex: outer region of the brain, much folded. Receives information from

sense organs and receptors of the body. Determines muscular responses. Different specific areas are responsible for different regions of the body

● Cerebrum: two halves of the brain – contains centres for memory, emotions and cognitive thought
● Corpus callosum: a connecting bridge of tissue linking the two sides of the brain
● Cerebellum: fine tunes muscle actions helping us walk, balance and play musical instruments
● Medulla: primitive part of the brain – controls heart rate, swallowing and breathing
● Hypothalamus: regulator involved in homeostasis

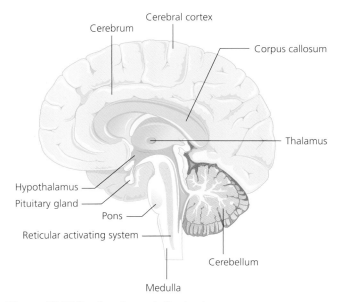

Figure 12.15 Section through the brain

Pituitary: produces hormones usually under direction of hypothalamus.

Activity

Use your imagination and any materials you have available to make models of nerve cells. Simple representations can be made from paper, card and wire.

Muscular system

Key terms

Contraction is when a muscle shortens and does work using energy in the form of ATP. It is the result of special proteins moving between each other

Relaxation is when a muscle is not contracting. In this state the proteins can be pulled out from between each other and the muscle stretched to its original length. This is done by another muscle pulling it back. Thus muscles can pull but not push

Antagonistic muscle pairs are muscles that work as a pair to carry out opposite actions. For example one muscle may raise the arm, and the other pulls it back down. One is contracting when the other is relaxing

Muscles are a form of tissue that are able to shorten their length. They can be individual cells or multicellular structures. There are three categories – skeletal, visceral and cardiac.

Visceral muscles can also be referred to as smooth or involuntary muscle. These tend to be found in the respiratory tubes, arteries, gut, bladder and uterus. They also work in pairs running in sheets that are at right angles to each other. In tubes this means that some run around the circumference of the tube and others down its length. The former will constrict the tube; the other will dilate it.

Skeletal muscle sometimes called voluntary muscle is associated with bones and joints and is arranged to bring about movement of a bone at a joint. They are also used to lock joints in position to hold the body still or upright. They work in antagonistic pairs – one pulls a bone in one direction; the other one pulls the bone back. This is because muscles can shorten through **contraction** and so pull but they cannot extend and push. A muscle is said to be relaxing if not contracting and can in this state be pulled long again by the action of another muscle. Thus one muscle of the pair opposes the action of the other – as one contracts the other relaxes, allowing movement to occur.

Skeletal muscle is a multinucleate structure caused by the fusion of many cells into fibres. Each muscle contains many bundles of fibres and each fibre consists of many strands known as myofibrils. These are made up of special proteins that allow a muscle to contract.

These proteins are arranged in units called sarcomeres within the myofibrils which give the fibres an obvious striped appearance.

Cardiac muscle is unusual in that it never fatigues, does not need a nerve impulse to make it contract and does not work in pairs. Embedded elastic fibres will return its shape after contraction. It is only found in the heart. The cardiac cells are branched and interconnect to neighbouring cells providing strength. They also appear striped due to having sarcomeres.

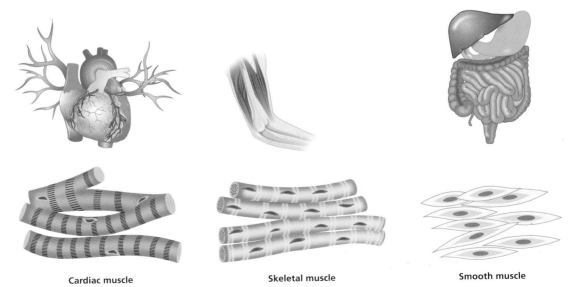

Cardiac muscle   Skeletal muscle   Smooth muscle

Figure 12.16 Types of muscle

Muscle action

Muscle action is best described with reference to skeletal muscle. There are two main types of protein found in the sarcomeres – actin and myosin although there are other types associated with them. They are arranged as parallel filaments – alternatively thick and thin. The thick ones contain myosin, the thin – actin. These are held in place by bands called Z discs.

During contraction a nerve impulse arrives at a muscle fibre and secretes a neurotransmitter across the synapse. This results in a change of charge as in nerve cells that causes the release of calcium from within the fibre with the result that ATP is used to make connections between the neighbouring protein filaments. The myosin then slides the actin filaments past so shortening the sarcomere and hence the muscle. On relaxation these filaments disengage as long as the calcium is removed and so can be pulled apart by the action of the antagonist muscle.

Take it further

The microscopic structure and biochemistry of muscle action is very complicated. If you wish to cement your understanding or take it a little further try the links shown here:

https://youtube/CepeYFvqmk4

https://youtube/hr1M4SaF1D4

www.teachpe.com › Anatomy & Physiology › Muscles › Muscles Theory

Muscle fibres can be categorised according to how they contract: how fast, for how long and how quickly they become fatigued.

Type 1 are the slowest but less likely to fatigue and are used to support the body.

Type II are faster and stronger but are more likely to get tired. They are found in the arms and legs.

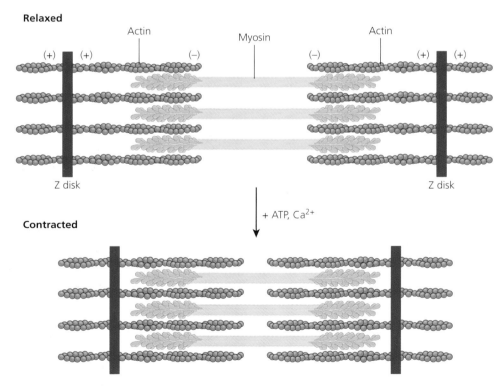

Relaxed

Actin   Myosin   Actin

Z disk   Z disk

+ ATP, Ca^{2+}

Contracted

Figure 12.17 Muscle action during contraction

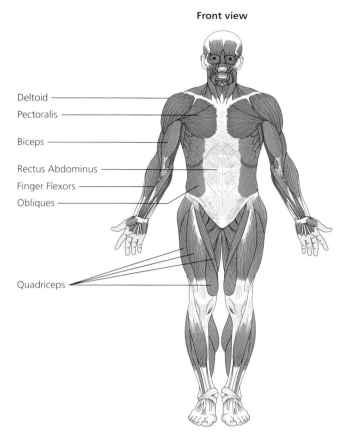
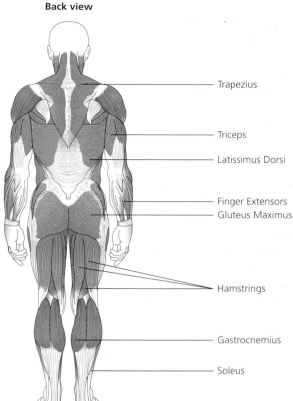

Front view

Deltoid
Pectoralis
Biceps
Rectus Abdominus
Finger Flexors
Obliques
Quadriceps

Back view

Trapezius
Triceps
Latissimus Dorsi
Finger Extensors
Gluteus Maximus
Hamstrings
Gastrocnemius
Soleus

Figure 12.18 Major muscles of the body

Muscles tend to be red coloured as most contain an oxygen-storing protein called myoglobin. They also contain the carbohydrate glycogen as a store of potential glucose.

The strength and duration of contraction depends on how many muscle fibres are stimulated and the duration of the stimulus. Muscles can go from merely twitching to full prolonged contraction – tetanus – which only stops if the nerve stimulation ceases and/or the muscle fatigues.

Muscle contraction that results in body movement is called isotonic contraction.

Isometric is partial contraction resulting in tension that is often used in maintaining posture.

Some skeletal muscle will stay partially contracted for long periods and this is known as muscle tone. Muscle tone is necessary to keep the body supported. Muscles in fact do not completely relax. Groups of muscle fibres contract at different times to prevent fatigue.

Skeletal system

Key terms

Cartilage is a flexible material made of protein that initially forms the skeleton but is mostly replaced by bone. It is found protecting the ends of bones from friction in joints

Bone a dense non-living material containing mineral salts such as calcium and phosphorus that is produced by **osteoblasts**

Osteoblasts are bone producing cells that arrange themselves in rings around blood vessels

Osteoclasts are bone destroying cells that remove bone from where it is not needed so allowing bones to respond to the forces exerted on them

Tendons are tough cords that connect skeletal muscles to bones at joints

Ligaments are tough cords that attach bones to each other especially at joints

Synovial fluid is an oily liquid that lubricates a joint and acts as a shock absorber

The human skeleton develops early in the embryo to form a skeleton of 270 bones at birth which reduces to 206 as various bones fuse together for additional strength.

Initially the skeleton is formed from proteins called chondrin and collagen that together form a tissue called cartilage. This is gradually replaced by bone producing cells or osteoblasts that surround blood vessels forming concentric rings. These cells produce salts containing calcium and phosphates – what we consider as bone.

The cells keep alive by connecting with each other and with the blood vessels. This is called a Haversian system and appears like concentric rings around a space containing blood vessels.

The cartilage persists at the ends of the bones and is also found where flexibility is needed in the ears and nose for example.

A typical bone is protected by a tough membrane on the outside and then an area of dense or compact bone. Beneath this is a fibrous area with many spaces – spongy bone and then at the centre of the long bones in particular is the bone marrow an area of active cell division and site of blood cell formation. Towards the ends of long bones are found areas of active bone growth – growth plates. These provide an increase in both bone and body length. A failure of these results in achondroplasia or dwarfism.

As well as osteoblasts there are bone destroying cells called **osteoclasts.** This allows bone density and distribution to vary during life reflecting the stresses and demands we place on our bones. For the most of our lives these two cells work in harmony but as hormone levels change as we age, especially in women after the menopause, the balance shifts towards the osteoclasts and bones become more brittle and can result in osteoporosis.

Our skeleton performs several functions:
- movement
- protection
- support
- store of minerals
- red blood cells are produced in the bone marrow.

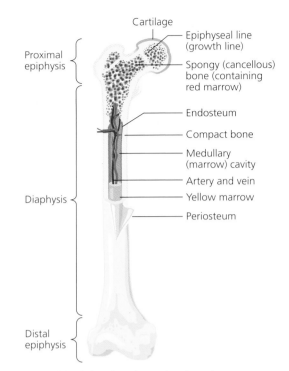

Figure 12.19 Section through a long bone

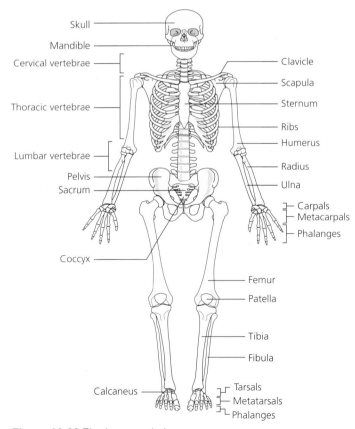

Figure 12.20 The human skeleton

The axial skeleton consists of the skull, spine and ribcage while the appendicular skeleton consists of the arms, legs, pectoral and pelvic girdles.

There are five types of bone found in the skeleton:

- Long bones: e.g. arms, legs
- Short bones: e.g. wrists, ankles
- Flat bones: e.g. bones of skull, ribs, shoulder bones
- Irregular bones: e.g. vertebrae, hips
- Sesamoid: e.g. knee cap

The vertebrae themselves are also divided into various types or regions:

- Cervical vertebrae of the neck with the specially adapted atlas and axis that support the head and allow its rotation
- Thoracic vertebrae which articulate with the ribs
- Lumbar vertebrae of the lower back
- Sacral that joins to the pelvic girdle
- Coccyx at the base. This is now redundant and is the remains of a tail.

Each vertebra has projections that allow connection with its neighbours allowing a small amount of movement. Magnified throughout the vertebral column this slight movement gives us our flexibility.

Between each vertebra is a spongy tough intervertebral disc that acts as a shock absorber. In the middle of the vertebra is a channel that protects the spinal cord.

The protective role of the skeleton includes the skull surrounding the brain, the ribcage and sternum surrounding the lungs and heart while the vertebrae enclose the spinal cord.

Support and movement both involve joints and there are several types of these:

- Fused: e.g. bones of skull
- Fibrous: non-moveable e.g. radius/ulna, tibia/fibula

- Cartilaginous: e.g. vertebrae
- Synovial: typical moveable joints that contain **synovial fluid** (see p. 279 for definition)

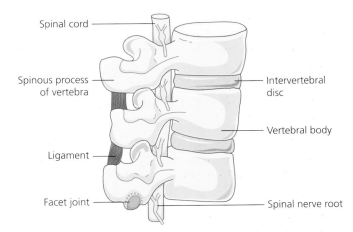

Figure 12.21 Lumbar vertebrae and discs

Synovial joints are further classified into:

- Ball and socket: e.g. shoulder/hip
- Hinge: e.g. elbow/knee
- Pivot: e.g. axis/atlas of neck
- Gliding: e.g. carpals and tarsals of hands and feet
- Saddle: e.g. thumbs and toes
- Condyloid: e.g. wrists and ankles

An example of a typical synovial joint is the elbow.

There are two main muscles that operate the lower arm at the elbow – the triceps and biceps, both found in the upper arm.

Muscles are not connected directly to bones but via fibrous cords made of tough connective tissue called tendons. This allows muscles to operate from a distance. You will notice the tendons operating your fingers rippling under the skin when you waggle your fingers. The muscles which operate the fingers are actually situated in the wrist.

Ligaments which are also made of tough connective tissue hold the bones together and in place.

The bones are also linked at the joint by the synovial membrane that forms and houses a thick oily substance called synovial fluid. This lubricates the joint and acts as a shock absorber.

Further reduction of possible friction and damage is provided by the cartilage that encases the ends of the bones.

Muscle action at the joints either moves the joint or locks it, providing support rather than movement.

Activity

Describe how the structure of bone, nerve and muscle tissue is related to their functions.

Take it further

Try using this link to explore more the ways bones and muscles work together:

www.bbc.co.uk › OCR 21st Century Triple Science Topics › Further Biology

Reproductive system

 Key terms

Menstrual cycle is about 28 days in length. It is the time from when the brain starts to stimulate the production of oestrogen from the ovary in order to repair the wall of the uterus, through ovulation at approximately day 15, the production of progesterone to prepare the uterus for a possible pregnancy and finally the breakdown of the uterus wall if pregnancy does not occur resulting in menstruation

Fertilisation is the joining of a single sperm cell with a released egg normally high up in the oviduct or fallopian tube

Meiosis is a special form of cell division used when forming sex cells or gametes. It is special because it causes the pairs of chromosomes we normally have in our body cells to separate so halving the total number of chromosomes from 46 to 23. Thus on fertilisation we end up with 46 again

Mitosis is normal cell division that occurs during growth. Our chromosomes duplicate themselves so that each new cell will have the same number (46) as the original cell

Implantation is when the ball of cells that has resulted from fertilisation embeds itself in the wall of the uterus and begins to develop into an embryo. This is normally about a week after fertilisation

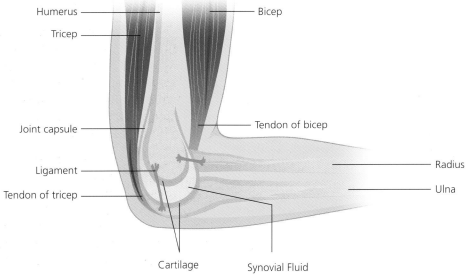

Figure 12.22 The elbow joint

The male system

The testes of the male contain a network of coiled seminiferous tubules whose walls undergo cell division to form the spermatozoa or sperm cells. The cells of the walls also produce the male hormone testosterone.

The testes are suspended outside of the body to be cooler as 35 degrees is the best temperature for sperm production.

The sperm are the result of two types of cell division – mitosis and meiosis. The latter separates the 23 pairs of chromosomes into a single set of 23.

The sperm are moved into a storage sac above the testis – the epididymis – for storage and a period of maturation. During this time they develop the long microscopic tail or flagellum that is used to propel them to the female egg. The rest of the sperm cell consists of the head containing the nucleus, a large mitochondrion to provide energy and a sac at the front – the acrosome – that contains digestive enzymes used to enter the egg.

Upon ejaculation the sperm are moved rapidly by muscular contractions to the penis. As they reach the urethra leading from the bladder to the penis two glands – seminal vesicles and the prostate gland – add fluids containing sugars, vitamins, alkaline salts and hormones. This is the seminal fluid which when mixed with sperm is known as semen. These fluids provide nutrients, energy and protection from the potentially hostile female environment – the vagina being acidic.

The semen is propelled along the penis and into the vagina. The penis contains many blood spaces and elastic connective tissue that expands with increased blood flow providing an erection. Mucus glands at its tip provide lubrication to help entry into the vagina.

The female system

The female system consists of two ovaries, partially linked to two oviducts or fallopian tubes which lead to the uterus which is separated from the vagina by the cervix.

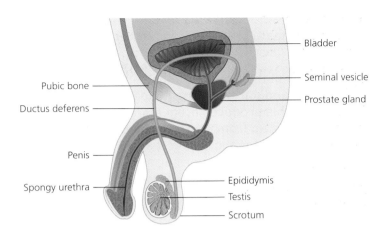

Figure 12.23 Side view of the male reproductive system

The woman is born with hundreds of thousands of potential egg cells already in place within the ovaries. Each month from about 12 years to menopause the brain using a hormone called FSH (follicle stimulating hormone) causes some of these potential eggs to develop into swollen groups of cells called follicles. As well as containing the egg or ovum these cells produce the hormone oestrogen which helps prepare the wall of the uterus for a possible pregnancy.

Some of the follicles expand and develop further into Graafian follicles and within these fluid filled structures the ovum grows and matures. At about day 15 of the menstrual cycle one of the Graafian follicles moves to the edge of the ovary and bursts releasing the ovum. This is ovulation.

The oviducts are not connected to the ovaries but they have frond-like fimbriae that surround their openings. During ovulation these fronds caress the ovaries like stroking fingers and the released ovum is scooped into the oviduct. Muscular contractions and cilia in the walls of the oviduct move the ovum along.

As it does so it may encounter sperm and if so, one sperm only penetrates and fertilises the ovum. It does this by enzymes in the acrosome of the sperm digesting a way into the egg. A lightning fast reaction then results in a protective wall forming around the egg which prevents any other sperm from entering.

Mitosis then occurs and the dividing ball of cells – the blastula – is moved further down to the uterus.

The remains of the Graafian follicle in the ovary become a glandular structure called the corpus luteum and this produces progesterone. This hormone picks up from oestrogen and prepares the uterus for pregnancy by increasing the blood supply and making the inner surface of the uterus – endometrium – more glandular and ready for possible implantation.

If implantation is successful the blastula becomes an embryo. After about three months the placenta forms and the embryo becomes human-like in appearance and is now referred to as a foetus. The placenta is a mixture of maternal and embryonic tissue that feeds the foetus via the umbilical cord while it floats in the protective amniotic fluid contained within the amniotic sac.

Normally after nine months the protective neck of the uterus, the cervix, opens up or dilates and the muscular outer layer of the uterus – the myometrium – begins contractions to give birth to the baby. Hormones are involved in all stages of labour. Relaxin prepares the mother for birth, oxytocin causes the contractions of labour and prolactin prepares the breasts for lactation or milk production. Adrenalin also plays a role during birth as do endorphins from the brain which act as natural painkillers.

Activity

Use a search engine to obtain some un-labelled diagrams of the brain and reproductive systems. Print these off and, working in pairs, identify the structures.

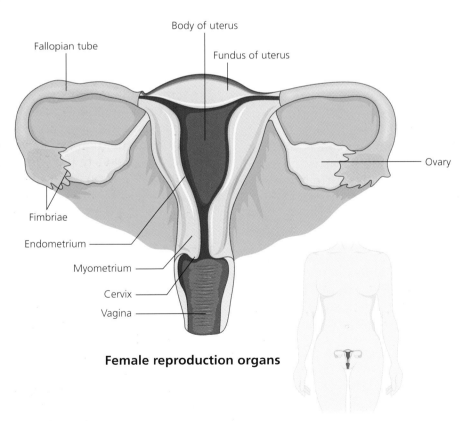

Female reproduction organs

Figure 12.24 A front view of the female reproductive system

Check your understanding

1. a. Distinguish between sensory and motor neurons.
   b. Distinguish between the sympathetic and parasympathetic nervous systems.
2. Explain the terms: stimulus, threshold value, all or nothing rule and action potential.
3. Explain the function of the myelin sheath.
4. Distinguish between skeletal, involuntary and cardiac muscle.
5. Describe what is meant by the term antagonistic muscle.
6. Explain how a muscle contracts.
7. Describe the functions of tendons, ligaments and synovial fluid.
8. Distinguish between bone and cartilage and between osteoblasts and osteoclasts.
9. Give functions for each of the following reproductive structures: vas deferens, testis, epididymis, prostate gland, ovary and uterus.
10. Describe the events of fertilisation.
11. What roles do the following hormones play in the female reproductive system: FSH, oestrogen, progesterone, oxytocin and prolactin?

Take it further

If you would like to watch the events of fertilisation follow the link:

https://youtube/_5OvgQW6FG4

If you would like to examine the nine months of human development in more depth look at:

https://youtube/WH9ZJu4wRUE

Command word activity

Describe (AC 1.1)

Produce either a wall chart/poster or a slide presentation that clearly and accurately describes in detail the structures of the main organ systems studied.

For each organ system described provide a brief description of its function.

Command word activity

Explain (AC 1.2)

Produce a small booklet for someone entering the care profession who does not have much biological knowledge. Provide them with explanations of how the main organ systems are adapted to carry out their functions.

1.3 Explain the relationships between the organ systems in maintaining healthy body functions

Inevitably when describing the functions of organs and systems reference will be made to how systems interact as they do not carry out their functions in isolation. In this section we will examine further examples of how these interactions maintain the efficient and healthy working of the body.

 Key terms

Ions are charged atoms. They can be positive (anions) or negative (cations). They are formed when molecules break down in a reaction through either gaining or losing electrons. If they gain electrons they acquire negative charge; if they lose them they become positive

Protons are positively charged particles found in the nuclei of atoms. As hydrogen is a simple atom with one proton and one electron if it loses the latter it becomes a positively charged hydrogen ion consisting of one proton. It is the concentration of hydrogen ions or protons that forms the pH scale. The more hydrogen ions/protons there are in a solution the more acidic it is

Gaseous exchange is the term used to describe how oxygen passes from the lungs into the blood and then to the tissues while carbon dioxide is transported in the opposite direction

Oxygen debt is a term used to describe events that take place during strenuous exercise. To gain additional supplies of energy in the form of ATP as well as aerobic respiration taking place some extra glucose is incompletely broken down to lactic acid providing some additional ATP. However as lactic acid is poisonous it must be broken down completely after exercising. This requires additional oxygen and explains our heavy breathing after exercise

Respiratory gases

Breathing draws air into our lungs. Approximately 21 per cent of this is oxygen, only about 0.03 per cent is carbon dioxide while the bulk of the rest is nitrogen which we cannot and do not utilise.

The oxygen dissolves first in the moist lining of the alveoli and then diffuses through their epithelial walls into the blood.

The red blood cells as they squeeze through the capillaries are deformed which, together with their ring doughnut shape, presents the maximum surface area to absorb the oxygen. This is picked up by the haemoglobin and is held in a form called oxyhaemoglobin. A property of this molecule is that as it encounters a low concentration of oxygen it changes back to haemoglobin releasing the oxygen into the tissues.

Carbon dioxide from respiration is carried back in the blood to the lungs but only about 3 per cent is carried directly by the haemoglobin. Most is transported in the plasma. Carbon dioxide dissolves in the water to form carbonic acid which then breaks down into hydrogen protons and hydrogen carbonate **ions** (see p. 285 for definition). When at the lungs these reform as carbon dioxide and are exhaled.

This passage of gases in and out of the alveoli is known as **gaseous exchange**.

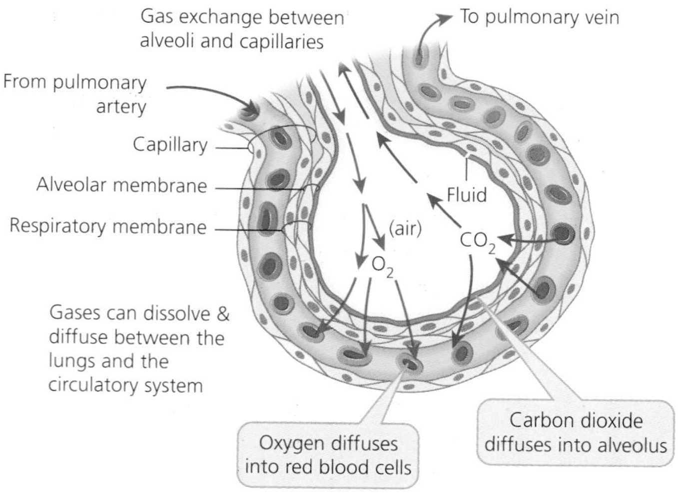

Figure 12.25 Gaseous exchange

The rate at which we breathe is regulated by the respiratory centres of the brain. They are located in the bottom part of the brain – the medulla or brain stem. They set up a rhythm that is initially not over ridden by a fall in oxygen levels as might be expected but by rising levels of carbon dioxide in the body.

The hydrogen **protons** produced as carbon dioxide dissolve in the blood and lower the pH making the **blood acidic** (see p. 285 for definition). This is harmful to the body as the low pH could result in enzymes being damaged. Cells within the respiratory centre detect this increase in acidity and increase our breathing rate to expel the carbon dioxide more rapidly. Thus we breathe deeper and faster.

Nerve cells of the autonomic nerve systems connect the brain to the respiratory muscle varying breathing rate, depth of breathing and how much air can pass through the respiratory tubes.

When our muscles are working hard we need as much energy from respiration as possible. To gain additional energy some glucose is partially broken down – not to carbon dioxide and water but to lactic acid. This releases a little extra energy to form ATP.

However lactic acid is a poison and its build up in muscles causes fatigue. So after we have finished exercising we have to get rid of it by completing the process of cellular respiration and breaking it down into carbon dioxide and water. To do this we need additional oxygen and so even though we have finished using our muscles we continue to pant hard as we draw in the extra oxygen. This is referred to as repaying the oxygen debt.

Activity

Using charts, slide presentations or a conventional written report explain the relationships between the respiratory, nervous, muscular, skeletal and cardiovascular systems in ensuring there is always an adequate supply of oxygen for cellular respiration.

Similarly explain the relationship between the cardiovascular and excretory systems in removing urea produced by the liver.

Take it further

Follow the links below to understand more about gaseous exchange:

https://www.youtube.com/watch?v=GCn47cko3lo

https://www.boundless.com › ... › **Transport of Gases in Human Bodily Fluids**

You may wish to explore further the nature and function of haemoglobin.

1. What is shown by the oxygen dissociation curve?
2. Find out why we have a different type of haemoglobin before birth.
3. Investigate myoglobin and its relationship with haemoglobin.

Command word activity

Explain 1.3

1. Using a minimum of two sources research the roles of nerves and hormones in controlling digestion.
2. Produce a detailed wall chart that explains how the nervous and endocrine systems control the movement of food material through the digestive system and regulate the secretion of digestive fluids and enzymes.

✓ Check your understanding

1. Describe how the alveoli of the lungs are adapted to their function of gaseous exchange.
2. Describe how both oxygen and carbon dioxide are carried by the blood.
3. Explain what is meant by an oxygen debt.

LO2: Understand homeostasis in the human body

2.1 Explain the process of homeostasis in the human body

We have seen that human metabolism is dependent on the action of enzymes, which as they are made of protein, makes them vulnerable to changes or fluctuations in both temperature and pH.

 Key terms

Optimum means the best conditions for the body to work efficiently, for example, a body temperature of 37°C or a slightly alkaline pH of 7.5

Negative feedback is when a change from the optimum is detected and the response is to bring the conditions back to the optimum again

Positive feedback is when a deviation from the normal is encouraged to increase further from the norm

However, metabolic processes are themselves producing the very conditions that could affect the performance of enzymes by producing heat and acidic waste products.

The body must therefore somehow maintain an internal environment that remains as near 'perfect' conditions as possible.

Any fluctuations that could be harmful must be detected and corrected. This maintaining of optimum conditions is known as *homeostasis.*

As well as maintaining optimal conditions of temperature and pH homeostasis is also involved in maintaining the equally important fluid concentration of the blood as well as levels of blood glucose.

Homeostasis is a *self-regulating process* working through the mechanism of feedback control.

In simple terms this can be imagined as trying to keep a see-saw level.

There is an increase in the level of a particular factor, for example a rise in blood glucose. The see-saw swings up.

As the rise is detected a response is triggered that attempts to reduce this factor. As the level falls the response is reduced or stopped so that the factor is brought back to the optimum level again. The see-saw levels.

If the level of the factor drops below the optimum (the see-saw drops) this fall is also detected and steps are taken to raise the level again. This is known as a **negative feedback mechanism.**

Take it further

To help make sure you understand what is meant by homeostasis you may wish to follow these links before exploring the more detailed examples that follow in LO2 and LO3 in this unit:

www.bbc.co.uk › Bitesize › GCSE › Science › Biology › Nerves and hormones

www.s-cool.co.uk/gcse/biology/homeostasis/revise-it/what-is-homeostasis

There are many parts of the body that are involved in detecting these fluctuations from optimal levels. Two important ones are a region in the lower part of the brain –the *hypothalamus* and special groups of cells in the pancreas called the *Islets of Langerhans*.

Most homeostatic mechanisms in the body tend to use negative feedback in order to maintain the ideal conditions but there are examples of **positive feedback** mechanisms being used. Here the stimulus that brought about the response is amplified and the response is strengthened or prolonged. One example is during birth.

The muscles of the myometrium in the uterus start to contract under the effect of a hormone from the brain – oxytocin. The more the muscles contract the more oxytocin is produced and so contractions increase in duration and intensity.

Another example is blood clotting. This is brought about by a chain of chemical reactions triggered by the platelets of the blood and involving a number of blood clotting proteins found in the plasma. These result in a fibrous protein net that traps red blood cells forming a clot. The start of the clotting mechanism encourages more platelets to descend on the wound triggering yet more clotting reactions and so on until the wound is plugged.

2.2 Explain how homeostasis maintains the healthy functioning of the human body

2.3 Examine the relationship between the nervous system and the endocrine system in gaining homeostatic control

How homeostasis maintains healthy functioning of the body is best explained by demonstrating how the nervous and endocrine systems work together to ensure this homeostatic control of body processes.

Examples of control
Blood glucose levels

A normal healthy glucose level is considered to be 4–6 mmol/L when fasting and up to 7.8 mmol/L within two hours of eating.

If glucose levels fall below normal for a period of time we may become hypoglycaemic and this can result in a coma and death. If levels rise above the optimum and stay there we become hyperglycaemic and two things are likely to happen.

The proximal tubule cells of the kidney are only capable of reabsorbing the normal levels of glucose found in the glomerular filtrate. Any additional glucose passes out in the urine causing blood glucose levels to drop resulting possibly in hypoglycaemia.

The other effect is that abnormally high levels of glucose damages blood vessels with significant consequences. Kidney glomeruli are damaged resulting in kidney failure. Nerve endings in the skin die resulting in a loss of sensation, which in the feet can cause wounds to go undetected. They then become infected causing gangrenous ulcers that result in possible multiple amputations. Damage to the retina of the eye that contains the light sensitive cells results in retinopathy – a type of blindness. The damage to blood vessels can also cause mini strokes in the brain leading to loss of cognitive function and possibly death. This inability to control glucose is the condition we call diabetes.

In a healthy individual a rise in glucose after a meal is detected by the Islets of Langerhans and these release the hormone insulin that works by making the cells of the body, in particular muscle and liver cells, take up glucose from the blood. As the levels decrease so insulin levels drop.

When normal metabolism uses enough glucose to drop blood glucose levels below the optimum level the Islets of Langerhans again detect this but now cause different cells within the islets to produce another hormone – glucagon. This promotes the conversion of the carbohydrate

Activity

1. How are normal blood glucose levels maintained?
2. Research the condition diabetes and use this to explain why the homeostatic control of blood glucose is vital for a healthy body.

Take it further

Use the NHS website to find out more about diabetes, its causes and effects.

www.nhs.uk/Conditions/Diabetes/Pages/Diabetes.aspx

store glycogen to break down into glucose which is then released back into the blood so restoring levels.

In Type I diabetes an autoimmune response destroys the cells that produce insulin and so people affected have to inject insulin. In Type II diabetes either the pancreas stops producing enough insulin or more commonly the body's cells stop reacting to insulin. In this case injections will have no effect and so lifestyle changes and possibly medication have to be used.

Thermoregulation

The hypothalamus in the brain acts like a thermostat in a domestic heating system. A rise in body temperature is detected as the warm blood flows through the hypothalamus and this causes a feedback mechanism using the autonomic nervous system to activate vasodilation and promote the secretion of sweat. This results in the body temperature being lowered.

A drop in body temperature is also detected by the hypothalamus and again the autonomic system is used to bring about a response – this time vasoconstriction, hair arousal, shivering and an inhibition of sweating. So body temperature is conserved and blood temperature returns to the norm.

Prolonged elevation of body temperature results in hyperthermia. This is a potentially dangerous example of positive feedback. Excess heat from metabolism will result in a further increase

in metabolism as an increase in temperature increases the rate of chemical reactions. So further production of heat occurs eventually resulting in seizures and death. This can be triggered by external factors like a long exposure to high temperatures or internal ones like a fever.

Hypothermia results from prolonged exposure to severe low temperatures. Here the metabolic rate slows down as a decrease in temperature reduces the rate of chemical reactions. Eventually a point is reached when not enough energy is produced quickly enough to sustain life.

Osmoregulation

Both blood and cell cytoplasm are solutions. It is vital that they are kept **isotonic**. If they become unbalanced the consequences are potentially disastrous.

If blood plasma becomes **hypertonic** then water will be drawn out of tissues by osmosis to try and equalise the concentrations. This will have the effect of shrinking and damaging the cells.

However if blood plasma becomes **hypotonic** then water will enter the cells by osmosis causing them to swell and possibly burst.

The homeostatic mechanism that ensures these two extremes do not happen is known as osmoregulation and involves interactions between the nervous, endocrine and renal systems.

Key terms

Semi-permeable membrane a membrane such as a cell membrane that will allow small molecules to pass through but not ones beyond a certain size

Hypotonic a solution that is less concentrated than a neighbouring one separated by a semi-permeable membrane

Hypertonic a solution that is more concentrated than a neighbouring one separated by a semi-permeable membrane

Isotonic when two solutions separated by a membrane are of equal concentration

Osmoregulation the process by which the body maintains an isotonic balance between the blood and body tissues

If we are exercising on a hot day, for example, we sweat to cool down. This loss of water results in the plasma becoming hypertonic to our cells. This increase in concentration is detected by special cells called osmoreceptors located in the hypothalamus. These cells are linked by nerve cells to a neighbouring gland in the brain called the pituitary. Nerve impulses result in the release of a hormone called ADH (anti-diuretic hormone). ADH passes into the blood and travels around the body in the plasma.

ADH is recognised by cells located in the walls of the collecting ducts of the kidney nephrons. It makes the walls of these tubes permeable to water.

The loops of Henle in the nephrons of the kidney carry out a complicated mechanism by which the tissues of the kidney medulla in which they are located build up a high concentration of salt. While this salt eventually returns to the blood it lingers in the medulla creating a hypertonic environment.

The collecting ducts also pass through this region and under the influence of ADH water in the urine is drawn out by osmosis into the medulla and from there back into the blood so restoring isotonicity with blood and body cells.

The urine produced under such conditions is sparse and concentrated.

If a day is cool and we are not exercising but still drinking a lot of water, the reverse occurs. The plasma becomes hypotonic and this suppresses or reduces the release of ADH so water is not reabsorbed in the collecting ducts back into the blood but stays in the urine.

We therefore urinate more frequently and more copiously producing dilute urine.

Blood pressure

Blood pressure is normally measured as two readings – one the systolic pressure is the higher value of the two and equates to the pressure exerted by the heart when contracting, the other is the diastolic which is the underlying pressure during the heart's relaxation.

A normal healthy reading is 120mm/80mm Hg pressure or 120 over 80.

Below 90/60 mm Hg our blood pressure is considered low – hypotension.

Above 140/90mm Hg our blood pressure is considered high – hypertension.

Hypotension can lead to fainting while hypertension can lead to cardiac disease and strokes.

Maintaining blood pressure is a very complex affair and is accomplished in a variety of ways that involve the cardiovascular, respiratory, nervous and renal systems.

Special cells located near the glomeruli of the kidney tubules detect a drop in blood pressure and this results in the distal tubule of the nephron absorbing sodium ions from the urine. This causes more water to be taken out of the urine so increasing blood volume and hence blood pressure.

Another set of cells nearby release a hormone called renin that activates a chemical produced in the blood vessels of the lungs. This angiotensin constricts blood vessels and increases blood flow to the heart so increasing cardiac output (how much blood leaves the heart) and so raises blood pressure.

This sequence of events also triggers the release of yet another hormone – aldosterone – from the adrenal gland. This promotes further uptake of salts and hence water from the distal tubule so too helping to increase blood volume and pressure.

Cells sensitive to pressure – baroreceptors – in certain blood vessel walls directly monitor blood pressure. Those found in the aorta and the carotid arteries which lead to the brain detect high blood pressure. These send information via the autonomic nervous system to the medulla of the brain resulting in vasodilation as well as lowering heart rate and force of contraction.

Baroreceptors in the vena cavae on the other hand register a low blood pressure and respond by increasing the secretion of ADH, aldosterone and renin which again all promote the uptake of salt in the kidney resulting in an increase in blood volume and hence pressure.

The section above shows how intricately the body systems are inter-related!

Blood pH

Key terms

pH is a measure of the concentration of hydrogen ions

Buffers are chemicals that absorb excess hydrogen ions preventing them from causing significant changes to the pH

Bases are chemicals that have properties opposite to acids thus making them alkaline

The more *hydrogen ions* there are in a solution the more acidic it is, that is, it has a low pH.

In the body a pH less than 7.2 or above 7.5 can cause cells, including the brain, to malfunction so a very slightly alkaline pH must be maintained.

If the body fluids become too acidic **buffers** absorb hydrogen ions; if they become too alkaline then the buffers release some of the hydrogen ions so restoring the balance.

We saw in LO1 and LO2 how carbon dioxide from respiration dissolves in water producing carbonic acid which then breaks down into hydrogen and bicarbonate ions. The latter are an example of a base.

The more carbon dioxide produced the more carbonic acid is made and hence more hydrogen ions are released thus lowering the pH.

If the carbon dioxide can be quickly removed then less hydrogen ions will need to be buffered and hence the pH will rise. Thus hyperventilating or breathing deeply and quickly results in *respiratory alkalosis*.

On the other hand breathing shallowly and slowly results in *respiratory acidosis* and a lowering of pH as carbon dioxide and hence hydrogen ion levels build up in the blood.

Basic bicarbonate ions are also selectively reabsorbed from the urine by the nephrons of the kidney so helping to adjust the body's pH. Other **bases** are also produced and released by the kidneys to fine tune blood pH.

Command word activity

Explain (AC 2.1, 2.2)

Produce a slide presentation that allows you to explain the process of homeostasis and why it is necessary. Use the example of glucose regulation to illustrate your explanation of the principles involved.

Use the examples of thermoregulation and osmoregulation to explain how homeostasis maintains healthy body function. Your explanation could be in the form of a slide presentation, a detailed wall chart or a conventional report.

Command word activity

Evidence (AC 2.3)

Someone you know has been diagnosed with high blood pressure and prescribed drugs to treat it. They wish to fully understand their condition.

Produce an information leaflet for them that examines and shows how both the autonomic nervous system and endocrine system work together to bring about the homeostatic control of blood pressure.

You will need to assume that your friend knows nothing about either body system. You will therefore have to provide enough basic information on the structure and function of both systems to support your explanation.

You may wish to incorporate some simple explanations as to how their medicine works in affecting the control mechanisms. This will require further reading and research on your behalf.

You may wish to provide them with some sources for them to read further or to confirm your information.

Take it further

You may wish to use one of the many colouring books to help you remember the various structures and their functions. One example is shown below but there is quite a choice!

Ross and Wilson Anatomy and Physiology Colouring and Workbook by Anne Waugh and Allison Grant (2014).

Check your understanding

1. What is meant by homeostasis?
2. What is meant by the terms optimum temperature and optimum pH?
3. Summarise how blood pressure is maintained.
4. What are buffers?
5. How is temperature regulation an example of homeostasis?
6. Why is it important to maintain a normal body temperature?
7. Why is it necessary to maintain an optimum pH?

LO3: Understand factors which may affect changes in physiological measurements

3.1 Explain factors which may affect changes in physiological measurements

Certain aspects of our metabolism or physiology can be measured and recorded. These are then used in helping to assess our state of health and if the values recorded indicate a health issue then they are used to monitor any improvement or deterioration.

Common values or **parameters** include pulse, blood pressure, temperature, respiratory rate and the oxygen saturation of the blood. You will have the opportunity to record these yourself.

Various factors can affect these parameters. These include the following: gender; age; ill-health; diet; level of activity; stress; emotion; drugs and hormones.

Gender

Females tend to have a higher pulse rate than men because generally they are smaller with less muscle and so to maintain their metabolic

Key term

Parameter is a measurable figure or value that limits the range of healthy body function.

rate they need to pump blood to the lungs and muscles more rapidly. Their breathing rate tends to be faster too.

Age

Blood pressure is affected slightly by age in that it is influenced by the resistance blood experiences as it is forced through the arteries.

Young healthy arteries are elastic and expand readily as blood flows through them. Elasticity declines with age in all tissues and so blood vessels become more rigid so offering more resistance – known as *arteriosclerosis.*

Also as we age there is inevitably some build up of plaque or *atheroma* in the walls of arteries as a result of lifestyle choices.

While age does not appear to have much effect on average pulse rates the maximum heart rate drops as the heart muscle becomes less efficient.

Diet

Too much salt in the diet will increase blood pressure as it causes an increase in blood volume as more water is needed in the blood to maintain isotonicity.

Similarly too many carbohydrates and fats in the diet will affect blood pressure as these excesses get stored as fat and we become overweight, which results in elevated blood pressure. Also some of these fats will form atheroma increasing resistance and hence pressure – *atherosclerosis.*

If cardiovascular disease results from the atheroma our pulse is likely to increase or become irregular – *arrhythmia.*

The process of eating can also raise pulse rate as the cardiovascular system responds to the digestive process.

Level of activity

Regular exercise will affect blood pressure, pulse and breathing rate if maintained and especially if it is intense.

Respiratory rate rises as demand for oxygen increases and there is a corresponding increase in pulse rate and initially blood pressure. However, athletes, in particular, will develop larger more efficient hearts and lungs and so pulse rate will ultimately decrease.

As weight is lost, overall blood pressure is reduced.

Temperature will increase with exercise as muscles give off heat from respiration, but as long as the thermoregulatory mechanism described already works there will be no significant rise in body temperature. If it is compromised then *heatstroke* or heat exhaustion will occur and this can lead to death.

Stress and emotion

Being stressed or feeling anxious will result in hormones like *adrenalin* and *cortisol* raising pulse, breathing rate and blood pressure. This is partly due to adrenalin being produced to prepare the body for action. A little stress is beneficial as it increases the efficiency of the body but if prolonged will be detrimental.

Cortisol, also produced by the adrenal gland, raises blood glucose as well as blood pressure.

High anxiety levels can result in hyperventilation which affects blood pH as previously described.

Calming emotions as with yoga and forms of meditation can lower pulse, blood pressure and breathing rates.

Drugs

Nicotine, caffeine and alcohol all raise blood pressure and will influence pulse. Alcohol, in particular, can lead to irregular heart rates. Medicinal drugs such as *beta-blockers* act by slowing the heart's rhythm and hence pulse rate.

There are numerous drugs used to combat high blood pressure with many of them acting on the renal control of blood pressure. Others are *diuretics* which are drugs that remove water from the body and hence lower both blood volume and pressure.

Some pain relievers and sedatives, as well as heroin and high alcohol intake, inhibit or suppress the respiratory centre in the medulla of the brain resulting in slowing and then the arrest of breathing.

Ill-health

There are many health conditions that will affect physiological parameters.

Atheroma contributes to an increase in blood pressure and pulse rate as well as breathing rate as the body struggles to get oxygen to the heart muscle.

Lung diseases like *emphysema* reduce oxygen saturation levels as in this condition, caused by smoking, the alveoli break-up and so the surface area for gaseous exchange is severely reduced. This results in an increase in breathing rate and depth of breathing as the body struggles to obtain enough oxygen.

Infections quite often result in a fever, which is considered any temperature above 37.8°C. A fever is a natural response to the presence of pathogens but this elevation of body temperature is likely to raise the pulse, breathing rate and possibly blood pressure.

Blood pressure is also increased as a result of severe *kidney disease* and conditions affecting the thyroid and adrenal glands.

Command word activity

Explain (AC 3.1)

Produce an illustrated information booklet for newly recruited health care practitioners. (This can then be extended in the evidence activity following LO4.)

Identify normal values for each of the following body parameters: body temperature, pulse, blood pressure, breathing rate and oxygen saturation.

Explain how at least two factors may affect each of the identified measurements.

You will need to show evidence of wider background reading by using at least four different sources. These sources could include books, websites, periodicals, videos/media sources and/ or primary data obtained by yourself.

You must provide a full system of referencing within your text that supports your explanations and also a bibliography.

Check your understanding

1. Which factors can affect physiological measurements?
2. How might these factors affect physiological measurements?
3. Identify five physiological parameters or values that can easily be monitored.
4. Give a typical value for each measurement likely to be recorded in a healthy individual.
5. Identify three factors that can cause these physiological values to vary from their normal values.

LO4: Understand how to obtain, record and report physiological measurements

4.1 Explain how to gain consent prior to obtaining physiological measurements

The law requires that valid consent must be obtained before physiological measurements can be made on a patient. In order to gain this the patient needs to be informed in a way they understand not only what the measurements entail but how they fit into their care and treatment. All patients have the right to say no, although there are certain circumstances in which they can be overruled. If consent is not given then the measurements must not be taken as this could be construed as assault.

Consent needs to be given freely with no undue influence exerted by relatives or the professionals. To give their consent the patient must be *legally competent*.

The National Institute for Health and Care Excellence (NICE) produces guidelines on procedures for obtaining measurements, as do the nursing bodies. Hospitals and health practices will also have their own **protocols** based on national standards laid down by NICE.

While carrying out the measurements the patients need to be reassured at all times and the procedures explained in terms they

Key terms

Legally competent generally speaking this is someone who is over 18 and is capable of weighing up any risks and who understands what procedures involve and the reasons for implementing them

Partnership working is also known as multi-disciplinary working and involves different professionals, services and agencies working together to provide the most effective care for an individual requiring treatment or support

Care plan is a personalised plan for the care and support of an individual identifying the personnel involved and their responsibilities

National standards framework are a set of clear policies issued by the NHS laying out the prescribed levels of care and procedures for a number of conditions and age groups

Framework of competence are those policies, knowledge and skills that a particular professional body or organisation requires from its members

Protocol is a set of rules that describes or explains the correct conduct and procedures to be carried out during a particular medical treatment

Appropriate person can also be described as a relevant person or advocate. They are usually an independent person who will make decisions on behalf of a patient if they are considered incapable of making their own informed decisions

Audit trail is a detailed record of actions taken with reasons stating times, any recordings and who was involved

can understand as the recording progresses, especially if repeat readings are required.

They also need to have feedback on the results and be kept informed at all times. Effective communication is the key.

4.2 Describe how to use equipment for measuring temperature; blood pressure; pulse; respiratory rate and oxygen saturation

Measuring temperature

Measuring temperature can be done in a variety of ways but there are issues of accuracy with some of them.

Old fashioned mercury filled glass thermometers should not be used as they are a potential risk due to breakage.

True body core temperature which is a true reflection of internal temperature can only be achieved *invasively* – that is by measuring temperature within the body.

Non-invasive sites include the oral cavity, the ear, under the arm, forehead and rectum though the patient is likely to think this last one also invasive!

When taking the oral temperature a digital thermometer should be inserted in the sublingual pocket that is just to one side under the tongue. It needs to be placed posteriorly rather than near the front where it can be cooler. Obviously this measurement should not be taken after eating or drinking as these will have influenced the local temperature.

Taking the temperature in the ear canal requires a special *tympanic thermometer* which needs to be used by a trained practitioner. Results are deemed a little variable.

Axillary temperature is that taken with a thermometer placed under an armpit with the arm held close to the chest. This is easy to accomplish but is again thought to be fairly inaccurate in recording *core temperature*. Core temperature is that deep inside the body.

Thermometer strips held across the forehead are easy to use but there also questions about its reliability as a method for determining core temperature.

The most accurate is rectal temperature but this is often unfavourable with patients. If using the rectal method a small amount of lubricant should be put on the end and the thermometer inserted no more than a centimetre into the anus.

Most digital thermometers will beep when the temperature has been recorded and so is held in position until this happens – usually within 15 seconds.

Pulse

Electronic pulse meters will record pulse automatically. Depending on the type they may take information from the fingertip, wrist or chest.

Manual readings are usually taken either at the neck or on the wrist. For the neck press two fingers gently in the soft hollow just beside the windpipe.

For the wrist place an index and middle finger on the inside of the wrist just below the hand.

Whichever method either count the number of beats for a minute or count for 30 seconds and multiply by 2.

Blood pressure

Blood pressure is measured using a *sphygmomanometer*. This measures the higher systolic and then lower diastolic measurements. It can be recorded using an electronic monitor or a conventional sphygmomanometer and stethoscope.

Either way the patient needs to be relaxed, wearing loose clothing and be sitting with one arm resting lightly on a surface like a table.

If using an electronic monitor the cuff should be placed around the arm according to the instructions supplied. The machine is switched on and two readings will be obtained. Repeat after an interval of at least two minutes.

If using a traditional sphygmomanometer the cuff is wrapped around the upper arm and inflated rapidly to 180mmHg. A stethoscope is placed over the brachial artery of the arm just below the cuff.

Figure 12.26 Using a sphygmomanometer

Air is released from the cuff at a moderate rate. A knocking sound will be heard that represents the systolic pressure. The pressure reading at this point is recorded. Air continues to be released until the knocking sound disappears. This is recorded as the diastolic value.

The cuff used needs to be of an appropriate size for the patient and is not placed over clothing.

Respiratory rate

The patient is placed in a resting position and the number of times their chest rises in a minute is counted and recorded.

Care must be taken to do this as unobtrusively as possible as most people will alter their rate of breathing if they feel they are being watched.

If available then a *stethoscope* could be placed gently on the chest and the sounds of breathing counted.

Oxygen saturation

The amount of oxygen being carried in the blood is given as a percentage of saturation. It is usually measured by using a device called a *pulse oximeter*.

The most common form resembles a clothes peg and clips onto a fingertip. It has a light source, a detector and a microprocessor.

Infrared and red light is shone through the finger to the detector on the other side. Haemoglobin absorbs differing wavelengths of light depending on how much oxygen is being carried. The probe takes several rapid readings and provides a readout of the average saturation.

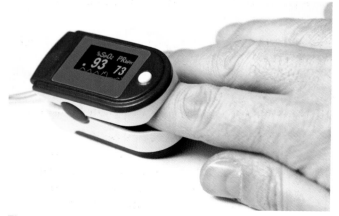

Figure 12.27 A pulse oximeter

4.3 Explain the reasons for accurate and timely recording of physiological measurements

In everyday life physiological measurements tend only to be taken if and when a problem arises. Exceptions to this will be those individuals whose work demands require regular health checks – sports people, service personnel, air crew, and so on.

Some businesses will insist on regular medicals as part of health insurance packages.

Most people will only have regular tests if they are diagnosed with a condition like diabetes or hypertension, or have had a cardiovascular issue such as a heart attack.

People who have been identified as at risk and have been prescribed medication often cannot automatically receive repeat prescriptions unless they present themselves for a check-up, which will usually involve blood pressure readings being taken together with blood tests.

Individuals with conditions such as diabetes and asthma will probably be self-testing several times a day.

In hospitals monitoring of essential parameters is also likely to be several times a day but outside of this situation it is likely to range from daily through to annually. It depends on the underlying health conditions.

For individuals with moderate to severe conditions this monitoring is part of their care plan, which is a personalised package of care approved by the individual and often including both medical and social care aspects. Care tends to be administered by a multi-disciplinary team or **partnership working** with different aspects being the responsibility of different practitioners (see p. 294 for definition). It is very important that they meet frequently so that they are aware of any changes required or implemented.

Professionals administering the tests must therefore be aware of any underlying health condition and will also need to be aware of what is considered to be an abnormal or dangerous reading.

It is therefore essential to obtain accurate results. To this end, readings must be noted accurately, not rounded up or down and ideally repeated at least three times to obtain a mean. In some cases the apparatus may need to be calibrated – that is, adjusted to ensure each reading is correct.

Any equipment used must be checked to ensure that it is not broken and that it is working accurately. If reliant on batteries then these must be regularly checked and if necessary replaced.

Any apparatus that is broken needs to be identified, labelled and removed from use and its repair actioned. This is all likely to be logged. Never should an individual use a piece of apparatus that they are unfamiliar with and are not trained to use.

For those individuals with underlying health conditions, regular and frequent testing is vital as it is important to recognise trends or variations over time.

Are values steadily increasing or decreasing? Depending on what is being measured either could be good or bad news.

If an individual receives medication for hypertension and their blood pressure readings are reducing steadily then it can be accepted that the medication is working. If their readings remain stubbornly high then perhaps a different drug regime is needed.

Similarly significant changes, for example, a sudden rise in pulse and blood pressure, could indicate a serious problem that requires immediate action. Practitioners need to know what values constitute a significant change.

All medical organisations will have policies and procedures set out based on national standards of care that their employees need to know and follow when carrying out physiological readings and monitoring.

4.4 Explain how to report physiological measurements that may be a cause for concern

There are *safeguarding* requirements that are laid out in *competency frameworks* for both children and vulnerable adults. This not only overlaps with the requirements of legal consent but also involves spotting and reporting any signs of abuse or neglect, either emotional or physical, to an appointed person.

It is essential that all measurements are recorded *accurately and precisely* on the appropriate document – likely to be a set form. This will provide an accurate log over time and allow worrying trends or abnormal values to be readily identified.

Any points of concern need to be readily and speedily communicated to a line manager who is likely to be a senior nurse or doctor/general practitioner. It may also be necessary to consult with an ***appropriate person*** (see p. 294 for definition).

Table 12.5 Physiological measurements

Measurement	Normal range/value	Cause for concern
Temperature	36.5–37.2°C	< 35°C > 40°C
Pulse	60–80 bpm	Irregular pulse Resting pulse < 60 Resting pulse above 100
Blood pressure	120/80 adult 110/75 young person 140/90 older person	< 90/60 Anything above 120/80 but especially above 140/90 > 180 needs urgent action
Breathing rate	8–17 breaths per minute	Above 25 Below 12
Oxygen saturation	95–99%	Below 90%

All steps taken, as well as the readings, need to be documented as part of an **audit trail** (see p. 294 for definition) and these will form part of the patient's records. This information is now available to the patient upon request by law but otherwise must be kept *confidential*. A patient's results must not be discussed publically nor files left lying around.

Yet again all agencies will have precise policies and procedures that staff are expected to follow.

Activity

Interview practitioners and ask them about the protocols involved in taking physiological measurements.

Case scenario (AC 4.1, 4.2, 4.3, 4.4)

Bill is in his mid-60s. He is a keen cyclist and cycles with his local club at least three times a week. He has never smoked and only occasionally drinks alcohol. He follows a vegetarian diet. When not cycling he is a keen walker and also enjoys tending his garden and growing fruit and vegetables.

Because of his age he has an annual review of his health at his local surgery. He has a blood sample taken and his blood pressure recorded.

His average resting pulse is 65 bpm and his blood pressure was recorded at 124/82 mmHg.

Jack is also in his 60s. He started showing the symptoms of early onset dementia in his 50s. He lives at home and is cared for by his wife. She continues to give him his favourite food of cooked breakfasts with pies, chops, fish and chips being typical evening meals. He has smoked since he was a boy although he now has to give them up, having developed a

chronic lung condition. This and arthritis resulting from a lifetime of heavy manual labour as a builder mean much of his time is spent sitting in a chair.

When in a recent visit by the health visitor his pulse was found to be 89 bpm; his blood pressure 154/96 mmHg; his breathing rate 27 breaths per minute and his oxygen saturation 91 per cent.

1. Comment on these two individuals and their different sets of readings.
2. Why did Jack have his breathing rate and oxygen saturation recorded while Bill didn't?
3. What trend might be expected in Jack's measurements?
4. What possible difference may Jack's dementia make to taking physiological measurements from him?
5. Suggest reasons for taking an annual blood sample from a man in his 60s.

Classroom discussion

Engage in a class discussion on the need for standards, frameworks, policies and audit trails.

Discuss the circumstances when advocacy may be needed.

Activity

Interview practitioners and ask them about the protocols involved in taking physiological measurements.

Check your understanding

1. What is a sphygmomanometer? How might one be used?

2. What is a disadvantage of most commonly used methods to record body temperature?

3. What steps must be taken before, during and after measuring an individual's physiological measurements?

4. Explain why communication throughout the monitoring process is so important. What factors or circumstances may make this more difficult?

Command word activity

Explain and describe (AC 4.1, 4.2, 4.3, 4.4)

If you haven't attempted Command word activity Explain (LO3) then:

Produce an illustrated information booklet for newly recruited health care practitioners

If you have already started this then it can be expanded to include the following evidence.

Provide an explanation of how health and social care practitioners should gain consent when attempting to make physiological measurements.

Give a full description of how to correctly use equipment to measure the following parameters:

- temperature
- pulse
- blood pressure
- respiratory rate
- oxygen saturation.

Provide an explanation as to why physiological measurements need to be accurate, giving at least two reasons.

Explain what you understand by 'timely recordings', giving at least two reasons for taking such measurements.

Provide an explanation of how to report physiological measurements that may be a cause for concern.

Emphasise the importance of recording and how to recognise values that may be of concern.

Explain the responsibilities of reporting such measurements within health and social care and to whom.

LO5: Be able to obtain and record physiological measurements

5.1 Apply standard precautions for infection prevention and control.

Standard precautionsare those steps taken to ensure there is no risk of cross-infection in a normal care environment including hospitals, health centres and home visits. It does not include the more specialised precautions found, for example, in an operating theatre.

Ensuring that cross-infection, that is, the passage of pathogens to and from individuals or through contaminated surfaces is part of *health and safety*

Key terms

Cross-infection is the transfer of disease causing microorganisms or pathogens from one individual to another or from a contaminated surface

Standard precautions are the steps or measures taken to prevent cross-infection. The term standard refers to measures that can be taken, like washing hands, cleaning surfaces that can be done in any health and special care setting including individuals' homes. It does not include the barrier nursing techniques used in intensive care units or operating theatres

legislation that applies to anyone working in a care setting.

It is a legal requirement for all care employers to give their staff appropriate training and it is a legal requirement for all staff to follow these stipulations and take personal responsibility for their clients or patients.

The most obvious standard precaution is *hand washing* and/or use of alcohol gel or wipes. This must take place before any physiological measurement is taken. Hand washing needs to be thorough and most care settings display posters showing how this should be done. Many basins will have special taps that can be operated by the elbows so that fingers do not get re-contaminated.

If there is a possible risk of cross-infection then disposable gloves and/or aprons should be used – these are examples of *personal protective equipment*.

Any equipment that is not disposable must be sterilised after use in an antiseptic solution. Just immersing in hot water is not appropriate as this is very likely to harm the apparatus. Cuffs of sphygmomanometers must be wiped down with an anti-septic cloth.

Organisations and health care agencies will all have their own policies regarding standard precautions and there may be policies involving personal jewellery, clothes, make-up and hair.

5.2 Use equipment accurately to obtain physiological measurements

In order to successfully complete your Skills Assessment you will need to complete the following tasks.

Working in pairs, take it in turns to obtain readings for temperature, pulse, blood pressure, breathing rate and oxygen saturation for each of you.

You must apply and demonstrate appropriate standard precautions to prevent infection and you should demonstrate good communication skills in obtaining consent and in explaining the measurements and any results. You may wish to film yourselves.

You must use the equipment appropriately following any instructions and take all necessary measures to ensure accuracy.

5.3 Record physiological measurements accurately

You must ensure that you record your results accurately and appropriately on a well-organised reporting sheet that allows for any results that may be of concern to be recognised.

Read about it

When supporting work on health and social care studies in the United Kingdom it is recommended that only UK websites are used; however, for anatomy and physiology it does not matter. However you may encounter different spellings, for example estrogen instead of oestrogen.

Care should be taken when using both books and websites as they can both turn out to be too complicated as they are directed at degree level or above. The suggestions below are general sources that should help consolidate your understanding.

BMA (2014) *A–Z Family Medical Encyclopaedia*, 6th edition, London: Dorling Kindersley

BMA (2016) *Complete Home Medical Guide: The Essential Reference for Every Family,* 4th edition, London: Dorling Kindersley.

Hark, L. and Deen, D. (2005) *Nutrition for Life*, London: Dorling Kindersley

Norris, M. and Rae Siegfried, D. (2011) *Anatomy & Physiology for Dummies*, 2nd edition, John Wiley & Sons

Waugh, A. and Grant, A. (2014) *Ross and Wilson Anatomy and Physiology in Health and Illness*, 12th edition, Churchill Livingstone

Waugh, A. and Grant, A. (2014) *Ross and Wilson Anatomy and Physiology Colouring and Workbook*, 4th edition, Churchill Livingstone

Wills, J. (2007) Food Bible, Quadrille Publishing Ltd

The Carer magazine

Caring Times magazine

NHS Choices **www.nhs.uk**

Nursing Standard journal

Nursing Times journal and **www.nursingtimes.net**

Unit HSC DM3.: How will I be graded?

For the Level 3 Technical Extended Diploma in Health and Social Care, this unit will be assessed via an exam. At Tech level, the unit will exclude any skills-based outcomes.

Your tutor will be able to offer more guidance with regards to the assessment of this unit.

Research Skills for Health and Social Care

About this unit

Research means 'finding out'. We research things every day; for example, we research holiday choices, menu options, and career options. Academic research uses many of the skills we use in everyday life. In this unit you will learn:

- about different ways research is approached and carried out in health and social care.
- about ethical considerations such as the duty of care researchers have and the role of the ethics committee;

- how to plan and carry out a research project, how to scrutinise the information you find and draw conclusions from your findings.
- how to present your findings, make recommendations based on what you found, and use your findings.

Finally, you will learn how to look back on the process, consider strengths and weaknesses in the methods you used and suggest improvements for any future projects you wish to conduct.

LO1: Understand research approaches and methodologies

Research helps to improve ways of doing things. Research in health helps us to understand the cause and spread of diseases such as Ebola, Avian flu, and meningitis and research finds vaccines that prevent us getting flu or meningitis. In social care, research tells us, for example, that when prisons are overcrowded and uncontrolled, more prisoners take their own lives. Research helps us find effective ways of reducing anti-social behaviour and unwanted teenage pregnancies. There are many ways of conducting research. The purpose of the research influences the choice of approach.

1.1 Describe research approaches

Watch what happens on a crowded bus. Do people speak to each other, make eye contact, and keep a personal space? How do they behave when their personal space is cramped? From this data, you may find patterns of behaviour which then give a theory of how people behave in crowded conditions. This is an inductive approach.

Key term

Research approach the angle or way you look at a topic. There are two main approaches – inductive and deductive

In contrast, a deductive approach starts with a theory such as, 'When personal space is restricted, individuals avoid eye contact'. Researchers set up an experiment to test the theory. They use selected volunteers, put them in a mock-up of a bus, and then add more people, until each person is squashed. Researchers observe what happens as each new person joins the bus. They might notice that when each person has their personal space invaded, they avoid eye contact with others. Evidence supports their theory. Or they might find that eye contact ceases long before that point, in which case the evidence does not support their theory.

These two approaches – inductive and deductive – are used in research. The approach used influences the tools or methods used.

Methods are the way the research is carried out. In the inductive example, the method used was observation of a given situation, a crowded bus. In the deductive example, the method was a controlled experiment where the researcher controls how many people join the bus and when they do so. They also use observation but it is not the main research method.

Inductive research

Inductive approaches to research generate data and then look for explanations of the data. One type of inductive approach is 'grounded theory' developed by Glaser and Strauss (1967), which starts with an open mind, generates data and then sifts through data to find patterns.

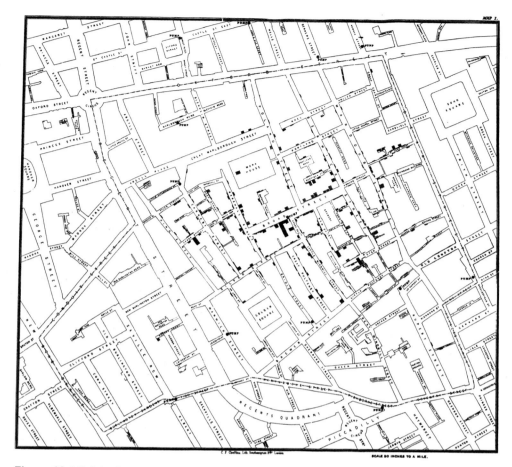

Figure 13.1 Original map made by John Snow in 1854. Cholera cases are highlighted in black

Action research is inductive. Action research does not start with a theory and does not aim to test a theory. Action research starts with a situation that is already in action, such as a large number of people dying, then draws out the common factors in the situation that is already happening. Generating data in this way then gives rise to theory. Inductive research involving action research was used in uncovering the cause of cholera. In 1854, Dr John Snow noticed that a lot of people in London were becoming sick. Many died. He wanted to find out why they got sick. He talked to people about what they ate and drank and their lifestyle, then mapped the cases of illness. People who worked at the local brewery drank beer, made with boiled water. They did not get sick. Everyone who took their water from the pump in Broad Street got sick. Dr Snow examined some water under a microscope and found cholera bacteria. He took the handle off the pump and the number of cases of cholera fell. Inductive approaches involve action research.

Deductive research

The second approach to research is deductive and often called the scientific approach. It starts with a hypothesis or theory then tests it. The aim of deductive research is to test a theory. Here is an example: according to Alzheimer's Research UK, Professor Jane Armitage at the University of Oxford will lead research to test the theory that taking aspirin or omega-3 fish oils may have an effect on memory and thinking skills in people with diabetes. A deductive approach may use experiments to test a theory, giving one group of participants medication and comparing their results with a control group who have not had the medication. This is a scientific approach.

Key terms

Inductive approaches generate data and then look for explanations of the data.

Deductive approaches start with a hypothesis or theory then look for evidence to support or disprove the theory.

Qualitative methods use case studies, unstructured interviews, and participant observation and focus on the content of what is observed or described

Quantitative methods use numerical and categorical data which can be analysed to show patterns

1.2 Describe research methodologies

Research methods used may be **qualitative**, concerned with opinions, or **quantitative** concerned with numbers and categories. Although qualitative research is often associated with inductive approaches, and quantitative research methods with deductive approaches, both qualitative and quantitative methods may be used in either approach.

Table 13.1 Qualitative and quantitative research compared

Qualitative research	Quantitative research
Is often small scale and is not representative of other situations. It is specific to that group in that situation	Is often large scale, e.g. Million Women study
Observes what is happening and then generates a theory from what is observed	Controls what is happening in order to test a theory or hypothesis
Uses interviews, focus groups, observation	Uses surveys, questionnaires, data already gathered e.g. Census
Data produced in the form of opinions and preferences, specific to the individual	Data produced in the form of numbers, scales, and classifications. Data is not unique to an individual
Data analysed using a predetermined framework or by reducing data to codes or key words and then picking out recurring themes	Statistical analysis of data such as how many male/female; or numerical values e.g. number of deaths from cancer

Qualitative methods

Qualitative methods use case studies, unstructured interviews, and participant observation where the observer is involved in whatever is happening. Information from qualitative methods is not concerned with numbers but with the content of what is observed or described.

Discourse analysis

Discourse analysis, which studies verbal, visual and other communication, is one qualitative method used to understand social interactions. In a study by C. Roberts *et al.* (2005), discourse analysis was used to study interactions between GPs and patients in Inner London. Video recordings of the interactions were analysed and the causes of misunderstandings identified as pronunciation and word stress; intonation and speech delivery; grammar, vocabulary and lack of contextual information; and style of presentation. The research recommended specific training for GPs in raising awareness of these issues. In the example for discourse analysis, the focus was on how things were said; by contrast, in narrative analysis the focus is on what is said.

Narrative analysis

In narrative analysis the researcher listens to accounts or stories given by participants and attempts to understand the experiences of the subject in relation to their social context. Narrative analysis was used as a method in a piece of research by Tara Young *et al.* (2014), where interviews and focus groups were used to examine the role of the family in gang formation, criminality and gang exit. Responses were recorded and analysed. The findings were used to help practitioners working with families involved or associated with gangs.

Grounded theory

Grounded theory, mentioned earlier as a type of inductive research, approaches a topic with an open mind and tries to understand what is happening and why. Young's research was concerned with exploring the role of the family in the formation of gangs, gang-related criminality and desistance. Researchers did not start out to prove or disprove a theory that family breakdown causes young people to become gang members.

Take it further

Tina Harris (2015) gives a detailed explanation of grounded theory in an article for the *Nursing Standard*. She gives examples such as research by Licqurish and Seibold (2011) which uses grounded theory to explore how midwifery students achieve competence on their final placement.

Key terms

Correlation refers to how often events occur together, increasing or decreasing at the same time (positive correlation) or when one increases while the other decreases (negative correlation). An example of negative correlation might be an increase in fitness levels and a reduced intake of chocolate. Correlation does not always mean causation. A child grows taller, pollution levels increase: two facts but they are not linked by cause and effect

Causation is an explanation or reason for something, cause and effect; for example, binge drinking causes liver damage

Instead they tried to find out what was happening and why. This is grounded theory.

It is used in health and social care research and in many other related disciplines. Researchers using grounded theory start with an open mind and consider everything is evidence, whether spoken words, tattoos, clothing or ways of interacting. Data is gathered, sifted and concepts emerge, bringing up new questions. Further data is gathered and compared with existing data until no more new concepts can be formed. Explanations emerge which then can be tested against more data. The process of grounded theory is iterative; processes are repeated and refined until core ideas emerge.

Quantitative methods

Quantitative methods such as questionnaires and surveys use numerical data which can be analysed to show patterns. The Census is an example of quantitative research. Large amounts of data are gathered and analysed. Methods of analysis focus on trying to pick out patterns and links.

Variable analysis

Variable analysis looks at the different variables or factors, so for example, data on deaths may include deaths of men, women, and infants under 1 year old, children 0 to 4 years, and people over 80. These are variables. If you want to compare variables, for example deaths of men compared to deaths of women, you would focus just on these variables. If you wanted to compare infant mortality in 2011 and 2001 you would focus on infant mortality in these two censuses, ignoring deaths of men and women.

Frequency distribution

Frequency distribution looks at how often an event occurs; for example, in a study of parent and child interactions you might count how often child A approaches its mother for reassurance and compare that with how often child B does the same.

Correlation

Correlation refers to how often events occur together, for example how often poverty and disability occur together in a population. A positive correlation indicates the variables increase or decrease together. For example ability and income: those with less ability experience least wealth, and those with full abilities experience the highest incomes.

A negative correlation describes the situation when variables move in opposite directions. In the case of ability and income, negative correlation would be where ability increases and income decreases. It is important to remember that correlation does not necessarily equal **causation**. A low income does not cause disability. (Some would argue that disability causes low income but others would argue that it does not.)

Tendencies and averages

Quantitative data can be used to look at measures of central tendency or probability, for example the probability of women having their first child in their twenties. We use types of

Command word activity

Describe (AC 1.1, 1.2)

1. Describe two research *approaches*, giving examples to support what you say.
2. Describe two research *methods*, giving examples to support what you say.

averages for this: mean, median and mode. For the mean we might add together the ages of ten first-time mothers and divide the total age by ten to give the arithmetical mean, commonly called the average. For the median we might line up all the mothers in order of age, from the 16 year old to the 40 year old, as shown in Figure 13.2.

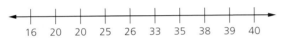

16 20 20 25 26 33 35 38 39 40

Figure 13.2 Median age in years of first-time mothers

The median falls between 26 and 33 so to get the midpoint we add 26 + 33 = 59 then divide it by 2 which gives a median of 29.5 years. The mode is the value appearing most often. In this sample it would be 20 years.

1.3 Explain how research approaches and methodologies are used for different purposes

Exploratory purposes

The purpose of the research decides which methods are used. The purpose of the research may be exploratory using case studies, observation and results from previous studies. For example, the National Institute for Health and Care Excellence (NICE) reviewed previous studies and data on the assessment and management of bipolar disorder and found that psychological interventions are effective and cost-saving compared with standard care based on medication. They also found psychological interventions, unlike medication, had no harmful effects and benefits continued after the interventions finished. The purpose of the study, to explore the most effective way of managing bipolar disorder, dictated that they review previous studies to find out what worked best.

Descriptive purposes

The purpose of the research may be descriptive, for example to identify and classify the elements or characteristics of the subject, which would be largely qualitative, using observation, case studies and surveys. An example of descriptive research is the work produced by the Mayor of London's office on London street gangs. It describes where gangs are based and what they are called. Descriptive research describes facts but makes no attempt to explain them.

Analytical purposes

Another purpose of research may be analytical. This research locates and identifies the different factors (or variables) involved. Dr Snow used analytical research to explain why people were dying, linking where they lived, where they got their water from and their occupation to track down the cause of cholera.

Predictive purposes

Research may be predictive, to speculate on future possibilities based on close analysis of available evidence. Public Health England use data on obesity to predict that by 2050, 60 per cent of men will be obese.

Take it further

You can visit the National Obesity Observatory website, now part of Public Health England website at **www.noo.org.uk** to see the latest research on changes in children's body mass index between 2006/7 and 2014/15.

Public Health England is a government body that collects and shares information about health and disease: **www.gov.uk/government/organisations/public-health-england**

Case scenario (AC 1.1, 1.2, 1.3)

Public Health England has a routine surveillance programme to collect information about the number of cases of meningitis. Infants aged less than one are most likely to be affected by MenB. For the past four years, an average of 74 cases were recorded each year in the winter period from September to May. A new vaccine was introduced in 2015. In the period September 2015 to May 2016 only 37 cases were recorded for the same age group.

Source: www.gov.uk/government/news/vaccine-cuts-cases-of-meningitis-and-septicaemia-in-uk-infants

1. Was the main purpose of this research:
   a. exploratory
   b. predictive
   c. descriptive, or
   d. analytical?
2. Is this an example of qualitative or quantitative research?
3. Is it inductive or deductive research?
4. Give reasons for your answers.

Activity

Find ONE piece of research from ONE of these sites:

https://www.alzheimers.org.uk

http://www.mind.org.uk/news-campaigns/campaigns/bluelight/blue-light-resources/research-and-evaluation/

http://www.nihr.ac.uk/ (The NHS Research site)

1. What is the purpose of the research?
2. Is the approach inductive or deductive?
3. Are the methods used qualitative or quantitative?

Command word activity

Explain (AC 1.3)

Explain with examples how the research approaches and methodologies you described in the all the previous activities are used for different purposes.

 Check your understanding

1. What is the difference between inductive and deductive research?
2. Give four different reasons why research might be conducted.
3. What is the difference between qualitative and quantitative methods?
4. Which method might use interviews and case studies?
5. Which method might use frequency data?
6. What does correlation mean?

LO2: Understand ethical implications associated with undertaking research in health and social care

Ethics are about what is morally right and what is wrong. Research should ensure the safety of people in the study and should ensure security of their information. There are ethical implications when conducting any research, but these are even more important in health and care research, where a duty of care is owed to patients and service users and a duty of care is owed to those involved in research.

2.1 Describe ethical issues to be considered when planning and carrying out research

Some key ethical issues are described here, but there may be others. Every researcher is responsible for identifying the ethical implications involved in their own research and for explaining how they will manage such issues.

 Key term

Ethics concerned with what is morally right or wrong

Informed consent

Informed consent can only be given after all the risks, benefits and alternatives have been explained. According to the NHS website:

'For consent to be valid, it must be voluntary and informed, and the person consenting must have the capacity to make the decision.'

Consent must be given voluntarily – there must be no pressure to make the person give consent.

The person must have the capacity to give consent, which means they must be able to understand all the information, and use it to make a decision.

Informed consent must be obtained before anyone can take part in research, and participants can withdraw their consent at any time.

Researchers often provide a handout summarising what is involved in the research. The NHS Health Research Authority publishes advice for ethics committees and researchers about ensuring information is easily understood by those who may have a different language or require different formats.

Take it further

Examples of consent forms for young children, people with learning disabilities and other vulnerable people are provided on the Health Research Authority website: www.hra.nhs.uk/resources/before-you-apply/consent-and-participation/consent-and-participant-information/

Privacy and confidentiality

Privacy and confidentiality must be maintained for those taking part in research. Individuals who take part are not named, or are given a different name so that they cannot be recognised when the research data is processed. The Research Governance Framework (RGF) for Health and Social Care sets out the principles, requirements and standards that apply to

research in UK health departments. The RGF at Section 2.2.5 says that:

'attention must be given to systems for ensuring confidentiality of personal information and to the security of those systems'

Data protection is a legal requirement under the Data Protection Acts 1998 and 2003. In addition to the rights of individuals to access and have corrected their own personal data and the responsibilities of professionals in maintaining, storing, processing and destroying personal data, researchers have other responsibilities. Section 2.4.2 of the RGF explains a researcher's responsibilities in ensuring commercial data is protected and that the timing of the research publication is sensitive to commercial requirements. A drug company may spend millions to develop a new drug and they do not want rivals to profit from their investment.

Objectivity

Researchers must be objective. They must not let their personal views influence the research in any way. This objectivity must be maintained throughout the research process; otherwise the research will be invalid. This is not easy. Researchers may introduce bias into the research at the start by the way they plan the research; for instance, they may not read all material available for a literature review. Or they may word the research aim in a way that loses objectivity. For example: 'The aim of the research is to find out how much racism there is in health care' is not objective. It assumes without evidence there is racism. A more objective aim would be: 'To examine the interactions between medical staff and patients in an outpatient's clinic'.

Bias may be introduced when selecting participants for the study. If 95 females and 5 males are selected, and they are all from the same age group, this may not be an accurate sample of patients attending the clinic. The method of gathering data may lose objectivity too. If a written questionnaire is used, visually impaired participants are disadvantaged.

Researchers cannot choose what evidence to include and what to disregard. They cannot make the evidence fit what they want to prove.

Deception

Deception, deliberately keeping participants unaware of some aspect of the study, is not allowed if it would:

'disguise the possibility of the subject being exposed to anything more than minimal risk and that nothing has been withheld that, if divulged, would cause a reasonable person to refuse to participate' 'Issues, Guidance & Evidence - Deception in Medical Research' (IGE paper (Deception in Medical Research) V1.1 July 2009, p. 1)

Researchers must provide detailed reasons why they need to deceive people and the Research Ethics Committee then decides whether the research will be allowed. Similarly, withholding information is rarely allowed and again must be approved by the Research Ethics Committee.

'The withholding of information or the misleading of participants is unacceptable if the participants are typically likely to object or show unease once debriefed' (IGE paper (Deception in Medical Research) V1.1 July 2009, p. 3)

One example of permitted deception might be when patients are randomly allocated to two groups. Group A receive a harmless non-active tablet, a placebo. Group B receive a new treatment. All participants have given consent to be in either the active drug trial or the placebo group but no one knows who gets what until after the end of the research.

Conflicts of interest

A conflict of interest may arise where a researcher has interests that impact on one another and may be tempted to put their own interests above the public interest. For example, a researcher paid by a soft drinks company may be under pressure to produce results showing that soft drinks do not harm teeth. There is a conflict between the need for objective research and the researcher's need for funding. A conflict of interest may occur when a researcher is testing whether vaccine A works, and sets up a company to produce an alternative, vaccine B. The interest the person has in his own company conflicts with his duty as a researcher to remain objective and independent. He may be tempted to select evidence that vaccine A does not work and so boost sales of his company's vaccine B. If he had set up a company to produce something else such as clothing, there would be no conflict of interest.

Sensitivity of subject matter and data

Sensitivity of subject matter and data has already been explained in relation to commercial sensitivity, but in health and social care we deal with issues that are sensitive on a personal level. Issues such as death and dying, bereavement and loss, cancer, HIV status and unwanted pregnancy are just a few. All these are personally sensitive and require careful handling on the part of the researcher if the participants are not to be harmed. The researcher must carefully consider how to manage the boundary between themselves and subject to ensure objectivity.

Safeguarding

Safeguarding policies and procedures in place for all organisations must be followed to ensure that vulnerable adults and children are kept safe. It is likely that the researcher will require a Disclosure and Barring Service (DBS) check. The NSPCC publish guidance for researchers on how to obtain informed consent, how to manage the risk of harm to participants and what to do with the information gathered during the research. Vulnerable adults may require extra support to understand the information given and to ensure they are not under any pressure to consent to take part in research. Mencap, the charity which supports people with learning disabilities, provides advocacy services to help individuals make their own decisions.

Take it further

Refer to Unit HSC CM3 for more detailed information on safeguarding.

Health and safety

Health and safety is important. Researchers and participants should complete a health and safety induction and be aware of emergency procedure for fire, accidents and incident reporting. Researchers should complete a risk assessment for any identified risks, for example risks relating to the place where interviews are conducted and the client group being studied. A researcher studying gang or drug culture will need to know how to ensure their personal safety. Arrangements must be in place for lone working or out of hours work, for example where a researcher studying homelessness may be out alone at night to interview people sleeping on the street. Section 3.6.3 of the RGF says for health and social care research, the chief investigator is responsible for ensuring that the research team gives 'priority at all times to the dignity, rights, safety and wellbeing of participants'.

Background of a participant

The participant's background must be considered as part of ethical issues. For example, a research project on the effect of trauma on individuals would be unwise to include participants who are suffering from unmanaged post-traumatic stress disorder (PTSD) because the research may bring back painful memories which negatively affect the person's health. For example, soldiers returning from a tour of duty may be experiencing PTSD, and participating in a study on stress might harm their health.

Command word activity

Describe (AC 2.1)

Identify and then describe three ethical issues to be considered when planning and carrying out research. Use examples to support the points you make and reference your sources. You may wish to consider ethical issues around funding treatment for children with rare life-threatening illnesses, or ethical issues around the quality of care of the elderly in care homes or hospitals.

2.2 Explain reasons for considering ethical issues when designing and carrying out research

One practical reason why researchers should consider ethical issues when designing research is that if they do not, they will not be given permission to conduct the research. All research proposals must be submitted to a Research Ethics Committee who scrutinise the proposal to ensure that participants will not be harmed.

A moral reason for considering ethical issues is that the researcher has a duty of care not to cause harm to participants.

Finally, if ethical issues are not considered, the research may not be accepted by others in the research community or it may be heavily criticised and the results dismissed as invalid.

Command word activity

Explain (AC 2.2)

Look back at the activity for AC 2.1. Explain the reasons for considering ethical issues when designing and carrying out the research you identified. Give at least three reasons. Support what you say with examples and reference your sources.

2.3 Describe the role of the Research Ethics Committee

In 2012, the publication Governance Arrangements for Research Ethics Committees set out the role of Research Ethics Committees (RECs) and the Research Ethics Service (RES). RECs are part of the Research Ethics Service. Research Ethics Committees safeguard the rights and welfare of those who are participating in research.

RECs are made up of lay people (members of the general public) as well as care professionals and they are independent of research sponsors. They examine research proposals from the point of view of participants to ensure the research is ethically managed.

The Health Research Authority grants approvals for all project-based research in NHS England after projects have been reviewed by ethics committees. The United Kingdom Ethics Committee Authority (UKECA) regulates the 104 Research Ethics Committees across England, Wales, Scotland and Northern Ireland. In addition to universities and the Ministry of Defence, which have their own RECs, there is a special Gene Therapy Advisory Committee dealing with stem cell research.

Take it further

You can read more about Research Ethics Committees and what they do on the Health Research Authority website:

www.hra.nhs.uk/about-the-hra/our-committees/

Command word activity

Describe (AC 2.3)

You have decided to undertake a piece of research and must present your outline to a Research Ethics Committee. Describe the role of the Research Ethics Committee. What is the purpose of such a committee?

Case scenario

In 2015, an American piece of research about combining drugs to reduce blood pressure in older people was stopped early because it had achieved its aim. The Systolic Blood Pressure Intervention Trial was funded by the National Institutes of Health. According to reports, 'at-risk older adults who reduced their systolic blood pressure (the top number in the blood pressure ratio) to 120, down from the recommended upper threshold of 140, also dropped their risk for heart attacks, heart failure, strokes and death.'

According to researchers, the method had succeeded in reducing blood pressure; therefore it was not fair to exclude others from the benefits of the findings.

Criticisms were made of the study by other scientists and researchers. The high-risk group selected were not fully representative of older people. A low-risk older age group taking a combination of these drugs might experience kidney problems, heart arrhythmias or an abnormally slow heart rate. The risks to this group have not been analysed.

The study has not yet been published. To read more about it, visit:

www.scientificamerican.com/article/raised-hype-about-lower-blood-pressure/

1. What ethical issues may be posed by this research?
2. How might future researchers manage these ethical issues?

 Classroom discussion (AC 2.1, 2.2)

Read about the social care project 'Improving mental health and emotional wellbeing support for children and young people in care.' Available on **www.scie.org.uk/children/care/mental-health/**

What ethical considerations would researchers need to consider when conducting this research project? Work in pairs to prepare a short presentation of your pair's ideas to the class.

 Check your understanding

1. What are ethics concerned with and why are ethics important in research?
2. What three aspects must be included in informed consent?
3. What data must be protected? Why?
4. Give an example of a conflict of interest and say why it is a conflict.
5. Which type of material may be sensitive?.

LO3: Understand how to plan a research project

Research is time-consuming and expensive. In order not to waste time, money and energy, it is important to plan research logically and in detail. Research should be useful. One way of assessing usefulness is to ask: 'So what?'

3.1 Describe the key stages in a research project

These are the key stages in a research project. Each stage can be complex.

Propose a topic: a general area of interest for your research. Choose something that interests you and that you can manage in the time you have.

Devise a research question/hypothesis: e.g. Question, 'Do people in my class eat healthy food at lunchtime?' Or hypothesis, 'People in my class eat healthy food at lunchtime.'

Review literature: what are the key resources available that have already covered your topic? You may need to read around key terms. For research on healthy food – what does the Government consider to be healthy food?

Design project: if you are following an inductive exploratory approach, you will need to design action research. If you are following a deductive approach, testing a hypothesis, you will need to design a study to support or disprove your hypothesis.

Select methodology: how will you ensure validity, i.e. that you are measuring what you intend to measure? How will you ensure reliability, i.e. that anyone who repeats the study with the same group will get the same results? How will you select the sample to reduce bias? How will you obtain informed consent?

Choose measurement tools: will you use observation, questionnaires, and interviews?

Design instruments such as questionnaires, interview questions: check that questions are clear, not biased. If you are testing a hypothesis, have you designed questionnaires with yes/no answers so the data can be analysed numerically?

Carry out research: how long will you need – one lunchtime or more?

Collect data: How will you ensure that people return questionnaires? Where will you interview them? If observing, how will you do this without influencing their choice of food?

Analyse data: action research – what patterns emerge? Do you need a framework to help analyse the content of interviews?

Report results: can you present results visually as bar charts or graphs?

Discussion: what do the results show?

Conclusion: what do the results mean? If you started with a hypothesis, do the findings support the hypothesis or not? If using action research, what patterns emerged?

Make recommendations: how do your findings link with Government aims to encourage healthy eating? What can be done to improve lunchtime meals?

Command word activity

Describe (AC 3.1)

Here are some potential topics for research in your class: the use of social media, diet, exercise, types of socialising. Choose one of these topics or pick your own topic.

Look through the headings of how to plan a research project and briefly describe the key stages in planning a research project on this topic.

3.2 Agree a research topic

When you conduct research, choose a topic that interests you because you will be spending a lot of time on it. Once you have your broad topic, refine it. A good way to do this is to write the topic in the centre of a page and then write any ideas associated with it.

Figure 13.3 Refining the topic

313

The research topic for Oxford University's Million Women Study (www.millionwomenstudy.org) is women's health ('What?'). Refining the topic narrowed it down to UK women aged 50 and over ('Who?'). It was conducted in a specific period between 1996 and 2001 ('When?') in the UK ('Where?'). Women were invited to take part in the study when they attended NHS Breast Screening Centres for routine mammograms ('How?'). Why choose women's health rather than men's health?

3.3 Identify aims of research project

Focus on a project where you have access to information so that you are able to find resources, materials and additional viewpoints concerning your selected topic for research.

The Million Women study researchers had access to women attending breast screening clinics. The study aimed to find out how reproductive and lifestyle factors affect women's health. The focus was narrowed even more to look at the effect of hormone replacement therapy on health. The study also looked at diet, exercise, employment patterns, oral contraceptive use, childbirth and breastfeeding, and family history of illness, in relation to cancers, fractures, gallbladder problems and cardiovascular disease.

3.4 Develop a research question

The research question is a statement identifying the issue to be studied. The Million Women study is a very big study so it was broken down into four research questions:

What effects do combined oestrogen and progestagen hormone replacement therapy (HRT) preparations have on breast cancer risk?

Are breast cancers detected at screening in women who have used HRT or oral contraceptives different in terms of size and invasiveness from the cancers detected in women who have never used these hormones?

How does HRT use affect the efficacy of breast cancer screening?

How does HRT use affect mortality from breast cancer and other conditions?

Each of these research questions gave rise to other pieces of research. You can read summaries of the published research online at www.millionwomenstudy.org/publications.

One study published in 2016, explores whether there is a link between high blood pressure in pregnancy and later coronary heart disease and stroke. This research has been made open access so you can read the report and see how a researcher writes up their research. Either see it on the Million Women site or put this into a search engine to find the article: 'Hypertension in pregnancy and risk of coronary heart disease and stroke: A prospective study in a large UK cohort', Canoy, Dexter et al. (2016) *International Journal of Cardiology*, vol. 222, pp.1012–18.

3.5 Review literature relevant to the chosen topic

A literature review is a way of finding out what has already been written about the topic. The researchers of hypertension in pregnancy refer to their literature review in the introduction, giving references of articles they read before starting the research. You can see the full list of their background reading at the end of their published research. Usually a literature review will consider publications in the last five years unless a very important study was done earlier that is still relevant.

The Cochrane Database of Systematic Reviews (CDSR) and the Campbell Collaboration produce systematic reviews of research and are useful places to start when doing a literature review.

Command word activity

Evidence (AC 3.5)

Review the literature available on your chosen topic. You may wish to use the Cochrane Library and/or the Campbell Collaboration as a starting point for your literature review, because they summarise what research has been done on a topic. Other useful sources are professional journals. Summarise what you find and say how it relates to your chosen topic.

Remember to reference the articles to which you refer. Your will need at least three sources but more are better in a literature review.

3.6 Devise a research proposal

In the research published by Canoy *et al.* (2016), mentioned in Section 3.4 above, researchers explain why they chose this topic. High blood pressure during pregnancy is an important cause of morbidity and mortality in both mother and baby in the perinatal period, and there is not much known about the impact in middle age of having had hypertension during pregnancy. This led to the research proposal: to 'study the relationship between a history of hypertension during pregnancy and subsequent risks of coronary heart disease and ischaemic and haemorrhagic stroke in a cohort of over a million UK women'. The purpose of this research is predictive, to find out if women who have hypertension during pregnancy go on to have coronary heart disease (CHD) and stroke in middle age. The research proposal was given ethical approval by the Oxford and Anglia Multi-Centre Research Ethics Committee.

When you produce a research proposal it should include:

- details of the project design
- how you will get informed consent
- a copy of the consent form
- an explanation of how you will select participants to ensure they are a representative sample of the group you intend to study
- appropriate methods
- an explanation of how you will ensure methods are reliable. **Reliability** in research means that if the test or question was repeated it would give the same results
- an explanation of how you will ensure validity, that the research is measuring what it intended.

Key terms

Reliability in research means that if the test or question was repeated it would give the same results

Validity means that the research is measuring what it intended

External validity means findings can be applied to other areas

Internal validity concerns the relationship between variables in the study

Validity

There are two types of validity: **internal** and **external**.

Internal validity is concerned with the variables in the study. In Canoy's research the variables are hypertension during pregnancy and later coronary heart disease and stroke. If later CHD and stroke is directly attributed to having been hypertensive during pregnancy, there is high internal validity. Other variables such as differing diet and lifestyle may reduce internal validity of the study, as they cannot be controlled. It would be impossible to restrict the lifestyle and diet of participants over decades. This is one reason why mice are sometimes used in research; their diets and lifestyles can be controlled.

External validity refers to how far results can be generalised. In Canoy's study of a very large population of middle-aged women, results might be generalisable to similar groups of women with similar lifestyles, but they may not apply to women exposed to different lifestyles, for example women where life expectancy is shorter, or women exposed to famine. Population validity refers to results that can be applied to other people. Historical validity refers to findings generalisable over time, for example from one century to the next.

Consistency of data

Consistency of data means that data is likely to remain the same. An opinion may be inconsistent, varying from day to day. A person may say they like dogs one day, but if you ask the same question when they have just been bitten by one, they may change their opinion. Factual data tends to be more consistent. If you ask if they own a dog, their answer is likely to be consistent (unless of course they have got one between the timing of the first and second time of asking).

Measurement tools

Choose measurement tools to suit the type of research you are conducting.

Quantitative studies use surveys and questionnaires, usually for large numbers of participants. Qualitative studies often use interviews and case studies and usually focus on a small number of participants.

Instrument design

Instrument design can make or break a piece of research. Instrument in this case means the tools you use to carry out the research. When asking questions, avoid giving a middle option. If you ask 'Do you like animals?' and give options of 'Yes', 'Perhaps', and 'No', most people will choose 'Perhaps'.

Devising questions

Do you want open or closed questions? If you put the open question 'What do you think of animals?' you will need to consider how you categorise the answers in order to process them. Answers to closed questions are easier to process but restrict responses. Asking 'Do you like animals? Yes or no?' gives data that is easy to process but misses detailed information of which animals they like and which they do not. One way round this is to give pre-set categories such as:

Tick which animals you like:				
Dog	Cat	Horse	Mouse	Other

Bias in questions invalidates research. Avoid making assumptions. 'Which football team do you support?' is a biased question. Participants may not like football. Avoid leading questions: 'Should concerned parents restrict their child's caffeine intake?' implies that if a parent does not, they are bad parents. The unbiased question could be 'Should children have caffeine?'

Key term

Rationale in science, a rationale is a reason

3.7 Produce a rationale for chosen research methodology

You will need to explain why you chose the methods you did. Why did you choose a quantitative approach or why did you choose a qualitative approach? Why choose a questionnaire or a case study or a survey or an experiment?

Canoy *et al.* (2016) produced a quantitative study using questionnaires and existing data records. The reason they chose this methodology was the availability of a large group of participants, 1.3 million UK women aged 50 to 64 years, who filled in questionnaires, and the availability of data from NHS data sources for hospital admissions and mortality.

Activity (AC 3.2, 3.3, 3.4, 3.6, 3.7)

Choose a topic related to health and social care that interests you and that you are able to research. Discuss the topic with your tutor and then present a research project plan on an agreed topic, to include:

● a detailed research question
● a detailed research proposal
● aims of the research topic
● a rationale for chosen research methodology.

Case scenario (LO3)

Zak is a second year student at a large university. He is on the student union social committee and wants to find out if the facilities provided by the student union meet the needs of new students. Current facilities are a bar, snooker tables, and a gym. He decides to do some qualitative research and gets together a focus group of his mates from the same year. He plans to hold the focus group in a corner of the bar area and record it. He has some introductory questions: 'What do you think of the student union?' and 'What do you think of the bar?' before moving on to key questions such as 'What facilities would you like to have?' Twelve students in his year were supposed to turn up but in the end only five came, all male.

1. What can you say about the validity of this research?
2. What can you say about the reliability of it?
3. What evidence of bias can you find?
4. Suggest how Zak could improve this research.
5. Why does validity matter?
6. Why does reliability matter?

Classroom discussion (AC 3.7)

1. What are the advantages and the drawbacks of each of these research methods?
   a. Questionnaires
   b. Case studies
   c. 1 to 1 interviews
   d. Focus groups for 6 to10 people
   e. Observation (participant)
   f. Observation (non-participant)
   g. Using secondary data such as Census data
   h. Experiment
   i. Using secondary data such as historical diaries, documents and letters.
2. Work in pairs, with one person considering advantages and one person considering disadvantages of one method. Make sure you do not choose the same method that another pair has chosen.
3. Present your findings.
4. As a class decide which methods are most suitable for your research projects.

Check your understanding

1. What are the key stages of a research project?
2. Give four possible aims of research projects.
3. What is a literature review?
4. Why do we do a literature review?
5. What is the purpose of a research question?
6. What is a rationale?
7. Why do we need a rationale for research?

LO4: Understand how to carry out a research project

In this section, you will carry out a research project. Your project supervisor is likely to be your tutor. They may help you to clarify your ideas around the topic and they will require regular updates on your progress. The best way to give updates is to keep a research diary and note down what you do each day towards your research. This will also help when you come to write up your research.

4.1 Carry out a research project

The research project should:

- follow a research proposal
- select a health or social care related topic
- include a literature review of the topic and justify why you chose that topic
- identify and justify the research approach and methodology to be used
- consider ethical factors relevant to the topic and research approach
- use a data collection tool identified in the proposal to collect data
- consider the reliability of the collection method
- analyse the data and consider the validity of the findings
- arrive at a conclusion and make recommendations for further study
- be presented in report format
- include an evaluation of the research process used.

Activity (AC 4.1)

Carry out your research project and keep notes in a research diary.

Provide detailed evidence of key stages involved in carrying out your own research project using the sections outlined earlier.

Include an evaluation of your research project.

Case scenario (AC 4.1)

Zak decided to do his research again and this time focused on first year students. He distributed a questionnaire to all the first year students and invited people to join a focus group. He selected ten applicants, with equal numbers of male and female, ensuring that every faculty was represented. Someone took notes for him during the focus meeting and he had some help in collating information from the questionnaires and from the focus group. It emerged that people were put off coming into the bar because of the noise of the juke box and they really wanted somewhere to get healthy food at a reasonable price. Several people felt the environment prevented socialising.

1. What should Zak include in his report?
2. What recommendations might he make based on the findings.

Classroom discussion (AC 4.1)

What problems did you encounter in conducting your research?

1. Work in pairs then in small groups. Share your findings.
2. What problems frequently occur?
3. What problems rarely occur – perhaps only one person had these problems?

Check your understanding

1. What is the reason for keeping a research diary?
2. What are the headings used in a research report?
3. Explain what to include under each heading.
4. What is the difference between a conclusion and recommendations?
5. How do you evaluate your research project?

LO5: Understand how to analyse data in relation to the research question

Analysing the information from your research is much easier if you consider how you are going to do this when first planning the project and designing your measurement tools.

5.1 Compare and contrast different methods of analysing data

The same method can be applied to analysing data whether it is from qualitative or quantitative research.

1. Describe and summarise the data.
2. Look for possible relationships between variables.
3. Look for similarities.
4. Look for differences.
5. Summarise results and draw conclusions.

Qualitative data is usually in the form of views, opinions, likes and dislikes, and preferences, whereas quantitative data may be in the form of numbers, and scales. There are, however, overlaps, for instance, when a questionnaire has a section for comments or when an interviewer asks 'On a scale of 1 to 10, how important is X to you?'

Qualitative data is analysed in a different way to quantitative data. The content of qualitative data is analysed using a framework. There are two types of framework. One has predetermined coding based on what the researcher is looking for, whereas the other starts by looking at the raw data and then picks out recurrent words.

Using a predetermined coding framework, in the case scenario above, Zak may have chosen the word 'socialise' or 'bar'. He would then read the raw data from the focus group and pick out words that match pre-set codes in the framework. This is a deductive approach, looking for evidence to confirm or disprove a hypothesis.

An alternative way of coding is to let the topics emerge using an inductive approach. In Zak's study 'healthy food' might emerge as a recurrent idea. Had he used a pre-set framework, he might have missed this. He can then write 'healthy food' on a sheet of paper. Another recurrent idea might be 'noise'. Zak then writes this on another piece of paper. This is the 'table top' method. By noting on each paper how many times the concept was mentioned we get an idea of how important it is to the group. Codes can be grouped into themes, such as 'social environment' and 'physical environment'. Patterns emerge, for example, the noisier the environment, the less likely people are to come to the union building, or the healthier the food, the more likely they are to buy food there.

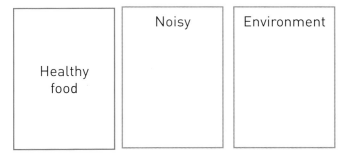

Figure 13.4 The table top method of coding qualitative data

Analysing quantitative data

Quantitative data is in the form of numbers, scales, or classifications. The variables may be categorical such as male/female, red/blue, or they may be numerical.

Category variables are counted and may be presented as percentages in a frequency table showing how often each variable occurs.

Table 13.2 Frequency table of category variables

Students from faculties	Number	%
Social sciences	2	20
Maths	1	10
Humanities	1	10
Arts	2	20
Sciences	1	10
Engineering	1	10
Medicine	2	20

Numerical variables may be presented using mean, median or mode averages as discussed earlier in the unit. A large amount of numerical data would be processed using a software package. Quantitative data enables the researcher to look for patterns and construct graphs and other views of the data. Standard deviation, which measures how far responses vary from the mean, can be calculated. All this data can be entered into a spreadsheet to make the process of analysing data easier. You can then select which graph or chart is the best to show your data.

In the following examples, graphs are used to show relationships or the absence of relationships between data. **Positive relationships** occur when two variables move in the same direction together, for example increasing fitness levels with improved health. Here the vertical axis shows distance run without getting breathless. Positive relationships may also show when variables decrease at the same time, for example decreasing mobility and decreasing fitness.

Key terms

Positive relationship variables increase or decrease together

Negative relationship one variable increases while another decreases

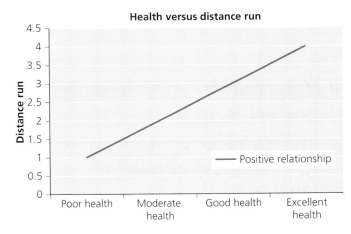

Figure 13.5 Both variables increase or decrease together in a positive relationship

Negative relationships may occur when one variable increases while another decreases; for example, Body Mass Index increases while fitness levels decrease.

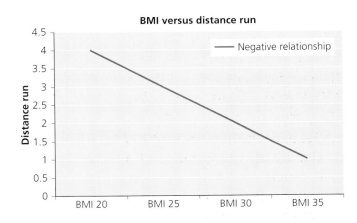

Figure 13.6 One variable increases while another decreases in a negative relationship

Command word activity

Compare and contrast (AC 5.1)

When you are analysing data, what similarities are there in the process?

How does the process of data analysis differ for quantitative and for qualitative research?

Sometimes there is no relationship at all; for example, there is no relationship between eye colour and fitness levels.

Command word activity

Analyse (AC 5.2)

Analyse the data from your research, making a note in your research diary of the methods you used.

For a reminder look back at Section 3.1 Describe the key stages in a research project, and, in particular, Section 3.7. Produce a rationale for chosen research methodology, where you produced reasons for your choice of methods.

What patterns or trends can you see in the data? Look for highest and lowest occurrences, or where a question seems ambiguous and results may not be reliable.

5.2 Analyse the data from own research

Now analyse your own research data. You may decide to use a spreadsheet to help you interpret the data patterns and relationships. Using spreadsheets can be helpful for when you later need to create bar charts, graphs and so on to present your data.

5.3 Draw conclusions on the analysis of the data

Conclusions should follow logically from your data, even if the results do not show what you expected. In the case scenario above, Zak's research brought up issues he had not considered such as the environment and healthy food, but he still had to bring them into his conclusions.

Activity (AC 5.3)

Draw conclusions from your data analysis, explaining how you came to that conclusion from the data presented. Final check, do the conclusions follow on from the data? Do any surprise you?

5.4 Make recommendations for health and social care provision

Recommendations follow on from your conclusions. In the case scenario, Zak's analysis showed there were more problems than he first realised. Noise and the masculine environment discouraged some students from using the student union. His recommendations to the student union committee were to reduce the volume of the music to a background sound, to introduce healthy and cheap food and to offer a wider variety of non-alcoholic drinks.

Activity (AC 5.4)

Make recommendations following on from your conclusions. Think about who will read the recommendations and outline your ideas clearly and simply. Are the recommendations specific, measurable, achievable, realistic and timed?

Case scenario: Kesia (AC 5.2)

Kesia has conducted a qualitative study, interviewing members of her local community on safety issues. She has the transcripts of six interviews and also the responses from twenty questionnaires to analyse. Some of the questions give numerical responses; for example, 'On a scale of 1 to 10, how safe do you feel walking from the bus stop to home in the dark?'

1. How could Kesia analyse the qualitative data?
2. How could she analyse the quantitative data?

Classroom discussion (AC 5.2)

Analysing the data is sometimes seen as the most challenging area of the research process. What errors might be introduced at this stage for both qualitative and quantitative research?

Make a list of potential errors and suggest how to avoid them.

Check your understanding

1. What are the advantages and disadvantages of a pre-set framework?
2. Which type of research produces numerical and categorical variables?
3. Give an example of a conclusion based on analysis of data.
4. Give an example of a recommendation based on a conclusion.

LO6: Understand how to present research findings

Research is only useful when it is shared. Academic research is submitted to a relevant journal and is peer reviewed by at least two other academics working in the same field. They critically read the research, checking methods for bias and inaccuracies. If feedback is positive, the research may then be accepted for publication in a prestigious journal.

Key term

Peer review research may only be published after it has been critically read and reviewed by at least two other researchers working in the same area. They will examine the methods used, data analysed and conclusions drawn to ensure the research is valid

6.1 Explain the elements of a research report

You will need to present your research report in the following format:

The title should tell the reader about the research.

Activity

Can you work out what these pieces of research are about?

Night Shift Work and Breast Cancer Incidence: Three Prospective Studies and Meta-analysis of Published Studies (http://jnci.oxfordjournals.org/content/108/12/djw169)

'Life satisfaction, ethnicity and neighbourhoods: Is there an effect of neighbourhood ethnic composition on life satisfaction?'

(http://www.sciencedirect.com/science/article/pii/S0049089X16302095)

Terms of reference: tells the reader about the scope of the work, what it covers, for example breast cancer but no other cancers. A hypothesis sets out the idea that researchers want to test. The aims are what the researcher intends to do. Is the research exploratory, predictive, descriptive or analytical?

Abstract: a one-paragraph summary of the purpose, main points, method, findings, and conclusions. It should be brief.

Introduction: this tells the reader why this research is being conducted; for example, there are suggestions that night working upsets the body clock and causes cancer. The introduction usually concludes by referring to the research question.

Literature review: an exploration and summary of what current research has to say on the topic.

Methodology: tells the reader how the research has been conducted, what methods have been used.

Results are the findings: the raw data may be included in an appendix, while the processed data is included in this section.

Discussion: this section interprets the results and also highlights any limitations in your study.

Conclusion: this final paragraph brings together the main points of the findings and answers the question 'So what?' Why are the findings important?

Recommendations: in this section draw on the conclusion to suggest a way forward. Are changes in practice required as a result of what you found? Is more research required to check if your findings apply to others?

References and bibliography: a reference list includes all the sources you used in your work, either by quoting or by paraphrasing them. A bibliography lists all the sources you read but did not quote or paraphrase.

Command word activity

Explain (AC 6.1)

You have been asked to talk to a group of people about research. They have no knowledge of the topic but are interested in knowing more.

Using at least three different sources, explain the elements of a research report.

Remember to reference your sources.

6.2 Present findings of research

Write up and present your research report using the headings given in Section 6.1.

Activity (AC 6.2)

Prepare a presentation about your research to include the main points of your research abstract. Use bullet points and present information in graphs or charts where possible. Use no more than five slides to show your audience why you did the research, how you did it, what you found, the implications of your findings and limitations of the research.

Classroom discussion

'Research is a waste of money'. (This is similar to an activity you did earlier in the unit.)

In pairs, prepare three arguments with evidence supporting this statement and three arguments against. Join another pair and share your ideas.

Your class is divided into two equal teams, A and B. One person from team A presents the case for the statement, then one person from team B presents the case against. Each speaker is given one minute. After the first speakers present their case, the floor is open to other speakers but each is limited to one minute.

A chairperson keeps time and gives each person permission to speak, ensuring both sides get equal turns. At the end of 10 minutes there is a vote on whether research is a waste of money.

Important point: has your opinion changed as a result of working through this unit?

Check your understanding

1. What is the purpose of an abstract?
2. Which section of the report tells you *why* the research was conducted?
3. Which section of the report tells you *how* the research was conducted?
4. Which section interprets the findings?
5. Which section answers the question *'So what?'*

LO7: Understand how to reflect on the research undertaken

Research is never perfect. Good researchers look back not just on what they found out, but also on how they did the research so that they can improve the process next time.

7.1 Discuss strengths and weaknesses in the research methodologies used

Look back at your research methods. Were they the best methods for what you wanted to find out? Or did you just choose them because they were convenient?

In the case scenario, Zak used questionnaires and focus groups. Would an experiment have worked? Or could data showing usage of the student union building have given him the information he wanted to find out? Did your research methods give the information you needed?

Command word activity

Discuss (AC 7.1)

Look back on your own research project and explain the strengths and weaknesses of each of the methods you used.

Use at least three sources of background reading; use them selectively and cite appropriately.

7.2 Discuss ways the research process could be improved

Look back at your research and consider how the process might be improved.

Start with the research topic: was it too big or too small?

Was your literature search relevant? Was your research question clearly defined?

Did the methods suit the research? If you wanted to know how many people smoke in your class, did you use quantitative methods such as a survey? If you wanted to know how people feel about smoking did you use qualitative methods such as interviews?

Was it easy to process data or did badly worded questions make results confusing?

Did your conclusions follow on from results? If you found that 15 out of 20 people wanted healthy food did you in fact talk about cheap food in the conclusion?

Do the recommendations follow from what you found? If results show more people want healthy food, did you recommend cheap food?

7.3 Reflect on own learning

Look back on what you have learned. Your research diary may help you to recall how you felt at different stages of the process. Doing research teaches you about three things:

1. The process of research such as research methods
2. The topic of the research
3. Yourself: your strengths and weaknesses, your attitudes, how you handle problems.

Command word activity

Discuss (AC 7.2)

Suggest three ways to improve your research. Use at least three sources of background reading; use them selectively and cite appropriately.

We have already looked at how you can reflect on the process and find ways to improve. Researching is hard work. It can be frustrating and leave you feeling disappointed when you put a lot of effort into something that is less than perfect. How you cope with the frustration, disappointment and hard work tells you about your strengths and weaknesses as an individual and links into Unit HSC CM9.

Here are some of the skills you develop through conducting research:

1. Reading skills improve. Reading around the topic for a literature search teaches you more about the topic. The jargon of research puts many people off, but by now you will be familiar with terms such as 'abstract' and 'qualitative'.
2. Communication skills improve as you write a research report, communicating complex ideas in an academic way.
3. You become an independent learner and learn how to find things out for yourself.
4. Time management and planning and organising skills improve as you plan each stage of the process and meet deadlines.

Your first piece of research is unlikely to be a masterpiece worthy of publication, but every researcher had to start somewhere. In research, as in life, we learn by doing and then by reflecting on what we have done. We make improvements each time until we become good at it. Who knows? You may be a future researcher!

Command word activity

Reflect (AC 7.3)

Reflect on your own learning during the process of planning, conducting and writing up research. Use at least three sources of background reading to help in your reflection. Use sources selectively and cite appropriately.

Case scenario

Zak listed the strengths and weaknesses of using questionnaires for his research.

Strengths	Weaknesses
Can reach a lot of people	They don't return them
Can standardise questions so everyone gets asked the same	They might be the wrong questions! Could be badly worded and confusing Misses information if they are not asked about it; don't get their suggestions
Easy to process data	

Zak was aware of the weaknesses of questionnaires and so chose to use focus groups with open questions to offset the weaknesses of questionnaires.

1. What are the strengths of using focus groups?
2. What are the weaknesses of using focus groups as a method?
3. What other methods might be used to conduct research?
4. For each method, list strengths and weaknesses.

Classroom discussion (AC 7.3)

Divide the class into four groups.

Each group finds a piece of research, identifies the methods in the research and then lists the strengths and weaknesses of the methods used.

Each group prepares a two-slide presentation to show the strengths and weaknesses in the research and suggestions for improving the research process.

Check your understanding

1. Why is it important to be aware of strengths and weaknesses of different research methodologies?
2. Why do we suggest ways to improve research?
3. What skills may be improved by doing research?

Read about it

Aveyard, H. (2014) *Doing a Literature Review in Health and Social Care: A Practical Guide*, 3rd edition. Maidenhead: Open University Press.

Bell J. and Waters S. (2014) *Doing Your Research Project: A Guide for First-Time Researchers*, 6th edition Maidenhead: Open University Press.

Charmaz, K. 'Grounded theory methods in social justice research' in Denzin, N. and Lincoln, Y. (2011) *The Sage Handbook of Qualitative Research*, Sage publications

Dickson-Swift, V., James, E.L. and Liamputtong, P. (2008) *Undertaking Sensitive Research in the Health and Social Sciences: Managing Boundaries, Emotions and Risks*, Cambridge: Cambridge University Press.

Glaser B. and Strauss A. (1967) *Discovery of Grounded Theory: Strategies for Qualitative Research*, Aldine Publishing Company.

Knies, G., Nandi, A. and Platt, L. (2016)' Life satisfaction, ethnicity and neighbourhoods: Is there an effect of neighbourhood ethnic composition on life satisfaction?', *Social Science Research*, vol. 60, pp. 110–24. Available at http://dx.doi.org/10.1016/j.ssresearch.2016.01.010, (http://www.sciencedirect.com/science/article/pii/S0049089X16302095)

Harris, T. (2015) 'Grounded theory', *Nursing Standard*, vol. 29, no. 35, pp. 32–9. Available at http://journals.rcni.com/doi/pdfplus/10.7748/ns.29.35.32.e9568

Health Inequalities, Public Health England. Available at www.noo.org.uk/NOO_about_obesity/inequalities

Canoy, Dexter *et al.* (2016) 'Hypertension in pregnancy and risk of coronary heart disease and stroke: A prospective study in a large UK cohort', *International Journal of Cardiology*, vol. 222, pp. 1012–18.

http://dx.doi.org/10.1016/j.ijcard.2016.07.170

0167-5273/© 2016 The Authors. Published by Elsevier Ireland Ltd. This is an open access article under the CC BY license (http://creativecommons.org/licenses/by/4.0/)

'IGE paper (Deception in Medical Research) V1.1 July 2009'. Available at http://www.hra.nhs.uk/documents/2013/09/ige-paper-deception-in-medical-research.pdf

'Improving mental health and emotional wellbeing support for children and young people in care'.

Available at www.scie.org.uk/children/care/mental-health

Licqurish, S. and Seibold, C. (2011) 'Applying a contemporary grounded theory methodology', *Nurse Researcher*, vol. 18, no. 4, pp. 11–16.

'Methods of data collection and analysis, Monitoring, Evaluation, Accountability and Learning (MEAL)', Open University and Save the Children. Available at www.open.edu/openlearnworks/mod/resource/view.php?id=52658

DoH (2005) *Research Governance Framework for Health and Social Care*, 2nd edition, Department of Health. Available at www.gov.uk/government/publications/research-governance-framework-for-health-and-social-care-second-edition
https://www.gov.uk/government/uploads/system/uploads/attachment_data/file/139565/dh_4122427.pdf

Research Support, University of Oxford. Available at www.admin.ox.ac.uk/researchsupport

NSPCC 'Research with children: ethics, safety and avoiding harm: What to consider when conducting research involving children'. Available at www.nspcc.org.uk/services-and-resources/impact-evidence-evaluation-child-protection/conducting-safe-and-ethical-research/

Roberts, C., Moss, B., Wass, V., Sarangi, S. and Jones, R. (2005) 'Misunderstandings: a qualitative study of primary care consultations in multilingual settings, and educational implications', *Med Educ.*, May, vol. 39, no. 5, pp. 465–75, PMID: 15842680. Available at https://www.ncbi.nlm.nih.gov/pubmed/15842680

Travis, R., Balkwill, A., Fensom, G., Appleby, P., Reeves, G., Wang, X., Roddam, A., Gathani, T., Peto, R., Green, J., Key, T. and Beral, V. (2016) *Night Shift Work and Breast Cancer Incidence: Three Prospective Studies and Meta-analysis of Published Studies*, JNCI J Natl Cancer Inst, 108 (12), djw169 doi:10.1093/jnci/djw169, first published online 6 October 2016 (9 pages)

Young, T., Fitzgibbon, W. and Silverstone, D. (2013) 'The role of the family in facilitating gang membership, criminality and exit – a report prepared for Catch22', London Metropolitan University. Available as a pdf at https://www.catch-22.org.uk/wp-content/uploads/2013/06/Catch22-Dawes-Unit-The-role-of-the-family-June-2013.pdf (full report)

Young, T., Fitzgibbon, W. and Silverstone, D. 'A question of family? Youth and gangs', *Youth Justice*, August 2014, vol.14, pp.171–85, doi:10.1177/1473225414537569. Available at http://yjj.sagepub.com/content/14/2/171.abstract

Websites

Alzheimer's Research UK
www.alzheimersresearchuk.org/oxford-researchers-ask-whether-fish-oils-aspirin-delay-dementia

Analysis and Presentation of Data. Available at www.open.edu/openlearnworks

The Campbell Collaboration
www.campbellcollaboration.org

The Cochrane Database of Systematic Reviews (CDSR)
www.cochranelibrary.com/cochrane-database-of-systematic-reviews

Data Protection Acts
https://ico.org.uk/for-organisations/guide-to-data-protection/key-definitions/

Health Research Authority
www.hra.nhs.uk

Mayor of London
www.london.gov.uk/what-we-do/mayors-office-policing-and-crime-mopac/data-and-research/crime%20/gangs-dashboard

The Million Women Study, Oxford University
www.millionwomenstudy.org

National Institute for Health and Care Excellence: Bipolar disorder
www.nice.org.uk/guidance/cg185

The National Institute for Health Research
www.nihr.ac.uk

Scientific American
www.scientificamerican.com/article/raised-hype-about-lower-blood-pressure

Unit HSC DM4: How will I be graded?

The table below shows what the learner must do to achieve each grading criterion. Learners must achieve all the criteria for a grade to be awarded (i.e. criteria D1 to D3 must be achieved to pass this unit assessment at grade D). A higher grade may not be awarded before a lower grade has been achieved in full, although component criteria of a higher grade may have been achieved.

Grade	Assessment criteria number	Assessment grading criteria	Assessment of learning / What you need to show
D1	1.1 1.2	Describe research approaches. Describe research methods.	Provide information to describe more than one: ● research approach ● research method.
D2	1.3	Explain how research approaches and methodologies are used for different purposes.	Explanation must show understanding of the use and purpose of the research approaches and research methods described for D1.
D3	3.1	Describe the key stages in a research project.	Provide information to describe key stages involved in carrying out a research project.
D4	6.1	Explain the elements of a research report.	Provide information to explain key elements of a research report.
D5		Show evidence of reading and use of sources.	There should be evidence of learners' reading or use of sources. Learners must use a minimum of two traceable references to support the discussion.
C1	3.2 3.3 3.4 3.6 3.7	Agree a research topic. Identify aims of research project. Develop a research question. Devise a research proposal. Produce a rationale for chosen research methodology.	Present a research project plan on an agreed topic, to include: ● a detailed research question ● a detailed research proposal ● aims of the research topic ● a rationale for chosen research methodology.
C2	3.5	Review literature relevant to the chosen topic.	Refer to the chosen research topic to produce a review of a range of relevant literature.
C3	2.1 2.2	Describe ethical issues to be considered when planning and carrying out research. Explain reasons for considering ethical issues when designing and carrying out research.	Information must focus on ethical issues considered when planning and carrying out research to show understanding of: ● more than one ethical issue ● a range of reasons for considering ethical issues.
C.4	2.3	Describe the role of the research ethics committee.	Understanding of the role of the research ethics committee must be shown in the description.
C.5		Show evidence of reading or use of sources with referencing relevant to the explanation or description. Good use of vocabulary and grammar.	Show evidence of reading and use of sources with referencing relevant to the explanation or description. Good use of vocabulary and grammar.
B1	4.1	Carry out a research project.	Provide detailed evidence of key stages involved in carrying out own research project.

Grade	Assessment criteria number	Assessment grading criteria	Assessment of learning / What you need to show
B2	5.1	Compare and contrast different methods of analysing data.	Provide information to consider the similarities and differences between: ● quantitative data ● qualitative data. Examples may be included to support the comparison.
B3	5.2 6.2	Analyse the data from own research. Present findings of research.	Refer to own research project to accurately present: ● analysis of data produced ● findings from research.
B4		Show evidence of reading or use of sources. Referencing supports the compare and contrast or analysis.	Use of reading or use of sources should be shown through a range of relevant referencing. Referencing supports analysis, or compare and contrast.
A1	5.3 5.4	Draw conclusions on the analysis of the data. Make recommendations for health and social care provision.	Refer to own research project to accurately discuss: a range of conclusions that can be drawn from the data analysis a range of recommendations for health and social care provision.
A2		Show evidence of wider background reading and use of sources.	Show evidence of wider background reading and use of sources: referencing supports conclusions or recommendations.
A*1	7.1 7.2 7.3	Discuss strengths and weaknesses in the research methodologies used. Discuss ways the research process could be improved. Reflect on own learning.	Information must include an appraisal of the research process to reflect on: ● benefits and limitations of the methodologies used ● ways that the research process could be improved ● own learning as a result of carrying out the research project.
A*2		Show evidence of a range of background reading or use of sources used selectively.	Learners should show the ability to consider or explore relevant issues which contribute to the discussion or reflection. An extensive range of background reading or use of sources should be used selectively and cited appropriately.

HSC DM5
Personal and Professional Development

About this unit

This unit aims to provide an introduction to personal and professional development. Professional development is about progressing and improving in the role of a health and social care practitioner. It might be about learning new skills or knowledge to undertake a more specialist role, or keeping up to date with changes in working methods or legislative requirements. Personal development is about developing your own specific skills required to achieve results. This may be different for each practitioner. Both are interlinked and essential for every career within health and social care.

Within this unit, job roles are explored along with opportunities to continue further study. You will learn how to reflect on personal development and create, review and implement a personal development plan. Finally, the need for professional development in the health and social care sector is critically evaluated. This unit will bring together many of the learning experiences within the course including any placement that you have undertaken.

LO1: Understand progression opportunities within the health and social care sector

This section explores a variety of careers within health and social care, along with a range of opportunities for further study. Some job roles require formal qualifications; all will require core skills such as communication, teamwork, problem solving, as well as English and numeracy skills.

1.1 Research job roles within health and social care provision

Health care assistant

Health care assistants work within hospital and community settings and help with the day-to-day care of individuals. They undertake a variety of tasks. In a hospital ward they may help with personal care, serving dinners or supporting individuals to eat, taking and recording observations such as temperature or blood pressure. In the community, such as a GP surgery or individuals' own homes, tasks may include carrying out health checks or taking blood samples. With extra training, some health care assistants can carry out some vaccinations or change wound dressings. Previous experience is helpful, which could include caring for a relative or doing some voluntary work in a health and social care organisation, although this is not always essential. Health care assistants need to be caring, have good communication skills, be patient and able to work both as part of a team and on their own.

Case scenario: Benjamin

Benjamin is a health care assistant in a GP's surgery. Today he is seeing three patients: Ahmed, Barbara and Carol:

1. Ahmed is having a new patient check so Benjamin will take some measurements including blood pressure and heart rate. He will weigh Ahmed and measure his height to work out his BMI.

2. Barbara needs a urine analysis so Benjamin will require her to provide a urine sample, which he will then test with a urinalysis kit and report on the results.

3. Carol is going to the surgery for her annual influenza vaccine. Benjamin will have to ensure he uses the right vaccination and be prepared for any adverse events, for example if Carol were to have a life-threatening anaphylactic reaction, by ensuing the medication and equipment to treat this are accessible.

For each patient, identify the skills that Benjamin requires to be able to do his job.

Key terms

Anaphylaxis a serious and potentially life-threatening allergic reaction

Urinalysis a screening and diagnostic tool carried out by dipping a testing stick in urine and interpreting the results

Care assistants and senior care worker

Working either within the community, or a care home, care workers support individuals with all their daily activities. This could include dressing, bathing, shopping, laundry or managing finances. Care assistants will need to be friendly and caring, respectful and be flexible to work with and support a range of individuals in different situations. Training is provided and if working in England in adult social care, all practitioners will undertake training based on standards of care. Senior care workers will do similar jobs to care assistants, but will supervise and take responsibility for the day-to-day running of the workplace. They will therefore need skills in managing people, along with a good knowledge of their workplace. Some may have specific responsibilities for particular areas, such as infection control.

Key term

Standards of care the basic level of care that should be provided to all individuals

Figure 14.1 Care assistants undertake a variety of tasks

Support worker or personal assistant

Personal assistants work under the direct supervision of the individual who requires care and are generally employed directly by them, working from the individual's own home. Personal assistants undertake a variety of skills such as personal care, domestic tasks or supporting an individual to engage in community activities. Often no formal academic qualifications are required, but practitioners will need to have the right values and skills, for example communication skills.

Social worker

A qualified social worker provides information, advice and support to help individuals and their families or groups of individuals to improve their lives. They also intervene when vulnerable adults or children need safeguarding. A social worker requires a qualification that is approved by the Health Care Professionals Council; this is generally a full-time university course, although part-time courses are available and some qualifications may be obtained through work-based learning. Social work courses are available at undergraduate and postgraduate level. Social workers are employed in a variety of settings such as the community, service users' own homes or hospitals and can be employed by different organisations including the local authority, voluntary organisations and the NHS.

Take it further

Explore the role of a social worker at: **https://www.healthcareers.nhs.uk/explore-roles/clinical-support-staff/social-worker**

Key terms

Undergraduate academic study leading to a degree, often undertaken after a learner has left secondary school

Postgraduate academic study undertaken at a higher level and after a degree has been obtained

Occupational therapists

Occupational therapists work with individuals with a range of difficulties to promote independence. The difficulties people experience may be present from birth, as a result of an accident or life stage such as older age. Some examples of measures that can be implemented to promote independence include grab rails in bathrooms or large handled cutlery to enable an individual to eat without the need for assistance. Occupational therapy requires a qualification that is approved by the Health Care Professionals Council. Individuals will require good communication skills, be able to manage a workload and be able to work independently and as part of a team.

Take it further

Explore how individuals have benefited from occupational therapy at **https://www.youtube.com/watch?v=FSpsq1Spixg&t=5s**

Outreach worker

The role of an outreach worker is to help people live independently. Although similar to other roles, an outreach worker will tend to focus on support and enabling rather than personal care. They are often involved in providing advice and guidance and will work in teams with a range of other professionals such as drug action groups, youth offending services and local authorities.

Outreach workers will need to be able to work on their own as well as part of a team and be able to problem solve and manage their own time. Some positions will require a Level 3 qualification, whereas for others no formal qualifications are required.

Activities worker / co-ordinator

An activities worker plans and puts into place activities to meet the needs of the individuals they are looking after. This includes groups of individuals such as older people, carers or people with learning disabilities and can be on an individual basis, such as catering for an individual and their hobbies, or a group event. The activities may take place within the individual's own home or in the community. Activities workers will need to have experience of working with the vulnerable individuals they are preparing activities for. Skills they may require include being able to communicate effectively, and writing a risk assessment for an activity.

Activity

Identify three activities that older people may enjoy and for one of these explain the benefits of undertaking that activity.

Advocate

An advocate is someone who offers support by speaking on behalf of someone to ensure their views, needs and preferences are heard. This may be for a variety of reasons such as someone with learning disabilities who may not be able to communicate effectively or persuasively. Their role is to help the individual to make choices and have control over their lives, ensuring that there are equal opportunities and inclusion. They do not replace the role of other members of the multi-disciplinary team, such as social workers.

Take it further

Read about advocacy in Unit HSC CM4, Section 2.6.

Admin/office

Administration or office staff will undertake very little one-to-one work with individuals who are being looked after. Staff may work in different departments, for example **human resources** or **payroll**. The different roles that these workers will have such as sending letters to patients, contacting previous employers for references for new staff, and processing pay claims. Each role will require different qualifications and experience.

Activity

Outline three skills needed for working in human resources and three for working in payroll.

 ### Key terms

Human resources the part of an organisation that oversees areas of work connected to the effective use of staff

Payroll the part of the organisation that manages payment of employees' wages and any additional benefits, along with contributing to financial management

Ancillary staff

Ancillary staff are additional support staff who will not have a specific hands-on role, but will have a vital role in helping an organisation to run. For example, some organisations will require chefs, gardeners or maintenance professionals. The skills and entry requirements for these roles will be different depending upon the role.

Activity

Identify five ancillary staff required in a hospital and outline the skills required to complete the role.

Nurse

Nurses work in a range of settings including the community as well as hospitals. Nurses will work in one of four specialist areas: adult, children's, mental health and learning disabilities. Adult nurses work with patients that are aged over 18 years. They might further become a specialist in a specific area such as accident and emergency or cancer care.

Children's nurses work with children and young people up to the age of 19 years. Children often react differently to illnesses than adults and so having this specialist knowledge is extremely useful.

Nurses who work in mental health settings work with individuals with mental illness. This may be either in the community or in hospitals, planning, delivering care, and monitoring and evaluating its effectiveness.

Nurses who work with people with learning disabilities will do so in a range of settings. They may have specialist training in one area such as working with people with challenging behaviour or sensory processing disorder, where an individual has difficulties in interpreting the messages from the senses (such as touch, hearing or sight).

To become a nurse, a person will need to meet any formal entry requirements, have excellent communication skills, along with being compassionate and caring. Nurses will need to complete a course that is approved by the Nursing and Midwifery Council.

Figure 14.2 Nurses work in a variety of settings

> ### Command word activity
>
> #### Outline
>
> Numeracy and literacy skills are essential within nursing. Outline the reasons why a nurse requires each of these skills.

> ### Command word activity
>
> #### Evidence (AC 1.1)
>
> You have been asked to contribute to health and social care provision in the local community. In the complex there will be provision for health and social care for all ages. It includes a children's centre, a general practice surgery, a dentist and a day centre for adults with learning disabilities.
>
> Create a recruitment page for the website of the care village. Include an outline of one of the services provided and information on two different job opportunities for practitioners within each organisation. Present the job opportunity as a 'day in the life' with information on the role, salary, examples of day-to-day activities the practitioner may undertake, who they make work with and career prospects within the organisation. You could work in groups to cover all the services on offer in the community.
>
> Use a minimum of two sources for your research. Ensure you keep accurate details of your references.

1.2 Research opportunities for further study in relation to the health and social care sector

All job roles within health and social care will require a period of further study. This may be before starting the job, although some roles will offer training alongside working. There is a variety of opportunities available for practitioners to study, face to face or online.

Qualification requirements

Qualifications are obtained at the end of a successful period of study. Each job role will have specific qualification requirements, such as a requirement for a degree in social work, or maths and English GCSE grade C or equivalent. Certain job roles require a degree that enables registration with a professional body; for example, to be a paramedic will require a qualification that enables registration with the Health Care Professionals Council.

Qualifications have different levels of difficulty. Guidance about the level of difficulty can generally be determined by a numerical level attached to the qualification. A qualification at Level 2, for example, is a GCSE grade A*, A, B or C; a Level 5 qualification is a foundation degree from a university.

Qualifications at the same level will often specialise in certain areas or in proportionate depth. A Level 3 Certificate and a Level 3 Diploma are both Level 3 qualifications, but the subject will be studied in more detail and for longer in the Level 3 Diploma. Level 4 and above are university qualifications or post-qualifying development.

Courses

A course describes the study that a practitioner may undertake. Courses are offered in a range of subjects which are related to the practitioner's profession and may be either accredited or non-accredited. Courses that are accredited by an awarding body will include an assessment and lead to a qualification, such as a degree in nursing and registration with the NMC. Non-accredited courses are often more informal and a certificate of attendance is awarded upon completion; such courses include study days or workshops, which are often taken as part of the practitioner's work time. Courses may be funded by the employer and taken within work time, or the practitioner may fund them for themselves. Some courses may be free.

Further education (FE)

FE colleges offer a range of courses at different levels. The courses are generally vocational-based ones, for example Health and Social Care, along with maths, English and other core skills. Some FE colleges will work in partnership with universities and deliver university courses. Many will deliver work-based qualifications such as

apprenticeships. Apprenticeships can be offered at different qualification levels and in a wide range of careers. Within health and social care, apprenticeships can include a range of roles such as a health care assistant, administration and support staff or a specialist role in a range of settings such as nursing homes, pharmacies and health centres.

Key term

Apprenticeships a learner will gain a qualification through a combination of study and practical training in a workplace

Take it further

Find out about apprenticeships at **https://www. gov.uk/apprenticeships-guide.**

Higher education (HE)

Higher education establishments, usually universities, generally run diploma, undergraduate and postgraduate courses. Many also run CPD courses. Many run courses linked to health and social care, for example nursing, social work or occupational therapy. Study can be completed full time, although there are also many examples of part-time and distance-learning courses. Some are run alongside learners working.

Figure 14.3 A variety of courses provide study opportunities for staff

Job descriptions

A job description provides information about the role that a practitioner will be expected to perform within the workplace. Alongside skills and qualities, it will list the competencies that a potential practitioner should be able to demonstrate, as well as any formal qualifications or training required. These may be broken down into essential and desirable. Essential criteria are those which are definitely required for the job, whereas desirable will be useful but are not a requirement. Examining job descriptions of jobs that someone would like to do can provide useful information to identify skills gaps. This, in turn, can lead to understanding what someone needs to do in order to secure that job.

Take it further

For further detail on CPD see HSC CM9, Section 1.2.

Training

Many jobs will offer training as part of the development of the employee. It may be an initial part of training when the employee commences work or training for a new aspect of a job, for example where a new computer system is implemented or a new way of working. These can be run by the organisation that the practitioner works for, specific companies or external agencies.

Continuing professional development (CPD)

CPD is a term used to describe the activities undertaken by professionals to develop or update their skills and knowledge. All jobs within health and social care will require continual training known as CPD – continuing professional development. Many health and social care practitioners that are on a professional register are required to undertake a minimum number of hours to maintain their current practice. This is important to ensure that their skills are developed to reflect current best practice in terms of new knowledge and new techniques.

Take it further

For further detail on CPD see HSC CM9, Section 1.2.

Activity

Identify two jobs that require registration with a professional body. For each one, identify the number of hours and type of CPD required each year to remain on the professional register.

 Check your understanding

1. Identify two jobs that do not require a university degree.
2. Identify two jobs that require a university degree.
3. Compare the role of an occupational therapist and a nurse.
4. Describe three sources of further study for furthering knowledge.
5. Explain the importance of CPD.

It can ensure that the public have confidence in the profession, as they know that practitioners are maintaining their skill base. It can also help practitioners to advance in their career or undertake a specialist role.

LO2: Understand how to reflect on own personal development

2.1 Produce a learning journal

A learning journal is a collection of evidence that demonstrates learning and development across a period of time, normally to accompany a period of study or placement experience. The learning journal will be personal to each practitioner or learner and provides an opportunity to reflect upon learning experiences, reviewing knowledge obtained and skills developed either through practical or theoretical learning. Reflection is a process by which the practitioner explores an experience they may have had, and analyses what has occurred using theories to identify learning and ways to improve their own work in the future. It can provide a source of the next steps that a practitioner may take to further develop their knowledge and improve their skills.

> **Take it further**
>
> For more information on reflective practice see Unit HSC CM9, Section 2.2.

Review of knowledge

Knowledge reviews will summarise the things that have been learned. For example, each module undertaken on a course can be summarised with evidence of what the learner has achieved, or what content has been covered through class notes and assignments. Knowledge can also be recorded in journals or notes made on extra information that has been gained after reading about a topic. Once evidence of knowledge has been gathered, this should provide information on what has been learned so far and which resources have been useful. Reviewing knowledge will enable reflection, for example identifying further learning needs.

Understanding and skills

Information could be included on the learner's understanding and skills gained by assessment feedback and a unit achievement log. Throughout this course and placement a number of skills may have been developed. Evidence of using skills such as hand washing and PPE from Unit HSC CM5 could include observation sheets or feedback from placement experiences. Reflection could then take place on the skill and any further development required, for example reading comments to identify which elements of a skill need improvement and then planning how these may be improved.

> **Activity**
>
> Identify four areas of knowledge or skills developed so far. Describe what has been learned so far, and then explain how this can be further developed and what actions you could take to achieve this

Individual learning plans (ILP)

An ILP is a document that provides an opportunity to identify current strengths and areas that need further development. It allows the learner, along with their tutors, supervisors or mentors, to create a personal plan of how to develop skills, such as by setting goals, along with detailing support available to help achieve these goals. This document should be reviewed at regular intervals to ensure that goals remain realistic and achievable, along with any adjustments or extra support that may be required.

Placement progress reports

These reports could be produced by the placement or visits from a placement officer or tutor. At the start of a placement, it is a good idea to detail objectives that should be achieved during that placement. This will help to focus learning goals and also provide a benchmark to review progress. Placement progress reports will detail areas of strength on placement, and areas to develop. If more than one visit or review has occurred in a placement then analysis and reflection on skills and learning developed during that placement itself could be included.

Volunteering / other employment

Volunteering or other employment in any workplace can enhance the learning process. Within these roles a learner may develop a number of skills that can be applied to future working goals. Some examples include time management, prioritisation and communication skills. Volunteering can also prove invaluable in gaining experience and knowledge of what would be required to enter that job role.

> **Activity**
>
> Consider any part-time job or volunteering experience that you have had in any sector (for example, sales assistant, waiter), or if you have not had any work experiences, think of a job role that you know something about or would like to try. Consider a possible career you may like to do and outline skills that you have obtained that can be transferred to your chosen role.

Feedback

Feedback can be obtained from a number of different sources such as personal tutors, teachers, mentors (both academic or workplace) or placement staff. Feedback can be written or oral, such as a report or skills observation, or a conversation at the end of your working day. Feedback is useful to help identify areas of strength and areas that need development. Listening to and taking in feedback about your coursework can also improve your skills; for example, discussing the structure of an assignment might help to change an approach to writing and improve writing style. Feedback should also contain areas of good practice which can help to identify progress towards goals and help to continue in the right direction.

Activity

Obtain some feedback on an assignment or from placement experience. Identify two comments on what you are doing well now, and two comments that will help you improve in the future.

Development opportunities undertaken

Opportunities to improve your skills and knowledge can occur both within and outside a workplace. There may be informal opportunities, such as developing communication skills when looking after relatives, or formal opportunities, for example taking the lead on a task or extra responsibilities such as setting up an activity. Each opportunity can be examined before, during or after it has occurred to identify any skills developed. There may be an overlap between different development opportunities. For example, interpersonal skills can be developed from talking to friends, relatives, workplace and placement settings, but these skills can also reinforce learning.

Personal experiences

Personal experiences will be unique to each person. Something that is significant for one person may be less so for someone else. It can be useful to analyse that experience to find out what made it significant, consider any thoughts and feelings at the time, what has been learned from it and include this in a reflective diary. Personal experiences can be gained from different settings such as school, placement, a part-time job, friendships, or home and family life.

Application of knowledge to practice and practice to knowledge

Knowledge that is learned in classroom situations can be applied to practice, and practice in turn can lead to the development of knowledge. For example, using the principles of infection control in HSC CM5 while on placement may further develop knowledge of how to break the infection cycle by practising the steps of hand washing and decontamination. Discussion with individuals about the effects of life events in HSC CM2 may lead to further knowledge and understanding of the impact of these events.

Professional practice skills

Skills such as hand washing and the use of personal protective equipment are essential in health and social care. Using these skills regularly and practising them repeatedly can improve the skills and therefore the practitioner will become better at doing them.

Activity

Make a list of skills developed over the course. Complete a self-assessment on whether these can be performed competently or if further development is required. How can these skills be further developed?

Link to reflective models

Reflective practice is a process where a health and social care practitioner stops and thinks about how they are carrying out their job, and then uses theory to help understand what has occurred. There are different models which can be used to reflect on learning and these were discussed in HSC CM9 (LO5). The practitioner will find it helpful to use these tools in order to identify what has occurred, understand this and plan areas for improvement. They are essential tools for learning for many health and social care professionals.

Take it further

Reflective practice was covered in detail in HSC CM9, page 200.

Case scenario

Read this extract from Sian's placement diary.

Today was a really difficult day in placement. One of the individuals in my placement who has dementia threw a cup of tea and this really upset another resident. I found this difficult as I wasn't expecting the resident to do that. It does not normally happen. I felt that I did not know what to do and was glad that other members of staff were around. I discussed this with a member of staff who talked about how behaviour like this is a form of communication and it could just be that the tea was not right, wasn't what was wanted, or that there might have been another factor, such as pain. In future, I am going to try to remember that something like this could be a way of communicating and research alternative methods of communication that can be used. I am also going to do some further reading on challenging behaviour so I can understand this better.

1. What was the incident that Sian was reflecting on?
2. Using a model of reflective practice such as Gibbs, identify the parts of Sian's reflection that link to the reflective model.
3. Evaluate how reflective practice can help Sian to improve her knowledge and skills.
4. Describe how her reflection technique can be improved.

Activity (AC 2.1)

Compile a learning journal with evidence obtained from placements and your course. You could include some of the following:

1. Specific areas of learning, such as considering each unit studied so far and what has been learned
2. Feedback from tutors or members of staff and action you have taken since to improve
3. A time in placement where you have used knowledge from your course to help you understand a situation or act in a situation
4. A time in your study where you have used knowledge from your placement to help you understand your work.

Check your understanding

1. What is a learning journal?
2. Name two job roles that require evidence of CPD.
3. What is the importance of CPD?
4. Outline three pieces of evidence that can be used within a learning journal.
5. Describe the role of reflective practice within health and social care.

LO3: Understand how to create, implement and review own personal development plan

A personal development plan is specific to a learner and seeks to develop personal and professional skills. Personal skills relate to each practitioner individually, such as leadership skills or behaviours. Professional skills are more generic skills that relate entirely to a job, such as health and safety training; however, there is overlap between the two areas. There are three stages to a development plan:

1. Planning
2. Implementing
3. Evaluating.

There are also a range of factors that need to be considered prior to planning. A personal development plan should focus on a practitioner's own need for development. A SWOT analysis is useful to facilitate this. By identifying their strengths, identifying areas for improvement (weaknesses), opportunities to develop, and threats that may stop this from occurring, a practitioner's needs can be identified and a plan of action created.

Key term

SWOT analysis exploring strengths, weaknesses, opportunities and threat.

Activity

Philip is a children's nurse and wants to move up to a higher nursing position. He has five years of experience in nursing. He has excellent communication skills and is respected by the other staff on his ward. He has limited management experience, but is thinking of applying to a development programme run by his employer, which aims to train staff to move into higher roles. He is a bit worried though as he has a newborn baby so does not have a lot of time. The ward is short staffed to so he is concerned about being able to have time off.

1. Create a SWOT analysis for Philip.
2. Evaluate the usefulness of a SWOT analysis for Phillip.

3.1 Explain factors to consider when planning for personal development

Availability and access

Any goals set for a development plan must be achievable, with consideration given to the method of achieving the target. For example, if a chosen program of study is opted for, then the staff member must be available when the course is delivered or have access to the internet if an online option is chosen. If, as part of the development, a professional discussion or shadowing another member of staff is chosen, this must be feasible for both members of staff. Some personal development plans may require the availability of a combination of factors. For example, if a qualified social worker wishes to complete a course to enable them to assess those studying to be social workers, first they must complete a university qualification, and second they must be able to supervise learners in practice. If the social worker does not have access to both of these components, then they would not be able to complete the course.

The needs of learners and organisations

Choices of training and development can be influenced by the needs of either a learner or the organisation. Although someone may undertake CPD or extra training outside of work, any which is provided and supported by the organisation would need to be relevant to a person's job and contribute to effective running of the service.

At each practitioner level, there may be a skill that someone needs to improve or learn in order to be able to carry out their role effectively or to enable progression into a new role, for example improving leadership qualities or writing care plans. An organisation will consider the training needs of their staff and the short and long-term plans for the organisation before agreeing to fund or support CPD. Needs-based training and development at an organisational level, for example, would be introduced if a new system or policy was being implemented and all staff would require that training.

Cost

Cost is an important consideration. Many courses, especially at university level can be expensive and both the learner and the organisation need to consider the costs and other factors before committing to these. Is the course at an appropriate level? Is there time in the workplace and in the learner's personal life? Are the skills/knowledge they will acquire going to be of benefit, and to whom? It is not just the costs of courses that need to be considered; there will be additional costs to an organisation by covering for the member of staff to attend the course, and for the practitioner themselves who may need to buy books or other materials.

Frequency

Some opportunities for development, such as training courses, may appear infrequently and therefore if not undertaken as a priority, the opportunity may be lost. As part of workplace requirements in policies and procedures, some training aims to ensure that a skill or knowledge is updated annually, such as basic life support or manual handling. Therefore, if a member of staff requires up-to-date training in a specific skill it is important that this takes place, even if there are practical problems to be overcome.

Impact, context, relevance and application

There is a wealth of available courses and development opportunities for health and social care practitioners, along with opportunities to develop skills in the workplace. When choosing opportunities, context and relevance are important. For example, a children's nurse who studies for a Diploma in Working with People with Dementia, may find the course highly interesting and relevant to society but it may have less impact upon their day-to-day work than other courses. It is less likely that the nurse would be able to demonstrate to their employer the value of the knowledge they have acquired. How would they use this knowledge when working with children?

Some courses can be delivered to many people at once, which will increase their impact on an organisation, as these practitioners will then be able to apply and implement knowledge into practice more quickly. Other courses that are more specialist and time-consuming will only be delivered to a small number of practitioners at a time, such as a three-day first aid course, so while they are useful to the practitioner, their impact across the organisation is more limited.

If many practitioners have the same goal, one person can obtain the information and then disseminate this to others. For example, a practitioner who attends a course on using a new document to write patient notes in a hospital can then train everyone in their ward so that all practitioners in that department receive the information.

Training might also take place after a serious incident, such as a serious case review, or if an organisation has noticed trends in a particular type of injury, such as a high number of staff having needlestick injuries. By observing the needs and context of the organisation, the training will become more relevant and valuable.

The benefits of personal and professional development are apparent not only for the people acquiring the skills and learning, or the organisation they work for. Applying the learning from CPD in practice will benefit individuals: the patients and service users.

Accreditation

For learners wishing to train to become a health and social care practitioner that is regulated, such as midwifes, paramedics or occupational therapists, the course of study must be approved by the relevant professional body. Post-qualifying specialist roles, such as a mentor who has a role in assessing learners in the workplace, also require an approved course of study. Practitioners working with professional registration need to ensure that courses undertaken are approved by the relevant professional body.

Key term

Mentor a health and social care practitioner such as a nurse who undertakes a role in practice to guide and develop the skills of learners

Command word activity

Explain (AC 3.1)

Choose a job role in health and social care. Identify two courses that practitioners can take after qualifying that require accreditation with a professional body. Identify and explain two or more factors they would need to take into account when deciding whether to undertake this further training.

Classroom discussion (AC 1.3)

Why is it important that degree programs are approved by the professional body that regulates that profession?

3.2 Develop a curriculum vitae

A CV (or résumé) is a document that details personal and professional experiences including qualifications, previous employment, skills and interests. It is useful for an employer as it provides a summary of the professional, but it is also useful in providing guidance about what skills need to be developed. For the learner, a CV is useful for comparing against job descriptions of desired jobs to identify the skills, qualities and qualifications they have already achieved and which ones are still required. They may then formulate a plan of action to fill those skills gaps so that a similar job can be applied for in the future.

It is important that the layout of a CV is clear and logical. Ideally, it should fit on to one page if you have only recently started working (for example, if still in education or have just left). Once a person has had a variety of experiences and jobs, then a CV might need to be two pages long. Sometimes a job advertisement might even specify the length of CV they wish to receive from applicants. The CV should look appealing to read; headings, line breaks or bullet points can assist with this. The typeface is important and conventional typefaces such as Arial that are easy to read are usually the most acceptable.

Most CVs begin with personal details and an opening statement, then move on to detail work qualifications, educational background and work experience, although these can be presented with work experience first. A CV can finish with personal interests and hobbies to give an indication of personality. Make sure the CV is carefully checked for spelling errors. Common errors occur in the spelling of 'Personal', 'Curriculum' and 'Vitae'. You will find it helpful if another person reads through it for you to identify any errors or missing information.

Activity

Identify how Daniel Green's CV can be improved

Curiculuam Vitae

Daniel Green

yumchoccy@email.com

Personal Statement

I work hard and would like job in care home.

Education

8 GCSEs A*-C including English and Maths

2 A-Levels

Work

Burger Place - clean tables

Interests

Play football.

Table 14.1 What information is given on a CV?

Section	What to include
Personal details	Name, address, phone number and email Ensure email addresses are professional and obtain a new one if not. For example 'unicorns are real' or 'i hate work' are not going to create a good impression! Unless a requirement of a profession, such as acting, a photograph is not required
Personal statement	Not always required to be included, but should be powerful and brief
Education and qualifications	Present in reverse qualification order so the most recent is first. Ensure that grades are relevant to the job; for example, maths and English are listed. Do not be tempted to lie or inflate a grade on a CV as these will be checked by the employer Specific modules that are relevant to the job could be included, for example Infection Control or Communication if applying for a job as a health care assistant
Work experience	Try to relate the skills obtained in work experience to the position that is being applied for. Working in a busy restaurant will require teamwork, working under pressure, adhering to food hygiene policies and excellent communication skills This should be written with the most recent job role first Remember that it need not be only paid employment – volunteer work is also relevant Specific skills obtained such as IT skills should also be detailed
Interests	This should be fairly short and professional; for example, do not put I go out every Saturday night until 4 a.m. Avoid including too many solitary activities such as watching TV. Any interests that are relevant to the job and can provide examples of skills should be included; for example, being a team captain of a sports club demonstrates leadership skills

Activity (AC 3.2)

Begin to collate evidence to create a CV. Use the table given below to help you organise and analyse the skills that you already have. Think about all aspects of the role such as: attendance; any communications and interaction with members of the public, whether this is in person, on the phone or electronic; time management; as well as knowledge that you have obtained. Do you handle money? Or have particular responsibilities? Consider any feedback you have received, such as reports or meetings with managers, to help you.

Qualifications obtained	Skills and knowledge gained
Study and attendance at School / College	(e.g. time management to submit coursework, attendance)
Part-time job	
Voluntary work	
Informal work (e.g. babysitting)	
Placements through course	

3.3 Create own personal development plan

A personal development plan is devised to set goals and monitor progress against them to develop personal or professional skills, reviewing and evaluating. Although some skills that need to be developed may be the same as someone else's, the plan of how this is going to be achieved, along with reasons for choosing that area of development are likely to be different.

Evidenced based planning is about applying any research available to planning decisions about training. Organisations may observe trends around changes in population or health needs and train staff to work with these population groups. Organisations may also look for evidence about the benefits of the training; for example, if a way of working or new technique is seen to be beneficial, then they may train staff in a particular way.

Key term

Evidenced based planning using research and evidence available to plan a decision

Learning needs and career aspirations

A plan may reflect learning needs or career aspirations – things that a person wants to achieve in the future. Learning needs can be identified from completed activities, for example an assignment with feedback given that highlights areas for improvement, such as sentence structure or referencing. It can be a new skill that a practitioner requires in order to do their current job: a new way of working, for example writing a care plan in a new format, or using a new piece of equipment like an inhaler to facilitate teaching patients with asthma on how to use it. A personal development plan may also be linked to a career aspiration, for example becoming a specialist social worker, and then identify what steps are required in order to complete that goal. Sources of support available to help implement relevant training should be included within the plan.

SMART goal setting

A personal development plan must contain goals to be achieved that relate to the overall aim of the plan. Goals set must be SMART: Specific, Measurable, Attainable or Achievable, Realistic and Relevant, Timely/Time-bound.

Specific: The goal should be defined with whom the goal is for, what is going to be accomplished, it should include the reasons for the goal and who may be involved.

Measurable: How will it be known that the goal has been achieved?

Attainable: The goal should be possible within the time frame and resources available.

Realistic: The goal should be worthwhile and right for the situation.

Time-bound: There must be a date when the goal is going to be achieved.

Activity

Describe why this goal is not SMART. Rewrite it to create a SMART target.

I am going to do all my unit assignments by tomorrow morning.

Within a personal development plan it is good to have short-, medium- and long-term targets. Short-term goals may be goals that can be achieved within a month, medium-term within three months or one academic term, and long-term within a year or end of the academic year. The goals set should reflect the length of time that is required to achieve them. The goals may often interlink together. For example, Table 14.2.

Table 14.2 Short-, medium- and long-term goals

Goal length	Example of goal
Short term	Research on the internet to identify ten universities that offer adult nursing and write these in a table with **UCAS tariff points** required: within one month
Medium term	Book and visit three universities from the list on an open day and write down initial thoughts about each: within six months
Long term	Choose one preferred university for nursing and enter this on to the entry form: within twelve months

 Key term

UCAS tariff points are awarded for type and grade of qualifications and used when an offer is made for a university place

Activity (AC 3.3)

Begin to create a plan by considering a goal that you may have, such as a particular career or a skill that you want to develop. Now consider various smaller targets that will help you to achieve this goal.

Look at these targets and see if they meet the SMART criteria; for example, saying 'I will learn British Sign Language by the end of the year' would not be SMART, as this skill will take time to learn. Saying 'I will learn ten signs by the end of the academic year' may be more realistic.

To ensure the targets are SMART, make sure you have considered how this is going to be achieved and that you are able to access resources that will support you in your plan.

3.4 Implement own personal development plan

Implementing your own personal development plan involves putting the plan into action. The plan and agreed actions of the plan should be followed. If you find that the plan has not been realistic or achievable, then you may need to evaluate the plan or develop a new one.

A practitioner may have a number of goals that are short, medium and long term; but it is important not to do these one after the other, if they are intended to run concurrently, as they will not be achieved within the required time frame. For example consider this plan:

1. Short-term goal: identify and start at a new placement in one month
2. Medium-term goal: submit my coursework in four months
3. Long-term goal: submit reflective diary for assessment in nine months by writing a reflective entry after every attendance at placement.

To complete and meet the reflective diary submission, regular entries need to be made. If a learner started this only after the medium-term goal had been achieved, then it would be difficult to remember what had occurred previously in placements.

Activity (AC 3.3)

Julie is a health and social care learner on placement with individuals with learning disabilities. Three of the individuals use Makaton to communicate. Create a plan for her with one SMART short-term goal, one SMART medium-term goal and one SMART long-term goal. Include other people who may be able to help her to understand how she will know she has achieved her goals.

Keeping a written record, for instance a reflective diary, helps with learning and monitoring development. Collecting other evidence, such as certificates of attendance on a course, can help to prove skills and knowledge have been acquired. The plan should be updated to show progress against targets set and any amendments that have been made.

Activity

For the example above in Table 14.2, identify two types of evidence that could be obtained to prove that each goal has been implemented

3.5 Review own personal development plan

Your personal development plan should be reviewed regularly. This is to ensure that goals are being achieved and the plan can be amended if required. Regular reviews can also help with motivation as practitioners will feel they are making progress towards their long-term goals. This review can take place with a tutor or line manager or informally by the practitioner themselves.

Outcomes are the things that you've said you will achieve in your personal development plan. These should be evaluated at the end of a goal to determine the abilities and skills that have been developed and achieved.

When evaluating outcomes:

1. You should seek feedback from colleagues or line managers in the workplace
2. You can also seek feedback from tutors or organisers when achieving a qualification, or when attending a training event, by collating evidence or feedback on how you have performed in the training.
3. Make sure you reflect upon the outcomes you've achieved, how you have achieved them, the benefits of this to yourself and the organisation, what went well and what did not go so well.
4. Consider any next steps or new goals to be achieved, and add these to your plan. Identify which of these are the most important and which ones you should attempt to achieve next.

Check your understanding

1. What does SMART stand for?
2. Define short-, medium- and long-term target.
3. Identify three types of evidence that could demonstrate progress against a target.
4. Outline the importance of regular reviews of targets.
5. Explain the importance of evaluation of a personal development plan.

LO4: Understand the need for continuing professional development in the health and social care sector

4.1 Critically evaluate the need for continuing professional development in the health and social care sector

Continuing professional development is an essential element within all health and social care careers. Many practitioners have to ensure they keep a record of their CPD and ensure that this is a mix of activity relating to current or future practice, as well as those that have contributed to service provision and benefited individuals in care. Research is constantly being undertaken to evaluate practice and identify needs.

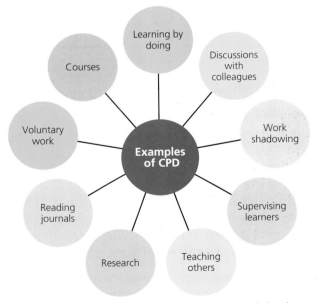

Figure 14.4 Examples of continuing professional development

Up-to-date knowledge and practice

The world of health and social care is constantly changing and evolving. For example, now many women who give birth with no complications are discharged with 24 hours, whereas previously they were often kept in hospital for a number of days. Changes with new medication and ways of working are seeing a use of technology for monitoring the health status of individuals, or prompting individuals with tasks such as taking medication, or helping to promote health such as exercising or quitting smoking. Changes are made when new evidence is available on how to carry out tasks and best practice. CPD should aim to improve the quality of work. A pre-registration course for a nurse, social worker and OT lasts for three years. If someone qualifies at 21 years then they have at least 35 years of working life, and knowledge and practice is not going to remain static. Learning does not stop when you finish school, college or university. There are opportunities, both formal and informal, to continue learning and developing skills. As well as keeping up with changes in the sector, lifelong learning provides opportunities for practitioners to specialise in areas such as working with individuals with dementia or infectious diseases.

Key term

Lifelong learning the formal and informal learning opportunities that occur throughout an individual's life to improve knowledge, skills and practice

Continuous improvements in provision and outcomes

The way in which health and social care provision is delivered can change so that care is continually improved for individuals. This can be at a national service delivery system, or local services that are set up in response to concerns. For example, walk-in centres to treat minor injuries were set up as a pilot project in the year 2000. Now there are many of these centres all across the country.

Immunisation programmes are another example of changing provision – changes to the Routine Immunisation Schedule are made regularly as new evidence emerges of immunity and disease patterns in the general population.

Health and social care practitioners need to ensure that their knowledge is up to date and the best care is administered to individuals to ensure decreases in morbidity. However, other factors can influence health and social care provision such as finance and resources available. CPD following incidents or serious case reviews can improve outcomes.

Key term

Morbidity a term used to describe the incidence of diseases in population groups

Activity

In placement or through discussion with a member of the health and social care staff, identify changes that have occurred throughout their career.

Reflective practice

Reflective practice can identify areas where improvements in knowledge and practice are required and can directly inform the chosen CPD. The critical analysis section of reflection is particularly helpful, as by focusing thoughts on existing knowledge and developing new ideas a plan for action can result. However, although useful it does not mean that if someone finds reflective practice difficult, they cannot identify how to improve or be aware of what they need to improve in practice. Reflective practice aims to identify new ways of working or exploring how a situation could have been handled differently. It is unlikely that the same situations would be replicated, so it can be difficult to evaluate the effectiveness of any learning.

Take it further

Information on reflective practice and how it can support the professional development of the health and social care practitioner can be found in HSC CM9, Section 2.2.

Regulatory requirements

As discussed in Section 1.2, CPD is for many professionals a regulatory requirement. Compliance will generally be monitored by the professional who will select individuals from the register of practitioners and request their portfolios to review. Some health and social care professionals will also require a line manager to countersign aspects of their portfolio, and evidence a certain number of hours in clinical practice. As part of the regulatory requirement, adherence to a code of practice will have to be demonstrated and information provided to show that the practitioner is upholding the values of their profession and the individuals in their care. Although there is a danger that some health and social care practitioners view CPD as a means to ensure they maintain the requirements of the registration, CPD has many beneficial aspects and should not be just a tick-box exercise.

CPD is essential to ensure the safe and effective delivery of health and social care. It benefits all staff that work in the sector. Factors that influence the amount of training being implemented into clinical practice include time, finance, resources and some reluctance to change practice, as staff may feel the older way has worked and therefore does not need changing, or they may find it difficult to learn a new skill. However, overall it helps to ensure that a health and social care workforce is able to meet the needs of the staff that work in it, and the individuals they care for.

Command word activity

Evaluate (AC 4.1)

Create a leaflet which explains the importance of CPD for an individual practitioner who is reluctant to change their way of working, Make your leaflet persuasive by using quotes and statistics in your explanation. Cover these points:

1. The need for up-to-date knowledge and practice (explain why this is important and give examples)
2. Continuous improvements in provision outcomes (include how the practitioner can contribute to these)
3. Reflective practice (explain why this is important and how reflective practice and CPD are linked)
4. Regulatory requirements (include examples from specific regulatory bodies such as the NMC).

Take it further

Research a profession such as mental health nursing. Collate evidence to include in your learning journal of different specialist areas and CPD that would be required to undertake that role.

You could look at universities, or organisations that relate to the professional bodies. You could also look at job descriptions of specialist roles to identify the additional skills a practitioner may need to enable them to be successful in that job.

Refer to a wide range of reading material and sources. Use the most relevant ones to back up your points. Ensure that you cite each reference accurately and correctly.

✔ Check your understanding

1. Outline one reason why CPD is important to improve knowledge.
2. Describe one reason why CPD is important.
3. What is meant by lifelong learning?
4. Outline one reason why CPD might not always be possible in a workplace.
5. What is the link between CPD and reflective practice?

Read about it

Gibbs, G. (1988) *Learning by Doing: A Guide to Teaching and Learning Methods*, Further Education Unit, Oxford Polytechnic: Oxford

NMC (2016) *The Code for Nurses and Midwifes*, NMC, London

Schön, D. (2006) *The Reflective Practitioner: How Professionals Think in Action*, Ashgate Publishing

Websites

HCPC (2016) *Our Standards for Continuing Professional Development.*
Accessed from http://www.hpc-uk.org/registrants/cpd/standards/
National Careers Service
Accessed from https://nationalcareersservice.direct.gov.uk/
Skills for Care, Think Care Careers
Accessed from http://www.skillsforcare.org.uk/Care-careers/Think-Care-Careers/Jobs/Job-types-available.aspx

Unit HSC DM5: How will I be graded?

The table below shows what the learner must do to achieve each grading criterion. Learners must achieve all the criteria for a grade to be awarded (i.e. criteria D1 to D3 must be achieved to pass this unit assessment at grade D). A higher grade may not be awarded before a lower grade has been achieved in full, although component criteria of a higher grade may have been achieved.

Grade	Assessment criteria number	Assessment grading criteria	Assessment of learning / What you need to show
D1	1.1	Research job roles within health and social care provision.	Provide information to identify a range of job roles within health and social care.
D2	1.2	Research opportunities for further study in relation to the health and social care sector.	Provide information to show a range of opportunities for further study in relation to health and social care.
D3		Show evidence of reading or use of sources.	There should be evidence of learners' reading or use of sources. Learners must use a minimum of two traceable references to support the discussion.
C1	3.1	Explain factors to consider when planning for personal development	Information must explain more than one factor for consideration when planning for personal development.
C2	3.2	Develop a curriculum vitae	Produce a curriculum vitae with information that includes: • qualifications • personal and professional experience • skills and interests
C3		Show evidence of reading or use of sources with referencing relevant to the explanations. Good use of vocabulary and grammar.	Evidence of reading or use of sources Vocabulary and grammar should be appropriate and accurate for purpose
B1	3.3	Create own personal development plan.	Produce a personal development plan which may include: • Evidenced based planning • identifying learning needs • links to career aspirations • SMART goal setting • other relevant information
B2	3.4	Implement own personal development plan	Provide information to discuss the implementation of the personal development plan produced for B1, which may include: • following agreed actions • short, medium, long-term goals, links to B1
B3	2.1	Produce a learning journal.	Produce a comprehensive learning journal, which may include: • review of knowledge • reflection • feedback • application of knowledge to practice and practice to knowledge

Grade	Assessment criteria number	Assessment grading criteria	Assessment of learning / What you need to show
B4		Show evidence of reading or use of sources. Referencing supports discussion.	Use of reading or use of sources should be shown through a range of relevant referencing. Referencing should be used appropriately to support discussion.
A1	3.5	Review own personal development plan	Provide detailed information to review the effectiveness of the personal development plan, which may include: • reviewing achievement • evaluating outcomes • prioritising next steps
A2		Show evidence of wider background reading or use of sources. Referencing supports the review.	Wider background reading should be evident or a wide range of source material should be used
A*1	4.1	Critically evaluate the need for continuing professional development in the health and social care sector.	The critical evaluation must include an appraisal of continuous professional development in the health and social care sector to include: • the need for up-to-date knowledge and practice • continuous improvement in provision outcomes • reflective practice • regulatory requirements
A*2		Show evidence of a range of background reading or use of sources used selectively.	Note: 'to include' means that all aspects must be covered in the assessment – ensure all aspects here are included. Learners should show the ability to consider or explore relevant issues which contribute to the evaluation. An extensive range of background reading or use of sources should be used selectively and cited appropriately.

Assessment

This section offers information and advice for the assessment for the Level 3 Technical Extended Diploma in Health and Social Care. You should also refer to the specification and your tutor will also be able to offer further guidance about assessment.

Information and tips

An overview of the qualification

This textbook will provide you with the knowledge and understanding required for the following qualifications:

The Technical Level 3 Extended Diploma in Health and Social Care (601/8435/8) and The Level 3 Extended Diploma in Health and Social Care (601/6110/3)

The content will support you if you are studying either of these qualifications. (Please note that if you are studying for a qualification that does not have Technical in the title, this book should only be used to support you with the knowledge and understanding that you need to complete your course. Follow the guidance provided by your tutor in relation to external assessment requirements.)

The award

The aim of the award is to provide you with an introduction to core topics within health and social care. From this, you can progress onto the Technical Level 3 Certificate in Health and Social Care and then to the Technical Level 3 Extended Diploma in Health and Social Care. In order to achieve the Level 3 Award in Health and Social Care, you must achieve at least a pass grade (which is at least a D) for the unit assessments for the

three mandatory units. Your tutor may recommend that you compile a portfolio of evidence.

The Technical Certificate

To complete the certificate you will be required to complete and achieve a pass grade (which is at least a D grade) in all the internally assessed unit assessments for the nine mandatory units, plus a pass grade for the externally assessed Certificate Assessment (HSC1), and complete a minimum of 75 hours of placement experience. Your tutor may also recommend that you compile a portfolio of evidence.

Once you have achieved the Technical Certificate, you will be able to progress to the Technical Level 3 Extended Diploma in Health and Social Care. The Certificate may also allow you to access Higher Education and progress to further learning at Level 4 and above. It will also allow you to access a wide range of job roles in the health and social care sector; these may include Care Support Worker roles in adult residential settings, and Community-Based Support Worker roles.

The Technical Extended Diploma

The aim of the Technical Level 3 Extended Diploma in Health and Social Care qualification is to provide you with the knowledge, understanding and skills that are essential to the health and social care sector, and to support your progression into Higher Education or the workplace, whichever you choose!

During the course, you will be assessed through internally marked and graded assessment, and externally marked assessments.

To gain the Technical Extended Diploma, you will need to achieve a pass grade in the internally assessed unit assessments for:

- 14 mandatory units
- three units from Option Group 1
- one unit from Option Group 2.

The range of optional units that are available will allow you to pursue an interest in a specific area of social care, heath studies or health sciences to suit the path you choose in which you choose to progress.

Units are graded from A* to D. They are internally assessed, with the exception of Unit DM3.1.

For the **external assessments**, you will complete a **Synoptic Assessment (HSC1)** covering the Certificate Mandatory units and **Synoptic Assessment (HSED2)** covering the Diploma Mandatory units. You will also complete a **Short Answer Examination (SAE) covering Unit HSC DM3.1**. This will be taken during the Diploma study stage.

You will not be able to achieve the qualification until all components are achieved. Unit certification will be available, which will provide confirmation of achievement in individual units, as appropriate. Your tutor will be able to advise you about this.

The work placement

For the Technical Extended Diploma, you will be required to attend placement in a real work environment to support your learning. The minimum required number of placement hours is 175 hours (or 100 hours if you have already successfully completed the Technical Certificate). This will support your learning by providing opportunities for you to apply knowledge to practice, receive feedback, and reflect on your own experience. The placement also provides opportunities for you to observe professional practice in action and gain valuable employability skills.

Your tutor will encourage you to reflect on your placement experience throughout your studies. Placement Handbooks, which include a Professional Skills Profile, will be provided to you and your placement mentor. They will be used to record your progress in several core subject areas. The following knowledge and skills within the Professional Skills Profile are covered by multiple mandatory units within the Technical Certificate and Technical Extended Diploma:

- positive role modelling
- policy and procedure
- communication
- valuing diversity
- inclusive practice
- health and safety
- professional development.

The Placement Handbooks must be completed with input from your placement mentor and tutor.

You should remember that the required placement hours do not contribute to the overall qualification grade; however, they are a mandatory element of the qualification. Your tutor will confirm your completion of the placement hours by completing the boxes in the Records of Grades Achieved Grid.

How long will the course take to complete?

You will usually be able to achieve the Extended Diploma in two years (or one year if you have already successfully completed the Certificate).

Grading

Your internal and external grade results will be used to calculate your overall grade and the UCAS points allocated. The record of grades in your Qualification Specification is a useful resource and your tutor will be able to support you with how to use this record.

What will I be able to do once I have completed the course?

When you achieve this qualification, you will be able to take a Higher Education course, or choose from a wide range of job roles in the health and social care sector, such as

- Care Support Workers in Adult Residential Settings
- Healthcare Assistants in Community, Primary Care and Acute Health Environments
- Care Support Workers in Domiciliary Services, Supported Living or Day Services
- Community-Based Support Workers.

Completing your assessments

As mentioned above, for the Technical Extended Level 3 Diploma, you will be assessed through internally marked units and also through externally set, externally marked assessments. Your tutor will be able to share the different types of assessment methods that you may be able to use to complete your internally marked work, as well as providing you with a schedule so that you know when your work needs to be submitted to your tutor.

You may be expected to complete assessment work outside of class time, so it is important that you plan your time to accommodate this.

There are a number of different methods that may be used to assess your work. These may include creating booklets, leaflets and posters, writing an essay or report, or through a presentation. Your tutor will be able to advise you further on this.

Know what the command words mean

Make sure you know the command words of your assessments as this will guide you in the different level of evidence and detail required. 'Identify', for example, requires you to name the main points accurately and could be a list; 'explain' requires more detail about what you are writing about, with reasons and examples. Your tutor will be able to advise you further on what you will need to do for each of the command words. Generally the more in-depth detail required or interpretation such as evaluations will be for the higher grades. Some examples of command words are included below with a brief explanation of what they require. Your tutor will be able to offer more in-depth guidance on this, but the following explanations may be helpful.

Term	Explanation
Apply	Explain how existing knowledge can be linked to new or different situations in practice.
Analyse	Break the subject down into separate parts and examine each part. Show how the main ideas are related and why they are important. Reference to current research or theory may support the analysis.
Clarify	Explain the information in a clear, concise way.
Classify	Organise according to specific criteria.
Collate	Collect and present information arranged in sequence or logical order.
Compare	Examine the subjects in detail and consider the similarities and differences.
Critically compare	This is a development of 'compare' where the learner considers the positive aspects and limitations of the subject.
Consider	Think carefully and write about a problem, action or decision.
Demonstrate	Show an understanding by describing, explaining or illustrating using examples.
Describe	Write about the subject giving detailed information in a logical way.
Develop (a plan/ idea which....)	Expand a plan or idea by adding more detail and/or depth of information.
Diagnose	Identify the cause based on valid evidence.
Differentiate	Identify the differences between two or more things.
Discuss	Write a detailed account giving a range of views or opinions.
Distinguish	Explain the difference between two or more items, resources, pieces of information.
Draw conclusions (which....)	Make a final decision or judgment based on reasons.
Estimate	Form an approximate opinion or judgment using previous knowledge or considering other information.
Evaluate	Examine strengths and weaknesses, arguments for and against and/or similarities and differences. Judge the evidence from the different perspectives and make a valid conclusion or reasoned judgement. Reference to current research or theory may support the evaluation.
Explain	Provide detailed information about the subject with reasons showing how or why. Responses could include examples to support these reasons.
Extrapolate	Use existing knowledge to predict possible outcomes which might be outside the norm.

Identify	Recognise and name the main points accurately. (Some description may also be necessary to gain higher marks when using compensatory marking.)
Implement	Explain how to put an idea or plan into action.
Interpret	Explain the meaning of something.
Judge	Form an opinion or make a decision.
Justify	Give a satisfactory explanation for actions or decisions.
Plan	Think about and organise information in a logical way using an appropriate format.
Perform	Carry out a task or process to meet the requirements of the question.
Provide	Identify and give relevant and detailed information in relation to the subject.
Review and revise	Look back over the subject and make corrections or changes.
Reflect	Learners should consider their actions, experiences or learning and the implications of this for their practice and/or professional development.
Select	Make an informed choice for a specific purpose.
Show	Supply evidence to demonstrate accurate knowledge and understanding.
State	Give the main points clearly in sentences or paragraphs.
Summarise	Give the main ideas or facts in a concise way.

Sources of information

There are a variety of sources that you can use to support your work on your assessments. These include books, websites and journals.

Journals: Journals are publications that relate to particular professions. They are issued regularly and provide the latest up-to-date information on relevant topics and skills. Some examples that may be useful to Health and Social Care include:

- *Nursing Times*
- *Nursing Standard*
- *Community Care*

Websites: There are numerous websites available. These can vary in reliability and validity. Different websites are set up for different purposes, which can be frequently identified from the website address: .gov.uk is from the government, .org.uk is often used by voluntary organisations and .ac.uk is an academic institution. Some examples that may be useful are:

- NHS Choices provides information on a range of health care topics: www.nhs.uk
- Gov.uk provides information on all government services: www.gov.uk
- Social Care Institute for Excellence provides examples of good practice and knowledge areas and is aimed at social care: www.scie.org.uk

Remember that Google and Yahoo are search tools not websites!

Books: Books are useful as they provide information on a range of topics. If you are using a textbook, then try to make sure that you are using an up-to-date one. The index at the back of a book can be helpful when you are trying to find information on specific topics.

Reading and referencing

With all course assessments, referencing is really important. You cannot achieve good grades without having a minimum of two traceable references. For the higher grade criteria, more are required and these should be from a wide range of sources. The references should be used to support the analysis and discussion of your ideas. This could be, for example, statistics from appropriate sources. However, references should not be used in place of your own words.

Decide on how you are going to do this, for example you may use the Harvard Referencing System. There are variations of the use of this, but one way is demonstrated in the section below on using a direct quote. Always try to use the most up-to-date sources you can, especially when quoting statistics. In some cases, such as a theory or legislation, you will not be able to do this, but again you need to ensure you are quoting the most up-to-date legislation.

A note of caution: Plagiarism

Plagiarism – which means taking someone else's work or ideas and using them as your own – is taken very seriously. If discovered in the external assessment it may result in it being unmarked and returned as a refer grade. It is therefore important to ensure you reference all the ideas, quotes and sources used.

Using a direct quote

If you are using a direct quote from a book or journal, then this should be illustrated with speech marks and the author's name, year of publication and page number. For example:

'As Green (2006 p. 7) states....'

or

'Quote' (Green 2006 p 7)

Long quotes should be avoided as this can detract from demonstrating your own understanding. However, if used, then these should be on a separate line to the main text and indented.

For two authors, make sure you reference both of them, for example: Green and Yellow (2006 p. 7).

Where there are three or more authors, you can use *et.al,* which is Latin for 'and others' and is academically accepted, rather than writing all the other names.

Paraphrasing

Paraphrasing an author or website's ideas should still be referenced. The reference can appear in brackets after the text. If you are using several sources that say the same, then these can all appear in the same bracket in chronological order. This can add weight to your argument.

The reference list

- Your reference list should be in alphabetical order.
- If there are six authors or fewer, all should be listed; if more than six, list the first three and then use *et.al*
- Journals should be presented as Author (year) Article Title. Journal Title. Volume (Issue number) pages of the article
- Websites should be presented as Author (year) Title of Website Page. Website Address. (date you accessed the website)

- Books should be presented as Author (year) Title of Book. Publisher, Place of Publication.
- It is often helpful to do your reference list as you go along, as you may get to the end and not know the source of a really good quote you want to use! It can also help avoid plagiarism.

External Assessment

Before you start

Before writing your external assessment, you will be informed about the controls for supervision by your tutor.

Resubmission and resits

Re-mark requests for external assessments

You may request a re-mark if you do not think that the result is a true reflection of your performance. This request must be made within 20 working days of the published results date. Following a re-mark, a grade may be decreased as well as increased.

Referral of an external assessment

A result that does not achieve a pass D grade will be graded as a referral and not achieved. If you intend to submit an external assessment for another attempt to achieve a D grade or above, you will be required to make a new submission of an alternative assessment.

Improving your grade for your external assessment (upgrading your result)

When you have achieved a D grade or above for your external assessments, you may want to improve your grade. If you intend to attempt to improve your grade, you will be required to make a new submission of an alternative assessment. The higher of the two grades achieved for the assessments will be the final result.

There is a maximum of two opportunities for you to attempt each external assessment in order to achieve a pass grade or improve a grade.

And finally, here are some tips to help you along the way:

- Reference and keep a bibliography as you go along
- Ensure you read each assessment criteria thoroughly
- Monitor your word count to ensure you do not go over the word limit
- Ensure your paragraphs have a beginning, middle and end and there are links between them
- Use a range of sources for your ideas
- Reflect, linking theory and practice
- Evaluate the evidence you have gathered

Good luck with your assessments!

Glossary

abuse action by another individual that causes significant harm

accountability being held responsible for one's own actions

action potential is the name given to a difference in electrical charge that is generated by the stimulus and which then travels along a nerve cell

active listening a method of listening to build rapport, trust and mutual understanding of the message that is being communicated

active participant relates to an individual being actively involved in all aspects of their life, care and support

active reabsorption is a process that occurs in the first section of tubule that the glomerular filtrate enters on leaving the Bowman's capsule. This section is surrounded by capillaries and useful substances such as glucose, salts (minerals) and amino acids are pumped from the filtrate back into the blood using ATP generated during respiration. As energy is used to transfer these molecules it is known as active reabsorption

advocacy supporting an individual to express their views and interests when they are unable to do so themselves

advocate an independent person that represents an individual's views and wishes

agreed ways of working relates to the working practices that are followed in a work setting, including policies and procedures

all or nothing rule a nerve cell will either fire an impulse or not. A stimulus will not create a weak impulse or a strong one

Alzheimer's refers to a disease that is the most common cause of dementia

amino acids long chains of these make up proteins

anaphylaxis a serious and potentially life-threatening allergic reaction

anatomical relating to the structures of the body

antagonistic muscle pairs are muscles that work as a pair to carry out opposite actions. For example, one muscle may raise the arm, the other pulls it back down. One is contracting when the other is relaxing

antibody is a specific protein produced by the B-cell lymphocytes in response to a particular antigen. It results in causing the microbes to clump together making them an easier target for phagocytic white blood cells

antigen is a chemical – usually a protein or carbohydrate that results in the production of antibodies by the immune system thus triggering an immune response

anxiety and panic attacks the physical and emotional negative sensations experienced as a result of worry and fear

aphasia and dysphasia are conditions where the part of the brain responsible for language is affected

apprenticeships a learner will gain a qualification through a combination of study and practical training in a workplace

approaches in psychology refer to methods of assessment and treatment based on a particular theory, e.g. psychodynamic approach

appropriate person can also be described as a relevant person or advocate. They are usually an independent person who will make decisions on behalf of a patient if they are considered incapable of making their own informed decisions

artefact theory any link between ill-health and class is artificially produced by the methods we use to measure

asymptomatic when an individual has no symptoms

audit trail is a detailed record of actions taken with reasons stating times, any recordings and who was involved

auto-immunity is when the immune system malfunctions and mistakes body tissues for invading organisms and so destroys or damages our own cells. Examples are diabetes, multiple sclerosis and nephrotic syndrome

autoimmune disease occurs when the immune system in the body attacks healthy cells

bases are chemicals that have properties opposite to acids thus making them alkaline

behaviour refers to a person's actions resulting from how they think and feel

behaviour modification describes a method of changing the way a person behaves

behaviourist theory suggests that all behaviour, except reflex behaviour, is a response to a stimulus in the environment. The temperature falls so we put on a jumper or turn up the heating. Our behaviour is a response to the stimulus of falling temperature

behaviours refer to specific actions such as screaming or self-harm

beliefs opinions not necessarily based on facts

best interests relates to taking into account an individual's circumstances and preferences before making a decision or choice for the individual

binary fusion a form of cell division that results in the cell dividing into two identical parts, each being able to grow to the original size

body language the movements of your body that express to others how you are feeling

body map an outline of the human body, which can be used to document and illustrate visible signs of harm or injury

body systems are made up of various organs that work together to fulfil a particular function, for example the digestion of food by the digestive system

bone a dense non-living material containing mineral salts such as calcium and phosphorus that is produced by osteoblasts

buffers are chemicals that absorb excess hydrogen ions preventing them from causing significant changes to the pH

Caldicott Principles a set of standards aimed at improving information handling in health and social care from a review commissioned by the Chief Medical Officer of England

cardiac cycle is the term given to the events occurring in the heart during one heart beat and includes the pumping of both the atria and the ventricles. The frequency of the cardiac cycle is known as our heart rate

care plan is a personalised plan for the care and support of an individual identifying the personnel involved and their responsibilities

Care Quality Commission (CQC) the regulator of health and social care services in England

cartilage is a flexible material made of protein that initially forms the skeleton but is mostly replaced by bone. It is found protecting the ends of bones from friction in joints

causation an explanation or reason for something, cause and effect; for example, binge drinking causes liver damage

cells are the individual building blocks of the body. There are about 200 different types in the body

cellular respiration sometimes called internal respiration is the process that occurs in all cells. This is where glucose is changed into carbon dioxide and water, releasing energy. Oxygen is required for this process

chemical digestion is the chemical change of proteins, nucleic acids, fats and carbohydrates from large insoluble molecules into smaller molecules that can be absorbed into and carried by the blood

children in need refers to children who are unable to attain the required level of health or development, or whose health or development may be affected without the provision of services

choices map a tool used to describe decisions that are made by the individual and the decisions made by other people

Christianity a religion based on the life and teachings of Jesus Christ

chromosomes thread-like structures in pairs in the nucleus of cells. Humans usually have twenty-six chromosomes. Each chromosome is made up of genes

chronic condition a condition such as a health condition or disease that lasts longer than three months

chyme is the name given to the pulverised or pureed food that is formed in the stomach and then passed on through the gut. It contains a lot of water and all the food nutrients in a digested, partially digested or undigested state

circadian rhythms sometimes known as the body clock. This is a process by which body functions are controlled or regulated, such as sleeping

clinical commissioning groups organisations that are responsible for the provision of NHS services in England

clinical commissioning groups (CCG,) are NHS organisations responsible for planning, agreeing and monitoring NHS services in England

clotting is the process by which the body detects a leak of blood and triggers a response that results in a fine net being weaved across the hole which then traps red blood cells forming a clot that then seals it preventing further blood loss

Codes of practice set out the standards or values that care practitioners must follow to provide high- quality, safe, compassionate and effective care and support

cognitive behavioural therapy a treatment that uses talking and listening to help individuals question negative thoughts, beliefs and attitudes that are causing them problems. It combines a cognitive approach, examining the individual's thoughts, with a behavioural approach, examining how they behave, so they can change their behaviour and their thinking

cognitive development relates to thinking and intellectual development

cognitive theory suggests that we understand the world through perception, language, thinking, and memory; for example, a baby learns to recognise faces then refines this perception until it recognises its mother's face

communication channel the method or way that communication is transferred

confidentiality means keeping information private. It is a legal obligation under the Data Protection Act 1998 and as a health and social care professional you must follow it

consistency the reliability of a service or working practice

continuity the uninterrupted provision of a service over time

contraction is when a muscle shortens and does work using energy in the form of ATP. It is the result of special proteins moving between each other

correlation refers to how often events occur together, increasing or decreasing at the same time (positive correlation) or when one increases while the other decreases (negative correlation). An example of negative correlation might be an increase in fitness levels and a reduced intake of chocolate. Correlation does not always mean causation. A child grows taller, pollution levels increase: two facts but they are not linked by cause and effect

CQC (Care Quality Commission) responsible for monitoring, inspecting and regulating health and social care services

cross-infection is the transfer of disease causing micro organisms or pathogens from one individual to another or from a contaminated surface

culture the beliefs, customs, ways of thinking and behaving of groups in society

cytotoxic refers to medication or treatments which are toxic to cells by preventing growth and are used to treat conditions such as cancer

data protection principles refers to the eight principles that govern the use of personal information under the Data Protection Act

day centre a setting that provides care and activities for individuals

DBS checks checks carried out to identify any criminal record

deamination is a process that occurs in the liver where excess amino acids from our diet have their amine component removed as ammonia. This is highly toxic and so is immediately converted to a slightly less poisonous molecule – urea. Urea is then transported by the blood and removed from the body in the kidney

deductive approaches start with a hypothesis or theory then look for evidence to support or disprove the theory

dementia refers to a group of symptoms that may include memory loss and/or difficulties with thinking or language

demographic data information that tells us about a population

depression a low mood that continues for a long period of time and affects day-to-day living

Designated Safeguarding Officer the person that takes on the lead for safeguarding in an organisation

diffusion is the movement of molecules from a high concentration (many in the same volume of space) to a low concentration (fewer in the same volume of space)

dignity self-respect

direct payments cash payments made to individuals to buy the care and support services they have been assessed as needing

disclosure to report or reveal information that is often sensitive or confidential

Disclosure and Barring Service a service that makes background checks for organisations, on people who want to work with children and adults

discrimination the unfair or unequal treatment of an individual or a group

discriminatory practices showing unfair treatment of individuals because of their differences

duty of candour a duty that requires health and social care providers to be honest and transparent about the provision of all care and treatment

duty of care a practitioner's obligation to act in individuals' best interests and keep them safe. This is a legal requirement under legislation such as The Care Act (2014) and under codes of practice such as the NMC Code

ego that part of us which has learned the rules of society and consciously moderates the primitive urges of the id

emotional development is the development and expression of feelings

empowerment enabling and supporting individuals to be in control of their lives

endorphins hormones produced in the body which influence mood

environmentalists those who consider that the environment has a greater influence than our genes do on how we develop

epilepsy a neurological condition that is characterised by the individual having seizures that start in the brain

ethics concerned with what is morally right or wrong

evidenced-based planning using research and evidence available to plan a decision

excretion is the removal of waste, usually poisonous, by-products of metabolism from the body. Examples are carbon dioxide from the lungs, components of bile from the liver and urea mainly from the kidney

experiences things that happen to us

external validity means findings can be applied to other areas

fatty acids and glycerol are the constituents of fats. There are many types of fatty acid

fertilisation is the joining of a single sperm cell with a released egg normally high up in the oviduct or fallopian tube

forced marriage when pressure or abuse is used to make a couple marry

forensic evidence evidence that can be used in a court, especially DNA

framework of competence are those policies, knowledge and skills that a particular professional body or organisation requires from its members

gaseous exchange is the term used to describe how oxygen passes from the lungs into the blood and then to the tissues while carbon dioxide is transported in the opposite direction

gene a basic unit of DNA that carries instructions for traits and diseases from one generation to the next. Genes are contained in the chromosomes. Every child has two copies of each gene, one from each parent. In total humans have between 20,000 and 25,000 genes

generativity a period of creativity, guiding the next generation of children

genetic the characteristics such as the physical, behaviour or medical conditions that are inherited from parents

genetic inheritance refers to the characteristics we get from our parents through their genes, for example, eye colour or the likelihood of developing breast cancer

guardian the lead person for safeguarding an individual's confidential information

handover passing information needed to continue the care of an individual from one member of staff to another

harassed unwanted conduct related to a 'protected characteristic'

Health and Wellbeing Boards where representatives from the health and social care sector work together to improve the health and well-being of their local populations

Health Education England oversees the education, training and workforce development in the health sector

Healthwatch England the national consumer organisation for the health and social care sector

heterosexual a person that is sexually attracted to people of the opposite sex

histamine a substance found in the human body that has a role in the immune system response

hoist a piece of equipment that enables an individual to move from one position to another

holistic development considering all aspects of development, not just one aspect

hormones are molecules released from secretory cells that travel in the blood to a specific target organ where they bring about an effect or response. This response may be rapid as with the hormone adrenalin or gradual as with the growth hormone somatotrophin

human resources the part of an organisation that oversees areas of work connected to the effective use of staff

hypertonic a solution that is more concentrated than a neighbouring one separated by a semi-permeable membrane

hypotonic a solution that is less concentrated than a neighbouring one separated by a semi-permeable membrane

id unconscious primitive instincts influencing the behaviour of the very young

immunity is our ability to detect and respond to possibly harmful chemicals and micro organisms like bacteria and viruses that have entered our bodies

impartial fair and objective

implantation is when the ball of cells that has resulted from fertilisation embeds itself in the wall of the uterus and begins to develop into an embryo. This is normally about a week after fertilisation

inclusive ways ways of working that provide individuals with equal opportunities so that they can be included

incubation period the time between exposure to an infectious microorganism and displaying signs and symptoms

independent regulator a public body that has authority to monitor and inspect a service

indicators are the signs and symptoms shown

individual budgets refers to the funding that is allocated to an individual for their eligible care and support needs

individuals persons accessing health and social care services

inductive approaches generate data and then look for explanations of the data

informed choices and decisions relates to having all the necessary information including the options available to make choices and decisions

internal validity concerns the relationship between variables in the study

intravenously giving directly into the veins through a tube known as a cannula

invasive infection an infection affecting the internal parts of the body that are normally free from pathogens

ions are charged atoms. They can be positive (anions) or negative (cations). They are formed when molecules break down in a reaction through either gaining or losing electrons. If they gain electrons they acquire negative charge; if they lose them they become positive

Islam a religion followed by Muslims that teaches that there is one God (Allah) and that Muhammad is its prophet

isotonic when two solutions separated by a membrane are of equal concentration

job description the duties and responsibilities that you are contracted to undertake in a job role

labelling theory a way for some sections of society with power and influence to control the behaviour of others

learning disabilities refers to individuals who have a reduced ability to learn new skills, carry out daily living activities, understand complex information and interact with other people

legally competent generally speaking this is someone who is over 18 and is capable of weighing up any risks and who understands what procedures involve and the reasons for implementing them

legislation laws made by the government which must be followed. Legislation includes Acts of Parliament as well as Regulations

lifelong learning the formal and informal learning opportunities that occur throughout an individual's life to improve knowledge, skills and practice

ligaments are tough cords that attach bones to each other especially at joints

Local Healthwatch organisations local consumer organisations for the health and social care sector

Makaton a language programme that uses signs and symbols to help children and adults to communicate

mechanical digestion is the physical breakdown of our food into smaller pieces or a puree. The food nutrients remain unchanged

meiosis is a special form of cell division used when forming sex cells or gametes. It is special because it causes the pairs of chromosomes we normally have in our body cells to separate so halving the total number of chromosomes from 46 to 23. Thus on fertilisation we end up with 46 again

menstrual cycle is about 28 days in length. It is the time from when the brain starts to stimulate the production of oestrogen from the ovary in order to repair the wall of the uterus, through ovulation at approximately day 15, the production of progesterone to prepare the uterus for a possible pregnancy and finally the breakdown of the uterus wall if pregnancy does not occur resulting in menstruation

Mental capacity refers to an individual's ability to make their own decisions

mental health needs refer to individuals that have a mental health illness that affects the way they think, feel and behave

mentor an experienced person in an organisation who provides training and guidance. In health and social care, a nurse mentor may guide and develop the skills of student nurses

meta-analysis a systematic review of other studies that may combine their data to produce findings with a greater statistical significance, or may draw together and compare their conclusions

metabolism is the sum of all the chemical reactions and processes occurring in the body that keep us alive and is particularly associated with those of cellular respiration

mitosis is normal cell division that occurs during growth. Our chromosomes duplicate themselves so that each new cell will have the same number (46) as the original cell

Monitor the regulator of health services in England

monitoring reviewing the quality and performance of a service on a regular basis

morbidity a term used to describe the incidence of diseases in population groups

morbidity rate the frequency with which a disease appears in a population

mortality rate the number of deaths per 1,000 people

National Institute for Health and Care Excellence (NICE) provides information, guidance and advice based on current research and best practice to the health and social care workforce

national standards framework are a set of clear policies issued by the NHS laying out the prescribed levels of care and procedures for a number of conditions and age groups

nativist a person who thinks that certain skills, abilities and traits are inherited

nature refers to our genetic inheritance. Inherited characteristics are decided by the genes we inherit from our parents

negative feedback is when a change from the optimum is detected and the response is to bring the conditions back to the optimum again

negative relationship one variable increases while another decreases

neglect failing to provide care that causes or is likely to cause harm to an individual

nerve transmission is the term given to the process by which nerve cells carry information (an impulse) along their length

NHS England has regional teams who work with organisations to oversee the funding, planning and delivery of healthcare

NHS Trust an organisation within the NHS that has specific responsibility for a geographical locality

non-pathogenic a term to describe microorganisms that do not cause disease

notifiable disease a disease which must be reported to the government by law

nucleic acids for example DNA (deoxyribose nucleic acid) are the chemicals we refer to as genes or chromosomes that determine our structure, appearance and behaviour by controlling the proteins we make in our cells

nucleotides are the building blocks of nucleic acids. There are four types that are found in DNA and their sequence determines which proteins are assembled in a cell

nursing home a residential care setting that provides nursing care

nurture refers to all the influences on us as we grow and develop

observable behaviour actions that can be seen by others

Ombudsman an official body appointed to explore unresolved complaints about public bodies in organisations

operant conditioning using reward to encourage the repetition of a behaviour, or using punishment or ignoring to discourage a behaviour

optimum means the best conditions for the body to work efficiently, for example, a body temperature of 37°C or a slightly alkaline pH of 7.5

organelles are the microscopic structures (very tiny structures that you will need a microscope to see) found inside the cell, as well as the cell membrane that surrounds a cell

organs are structures that are made up of different tissues that perform a particular function, for example the heart

osmoregulation the process by which the body maintains an isotonic balance between the blood and body tissues

osmosis is the diffusion of water through a semi-permeable membrane from a weak solution to a solution of a higher concentration

osteoblasts are bone producing cells that arrange themselves in rings around blood vessels

osteoclasts are bone destroying cells that remove bone from where it is not needed so allowing bones to respond to the forces exerted on them

others parents, carers, family, friends, colleagues, external partners and health and social care practitioners

oxygen debt is a term used to describe events that take place during strenuous exercise. To gain additional supplies of energy in the form of ATP as well as aerobic respiration taking place some extra glucose is incompletely broken down to lactic acid providing some additional ATP. However as lactic acid is poisonous it must be broken down completely after exercising. This requires additional oxygen and explains our heavy breathing after exercise

pandemic an outbreak of disease which affects a large number of people across different countries

parameter is a measurable figure or value that limits the range of healthy body function

parasites organisms that live in or on something, such as an animal, which is known as a host. The organism is then transmitted in various ways, for example as a bite from the infected animal

partnership working is also known as multi-disciplinary working and involves different professionals, services and agencies working together to provide the most effective care for an individual requiring treatment or support

pathogen is a collective name given to any microscopic organism such as bacteria that can cause us harm, illness and/or death

pathogenic is a medical term that describes any microorganism that can cause disease

payroll the part of the organisation that manages payment of employees' wages and any additional benefits, along with contributing to financial management

peer review research may only be published after it has been critically read and reviewed by at least two other researchers working in the same area. They will examine the methods used, data analysed and conclusions drawn to ensure the research is valid

perception how something is seen or thought about

person-centred care relates to an individual being in control of their care and support

personal protective equipment (PPE) equipment that protects a worker from health and safety risks at work

person specification the skills, experience, knowledge, qualifications and personal qualities that are required to undertaken a job role

pH is a measure of the concentration of hydrogen ions

phagocytosis the process of a cell taking in solid matter by flowing around it and engulfing it. Phagocytes are cells of the immune system that engulf and digest dead bacteria and body tissues

phlebotomist a member of the multi disciplinary team who takes blood samples from individuals

physical abuse unwanted bodily contact with an individual that causes pain, injury or harm

physical development how the body develops such as growing taller, or developing muscle groups

physiological relating to the functions of the body

policy is a statement of how an organisation works. This is normally linked to legislation. Examples include Confidentiality Policy and Health and Safety Policy

positive feedback is when a deviation from the normal is encouraged to increase further from the norm

positive relationship variables increase or decrease together

postgraduate academic study undertaken at a higher level and after a degree has been obtained

prescribed person independent bodies or individuals that can be approached by whistleblowers

private non-government-led organisations that run for profit such as independent organisations

procedures are a step-by-step guide of how to complete a task or implement a policy

prophylaxis refers to treatment given or action taken to prevent disease

protected characteristics refers to the nine characteristics protected from discrimination under the Equality Act

protection detecting and preventing harm and abuse

protocols are rules that describe or explain the correct conduct and procedures to be carried out

protons are positively charged particles found in the nuclei of atoms. As hydrogen is a simple atom with one proton and one electron if it loses the latter it becomes a positively charged hydrogen ion consisting of one proton. It is the concentration of hydrogen ions or protons that forms the pH scale. The more hydrogen ions/protons there are in a solution the more acidic it is

psychologist works with individuals to help them understand their thoughts, feelings and behaviour so that they can overcome problems. A psychologist has a degree and higher degree in psychology and usually specialises in a particular aspect of psychology

psychology the scientific study of people, the mind and behaviour

Public Health England provides advice and support on public health to local government, local authorities and the NHS

pyrexia a raised body temperature

qualitative methods use case studies, unstructured interviews, and participant observation and focus on the content of what is observed or described

quantitative methods use numerical and categorical data which can be analysed to show patterns

race an umbrella term that includes colour, ethnic origin, national origin and nationality

rationale in science, a rationale is a reason

reflective practice an evaluation of your working practices to improve the way you work

reflex an immediate and automatic response to a stimulus involving a pathway of usually only two or three nerve cells. It requires no conscious thought and is usually associated with avoiding danger or harm, for example, pulling the hand away from a flame

reflex behaviour an automatic response to a stimulus such as jumping when startled

registered manager a person appointed to have legal responsibility over the day-to-day running of any service regulated by the Care Quality Commission

regulate to maintain control

regulation governing the way a service operates

rehabilitation a specialised service that aims to improve or maintain an individual's independence after an accident or during an illness

relaxation is when a muscle is not contracting. In this state the proteins can be pulled out from between each other and the muscle stretched to its original length. This is done by another muscle pulling it back. Thus muscles can pull but not push

reliability in research means that if the test or question was repeated it would give the same results

repertory grid a tool to help individuals understand the way they see the world

research approach the angle or way you look at a topic. There are two main approaches – inductive and deductive

reservoir a store of the infection. It can live and multiply within the reservoir

revalidation nurses, midwives and doctors in the UK must revalidate, which means prove they are fit to practise by providing evidence that their skills and knowledge are up to date. Nurses revalidate every three years

Routine Immunisation Schedule a schedule of vaccinations offered at different ages (predominantly children and older adults) offered free of charge by the NHS

Safeguarding Adults Board where different health and social care sectors and agencies work together to help and safeguard adults with care and support needs

Safeguarding Adults Reviews involve different agencies reviewing and deciding how agencies and individuals involved could have worked differently to prevent harm or a death from taking place

saltatory conduction is a leapfrogging effect where an action potential is only generated at particular points along a nerve making the speed of transmission faster

schema patterns of how the world works, for example a hungry baby cries. This brings food. The baby learns the pattern of crying when it wants food

scientific study planned, rational, organised approach to investigating a topic

scrubbing a process of hand and forearm decontamination

secretion is the release of a chemical from a cell or a specialised collection of cells – a gland – that serves a useful purpose, for example water from sweat glands, digestive enzymes from the pancreas and hormones from an endocrine gland

self-esteem the value or confidence individuals place on themselves

self-fulfilment following and achieving hopes and wishes

self-reflection thinking about a situation that occurred, what happened and what could have been done differently

semi-permeable membrane a membrane such as a cell membrane that will allow small molecules to pass through but not ones beyond a certain size

serious case review an enquiry into the death or serious injury of a child or vulnerable adult where abuse or neglect is known or thought to be a factor. It aims to provide lessons that can be learned to prevent a similar incident occurring again

signs are outwardly visible to others, e.g. bruises

simple sugars are the carbohydrates used for energy, the most familiar being glucose. Complex carbohydrates like starch are broken down into glucose molecules

Skills for Care a not-for-profit organisation whose role is to inform policy and raise standards in the adult social care sector

Skills for Health a not-for-profit organisation whose role is to inform policy and raise standards in the health sector

social class divisions in society based on economic, social and cultural factors

social constructionism suggests that we build ideas of how the world works which seem 'common sense' to those who share them

social development is about learning skills to be able to develop relationships with others and be part of a group

social learning theory suggests that we learn from others in a social context. A baby learns behaviour by watching others

social realism is about seeing things as they are, highlighting structures that often disadvantage the weakest such as how addiction keeps people poor, while others profit from drug sales

sociological approach the way that sociologists tackle an issue. A sociological approach looks at groups of people. This contrasts with a psychological approach which looks at individuals

spores are produced by bacteria and fungi. They are able to reproduce by themselves and are adapted to travel and withstand unfavourable conditions

standard precautions are the steps or measures taken to prevent cross-infection. The term standard refers to measures that can be taken, like washing hands, cleaning surfaces that can be done in any health and special care setting including individuals' homes. It does not include the barrier nursing techniques used in intensive care units or operating theatres

standards guidance and rules regulating a profession or institution, including codes of conduct and practice, regulations, registration requirements, National Occupational Standards and the Human Rights Act

standards of care the basic level of care that should be provided to all individuals

stereotyping not seeing an individual as a person but prejudging them based on fixed ideas

stigma a behaviour or quality or reputation that is seen as socially undesirable and causes an individual to be rejected by that society

stimulus the event that makes a nerve cell likely to transmit an impulse. It may, for example, be pain, pressure, sound, light or a rise or fall in temperature. A stimulus often elicits a reaction

superego the ideal moralistic aspect which sometimes consciously and sometimes unconsciously influences behaviour

supported living scheme a scheme where individuals own or rent their own home and have control over the support they get and how they live their lives

SWOT analysis exploring strengths, weaknesses, opportunities and threats

symptoms are experienced by individuals, e.g. feeling upset, angry, alone

synovial fluid is an oily liquid that lubricates a joint and acts as a shock absorber

tendons are tough cords that connect skeletal muscles to bones at joints

theory a collection of ideas or concepts that attempt to explain a situation or behaviour, e.g. social learning theory

third sector also referred to as the voluntary sector, includes not-for-profit and non-governmental organisations

threshold value a stimulus has to be above a certain level for a nerve cell to fire an impulse. This value is its threshold

tissues are groups of cells, sometimes identical, that perform a particular function, for example nerve tissue

transsexual a person that may assume the gender role of the opposite sex and undergo treatment to acquire the physical characteristics of the opposite sex

ultrafiltration is the rapid movement of plasma through the walls of specialised capillaries found bunched within each Bowman's capsule of a kidney nephron. The basement membranes of the capillaries prevent large molecules such as blood proteins from leaving and so this modified filtered plasma is known as the glomerular filtrate. Ultrafiltration relies on a high blood pressure to work

UCAS tariff points are awarded to qualifications, which some universities use when making an offer to an applicant

undergraduate academic study leading to a degree, often undertaken after a learner has left secondary school

urinalysis a screening and diagnostic tool carried out by dipping a testing stick in urine and interpreting the results

validity means that the research is measuring what it intended

values are based on moral principles or beliefs that are important to an individual

vasoconstriction is the opposite of vasodilation. Muscles in the walls of blood vessels contract to narrow the vessel so restricting blood flow

vasodilation is the term used to describe when blood vessels open up and increase their diameter so allowing more blood through. It is brought about by muscles in their walls contracting

victimised when an individual is treated less favourably for making or seen to be supporting an allegation or complaint

voluntary not-for-profit organisations such as charities

zone of proximal development this describes tasks that the child cannot complete by themselves, but can be completed with the help or assistance of adults

Index